To Auntie F

THE DEATH OF DEMONS,
BOOK I - FULL CIRCLE

by

Leslie Ronald Smith

Lots of love Gaynore
x x v

With best wishes

Leslie Ronald Smith

1

A BLACKIE & CO PUBLISHERS PAPERBACK

© Copyright 2002 Eric Moran

Jacket Design by Eric Moran

The right of Eric Moran to be identified as the author of both the novel and the music, and as the creator of the cover designs for the book and the compact disc, has been asserted by him in accordance with the Copyright, Designs and Patents Act 1988.

First published in 2002

A CIP catalogue record for this title is available from the British Library.

ISBN 1-903138-72-8

Blackie & Co Publishers Ltd 1
07-111 Fleet Street
LONDON EC4A 2AB

About the author

Having overcome his early disadvantages through hard work and application, which took him to the top of the IT profession by the time he was 30, Leslie Ronald Smith quit the business world at age 42 and currently dedicates himself to the pursuits of family, music, writing and golf. Living with his wife and their young daughter in Scotland, the author feels that he has finally escaped his beginnings and now enjoys that elusive goal - 'a peaceful life'.

Dedicated to the five beautiful children
who brought me full circle and

to Val - you are the death of all my
demons

CONTENTS

FOREWORD 10
PROLOGUE 13

Song 1 - The Death Of Demons
Budapest, summer 1998 . . . .

PART ONE
Song 2 - Born Into Blues (1)
Chapter I . . . . .Glasgow, 27 March 1955 15
Song 3 - What'll Happen Now?
Chapter II . . . . .No Place to Hide 19
Chapter III . . . . .Just Cupboard Love 21
Chapter IV . . . . .Snick, click 23
Song 4 - Born Into Blues (2)
Chapter V . . . . .Irony, Ignorance and Selfishness . . 28
Chapter VI . . . . .Subjugating a Demon 31

PART TWO
Song 5 - Hard To Care
Chapter VII . . . . .Snick, click, bang! 33
Chapter VIII . . . . .Cawder Primary 38
Chapter IX . . . . .Knowledge hurts 44
Chapter X . . . . .Woody Hard-head 47
Chapter XI . . . . .Gammy Jenny 49
Chapter XII . . . . .Happy Times 54
Chapter XIII . . . . .Virgin Snow 56
Song 6 - Born Into Blues (3)
Chapter XIV . . . . .Lost Chances 63

Song 7 - On The Streets

Chapter XV	From CYT to the Cross	66
Chapter XVI	Mental Malkie	71
Chapter XVII	Hide your Daughters	78
Chapter XVIII	CYT Ya Bas	80
Chapter XIX	Wee Jimmy	82

Song 8 - Schoolboy Blues

Chapter XX	NK	90
Chapter XXI	The A Stream	97
Chapter XXII	Roxborough, Preston & Horsborough	101
Chapter XXIII	Winter Science	107
Chapter XXIV	Today's your Birthday	115
Chapter XXV	Classroom High Jinks	118
Chapter XXVI	Football, Religion and the Kirk	124
Chapter XXVII	Fear	133
Chapter XXVIII	John and Yoko, Man	139
Chapter XXIX	Jimmy the Pill	143
Chapter XXX	Enter the Dragon	147
Chapter XXXI	Hallelujah	156
Chapter XXXII	Camping out	160
Chapter XXXIII	Subjugating another Demon	172

PART THREE

Song 9 - Catching Fish With My Mind

| Chapter XXXIV | Closing Doors | 176 |

Song 10 - Makes Me Strange

Chapter XXXV	In the Scene, Man	186
Chapter XXXVI	Paranoia Pays	189
Chapter XXXVII	It's cool, Man	196
Chapter XXXVIII	Fatal Friendships	204

Song 11 - Brain Pudding

| Chapter XXXIX | Subjugating more Demons | 210 |

Song 12 - Time To Change

Chapter XL	Baptism	213
Chapter XLI	Apprenticeship	221
Chapter XLII	On the Piss again!	226
Chapter XLIII	Using my Head	231
Chapter XLIV	Muck away	233
Chapter XLV	Laugh - we certainly did!	241
Chapter XLVI	Ralph the Mouth	246
Chapter XLVII	Shane the Repressed	248
Chapter XLVIII	Crazy Pete	251
Chapter XLIX	The Cally Clan	253
Chapter L	Changing Places	255
Chapter LI	Insecurity breeds...	258
Chapter LII	End of an Era	262
Chapter LIII	Moving up a Gear	264
Chapter LIV	First Blood	267
Chapter LV	Moving on again	271
Chapter LVI	Pan-European Hippydom	275
Chapter LVII	Back to Squat	278
Chapter LVIII	Love's Young Dream	285
Chapter LIX	Massacre at the Squat	292
Chapter LX	Tolerance no more	298
Chapter LXI	Windsor and bust	304

Song 13 - Looking Inside The Fast Lane

Chapter LXII	Are there any Demons out there?	309

PART FOUR

Song 14 - It's Wicked

Chapter LXIII	Where have you been, Les?	313
Chapter LXIV	Back in the Old Life	315
Chapter LXV	From Hippy to Clippie	323
Chapter LXVI	Dizzy Dora	333
Chapter LXVII	Heading out of Town	338

Song 15 -My Roots

Chapter LXVIII	Back to my Roots	343
Chapter LXIX	Settling in	346
Chapter LXX	Crossing over	352
Chapter LXXI	Accepting Responsibility	356
Chapter LXXII	The Death of a Family	358
Chapter LXXIII	A Life on the Ocean Wave	361

Song 16 - It's Coloured Blue

Chapter LXXIV	Married Life	366
Chapter LXXV	Implementing the Plan	368

Song 17 - Full Circle

EPILOGUE		373
Now		

Acknowledgements

Without my children: Eve, Rachael, Sean & David, I would never have experienced the joy which brought me Full Circle. Thank you for every golden moment.

Without Valerie Murray, my demons would be very much alive and kicking - but what demons could survive the love, kindness and endless support given to me by such a very special person.

Also a very special thanks to Valerie for the hours that she spent reading and re-reading this work, for her final edits and for her classy inclusions it would not have been here today without the two of us.

And for my beautiful little Kate - she who provides continual smiles, hugs and the purest love only a child can offer without you it would have been so much harder to exorcise my demons.

It was the trust of Blackie & Co. and the support of Bettina Croft and Jonathan Millar that has allowed me to share this story. A very special thanks to both of you.

I would also like to acknowledge the many friends who have encouraged me to direct my energies towards creativity. In particular Georgette Verdin who kept telling me in Budapest that I MUST write this story It took a little longer than it should Georgette, but I never forgot your encouragement. As for the music, thanks to James Ward, who listened to the first pass with care and offered gentle and constructive criticism.

The main characters in this story are the people with whom I shared my early life. Although none of the names given in this work are related to the real names of the people mentioned I acknowledge each and every one of you. Without your influence, or the lessons I learned as our journeys crossed, I would not be where I am today. I hope you have all managed to exorcise your own demons and have found paths to happiness.

FOREWORD

During a period when I was making very frequent visits to Moscow, I was privileged to develop friendships with many creative Russian people. We would often get together for dinner, parties, or to just 'talk in the kitchen' - the warmest of Russian traditions. My contribution to our more or less sober evenings was to introduce an old story-telling game to the group. It is a simple game, which goes like this: one person will pick a beginning; one person will pick an ending; the rest of the participants, in turn, will take the story from its beginning to its nominated end. It turned out to be a lot of fun, and often sparked either some unusual flights of fancy or interesting, if shadowed, Russian/Scottish philosophy.

On one such story-telling evening, Oleg started with, 'He was plagued by his demons,' and Vera provided the ending, 'Then everybody died.' It wasn't a particularly inventive story-telling evening, although I remember enjoying a lot of laughter, good food, good wine and a mind-melting number of toasts with near-lethal Russian vodka; something about this particular story stuck with me, however, and acted as a catalyst to this eventual work. It had made me start to think seriously about the demons we build up and carry through our lives and the personal battles we fight in order to conquer these demons.

I, like many others, have shared my soul with many demons. I have often dramatically changed my circumstances and viewpoints, in effect killing the old me, in a bid to move forward and leave my demons behind. I have also lived in many social circles where it seemed that 'everybody died' - either swallowed up by their demons, consumed by their lifestyle, or imprisoned by the current trend or popular philosophy. In some of my old social circles, friends and acquaintances have let their demons get truly out of hand. These people, no longer with us, have paid the ultimate price for their choices.

I was determined that, if I ever found myself in a place where I was truly happy with who and where I was, I would use that vantage point to look back and write this story of the creation and vanquishing of my own demons. Although much of the resulting work is dark, it is not a negative story. The demons you will read about and listen to are demons that I have managed to overcome. Every experience - dark or light - taught me something and has contributed to a 'now' I would never change.

So, here it is: The Death Of Demons, book I, which I have called Full Circle. It starts where the character Leslie Ronald Smith is now, living in Budapest and sharing his life with Valerie, with the song that characterizes this time - 'The Death Of Demons'. It then drops back to the beginnings of his life and tracks significant influences until he completes a 'Full Circle'.

Although names have been changed to protect the guilty, everything contained in this work is a piece of my life, and writing this story has provided me with 'closure' on many issues. My hope is that, by reading and listening, it can provide you with something too.

Leslie Ronald Smith

SONG 1 - THE DEATH OF DEMONS

I'm grateful I hope you understand, babe - You stand
beside me all the time, babe
The demons knock at my door; I push and you pull them
over - You are - Death of my demons

Childhood, babyhood, baby in a jungle - Demons
Boyhood, school rules, all the rough and tumble - Demons
Innocence to adolescence, insecurity breeds - Demons
Everything that happens is packaged up inside me -
Demons

I've carried that load a long, long time, babe - One time I
thought that load was me, babe
Because of the girl you are, you melted away the fog - You
are - Death of my demons

Because of you is where I am, babe - No demon can
survive your skin, babe
The light of your eyes shines through, the worst of those
memories so blue
You are - death of my demons

Stepping out and hanging up my clothes - Feels so light
now, as all the armour goes
Not a stranger, there's someone else who knows - There's
no demons

Val, you are - Death of my demons

PROLOGUE

Budapest, summer 1998

I hear her voice.

'Are you OK, Les?'

Valerie is tired. She works pretty hard, and this day has been another one of stress and maximum effort for her. She has once again been at work for 12 hours today, and she is completely exhausted.

And yet she still thinks of my needs.

From a life-story starting with being born into an emotional winter, things today are pretty good. Demons nil, Leslie ten!

Valerie stirs in our bed. I look at her and know that, by the grace of God, I have reached a very special time in my life.

But it certainly didn't begin like that...

SONG 2 - BORN INTO BLUES (1)

Oh please hear me praying
My child is born today
I'm lost and alone here
They'll take my child away
Oh lord, I would keep him
If only I had the means
He'll go to another
How cruel can this life be?

PART ONE -
Childhood, Babyhood, Baby in a Jungle - Demons

CHAPTER I

Glasgow, 27 March 1955

Everyone is born to a stranger. Everyone has to get to know their parents and siblings, along with all the other myriad aspects of their environment. Leslie Ronald Smith was also born to a stranger and into a strange new world. Leslie, however, would never get the chance to learn about the woman who gave him life. Leslie would never get the chance to share his life with her; discover their commonality; argue, laugh and cry with her; or to share his hopes, fears and dreams with her.

On the 27th of March 1955, Leslie Ronald Smith was born, but it was far from being a happy occasion.

Leslie was born to a single mother called Betsy Dove Smith. She was a 30-year-old Dundee woman, working in a Glasgow hotel. In 1955 there was very little women's liberation - and Betsy, born in 1925, was raised with social values that amounted to virtual slavery for women by any modern standards. This was never going to be easy for her to deal with.

Betsy was a strong woman. She had left her home in Dundee to make her way in a strange city, alone, but with a strength born from surviving the normal hardships of her poor working-class background. She found herself a job in a hotel in Glasgow as a chambermaid, which also provided her with some meagre accommodation. She worked, saved a little for the occasional treat or undistinguished holiday, survived, and - occasionally - she loved.

It was the choices she made with her love life that eventually caused her a problem.

In 1955, Glasgow wasn't exactly a multi-racial society. It had a fair-sized group of coloured citizens, mainly from India and Pakistan, but just a sprinkling of Africans and other ethnic groups. Betsy found that she was drawn to one such citizen, whom she met at a Saturday night dance, and a relationship developed between them.

At this time society still very much believed in 'no sex before marriage' for women and 'he's some boy' for men who scored regularly (or at least bragged that they did). The dichotomy of a situation where men could be heroes for having sex as many times as possible, and yet the women with whom they had sex, or claimed to have sex with, were made social outcasts, will of course not have escaped you. Betsy chose to ignore the ridiculous sex prejudice and then further confounded her peers by loving a coloured man. After that she had only one other major taboo to adhere to, but when she broke this one, and became pregnant, it was purely accidental.

Betsy Dove Smith - single, poor and pregnant.

It got worse.

When Betsy approached her lover to tell him the news, she found out first that he was being sent overseas by his company to establish a new manufacturing plant. This was his big chance, and she loved him - so she kept the pregnancy quiet and he shipped out a few weeks later, with promises to come back and get her soon.

What was she going to do?

Everyone around her advised her to get rid of the baby by some means or other. When she refused to follow that course, the friends and relations she had shared her dilemma with told her that her only course was to have the child adopted. No one supported her. No one would believe that she could keep the baby and survive and the strongest voice raised against her keeping the child was that of her family doctor, a major icon in the Glasgow community of that time.

++++++++

Betsy sobbed. 'But I want to keep him.'

Doctor: 'Come on, Miss Smith, ye know that's no' a very good thing for you or your baby.'

Betsy: 'But I'd look after him, doctor. Maybe I could get somebody tae mind him when I'm working, or...' She sobbed again.

Doctor: 'Look, Betsy, we both know that the best thing for your baby is adoption. He'll go to a good family and, even if he is a wee bit coloured, he'll be brought up right. You know it's for the best. You've no man; you're living in tied accommodation and might lose your job because of this - where would you and the baby even stay? Come on now, Betsy; just sign the papers and it'll all be arranged when the baby's born in a week or two.'

Betsy could hardly speak she was sobbing so much. 'I suppose you're right, doctor. Oh, what have I done!'

++++++++

Two weeks before the birth, Betsy Dove Smith reluctantly signed away the care of her baby to the adoption society. On the 27th of March a healthy little half-caste baby boy was born. In a last bid for ownership, Betsy did not hand over the baby straight away, but took him home, registered him as Leslie Ronald Smith, and for three weeks suckled and loved her little boy.

It couldn't last.

The hotel didn't want her baby, her friends didn't rally round as she had hoped, and she had long ago cut ties with her family in Dundee. The inevitable happened and, under pressure simply to survive, Betsy handed her little boy over to the adoption society.

As the baby left the warmth of her bosom for the final time, Betsy cried uncontrollably. A small part of Betsy Dove Smith had left her life forever.

On that fateful day - a small piece of her soul died.

SONG 3 - WHAT'LL HAPPEN NOW?

This baby's taken, to his new abode - Wrapped
and swaddled, against the cold
He's smiling sweetly, new parents greet him - Baby new
found, child saved

Baby, taken away. Hold on now, he's here to stay
It isn't easy, there's lots to do - Why did no one explain
that to you?

New baby growing, in a troubled home - mother
frustrated, father drunk
Keeps crying nightly, sister beside him - father angry,
mother of stone

Little boy, you're crying again. Clumsy, noisy,
soul hungry and thin
It's all so scary, but what can you do?
You know this bad stuff keeps happening to you

Little one beaten, doesn't understand - Why he's hurting
and his sister's sad
He's learned to hide his soul inside - Still a child
but troubled like a man

CHAPTER II

No Place to Hide

'It's dark in here, but I don't want to come out.
They're looking for me, but I'm not coming out.'

Dad: 'Leslie! Leslie! What's wrong wi' that boy, Agnes? I think you need tae take him back tae the doctor's, there's definitely something wrong wi' that mental wee...'

Mum: 'No, I'll get the minister in, Pat; the boy listens tae him. I cannae stand this, Pat - I don't think folk know how hard it is for me in this hoose!'

Dad: 'Leslie! Leslie! - I'll kill that boy when I get him, Agnes! Leslie - you just wait! The minister's goin' tae speak tae you again. Ah'm phonin' Mr Fergusson, Leslie, so ye'd better come oot.'

Mum: 'Leslie! - Now what's up wi' you, Maggie; will you stop that bloody greetin' or yer dad will give ye something tae really greet aboot!'

++++++++

Snick, click - the bullet slides sweetly into the chamber as I hide in the cool, safe darkness of the hall cupboard.

In a home that comprises two small bedrooms, a living room, a bathroom, a kitchen, a thin hall that runs the length of the flat and a tiny broom cupboard, getting found is inevitable. But as a wee boy prone to spilling, breaking or talking at the wrong time, even this fragile and temporary reprieve in the cupboard is welcome.

Snick, click!

I can feel the weight of the barrel, clasped in strong hands, inside my head. Funny thing - I can't ever see it firing yet, but I can see it pointing, threatening, protecting. I haven't told Maggie or anyone about the gun, but it's all right, the picture in my head is right. The snick, click noise sounds clean and strong - stronger than them.

Maybe it'll protect Maggie too one day.

My head hurts a lot.

Maggie's still crying and now he's hit her. Mum shouted at her and he hit her too.

I wish I could understand why.

I suppose that I'd better get out.

++++++++

Cautiously, armed with his imaginary weapon, Leslie leaves his small, dark sanctuary to face whatever punishment his parents were serving up that day.

He emerges into the hall, and discovery brings the inevitable violence...

Snick, click!

Among the memories of Leslie Ronald Smith, transformed into memoirs through a haze of time, this very common incident rates as nothing less than a fundamental life-shaper.

This is a memory, which dominates.

When anger burned deep, or hopelessness prevailed...Snick, click!

Leslie rebelled inside and - his comforter awoke.

CHAPTER III
Just Cupboard Love

As a toddler, I was always hiding in the hall cupboard.

In my very small, two-bedroom council flat - 'with veranda', my mother would always add, with an attempt at a posh accent - there weren't many places to hide.

I would stand or squat in this small hidey-hole, where there was not much room for sitting without knocking over the Hoover, brushes or assorted household rubbish that the hall cupboard housed. I couldn't afford to make any noise and risk drawing attention to my sole, if temporary, refuge.

I'd have my hands over my ears, so that I could muffle my sister's wails as she was hit for some indiscretion or another, imagined more often than not, by our Bible-bashing household matriarch. Sometimes it was all too much for our mother and she would delegate the beating to dad. Punishment delegation was really just a clever ploy. It meant that our mum got a suitably harsh punishment meted out to her kids and at the same time she also got to berate dad about going too far.

When I think of any lessons I may have learned from my mother and father, the strongest are without doubt my courses on 'practical hypocrisy'. Hypocrisy was not a word I actually comprehended as a small boy, but, even at the tender age of ten, it was most definitely a concept burned deep into the dark side of my soul.

Hypocrisy. Even now that I have so often tasted that word, it doesn't diminish in its perfection as the most pure and all-encompassing adjective I could use to describe my adoptive parents - particularly my mother.

My mother *was* hypocrisy.

'The assumption or postulation of moral standards to which one's own behaviour does not conform.'

That was my mother to a T.

Her assumption was that, by going to church on a very regular basis; by 'soldiering on' through relative poverty; by always having a

21

Christian face for the public; and by knitting blankets with my aunt, out of recycled woollen jumpers salvaged from jumble sales, to give to the poor of the church, she was - therefore - a good person.

It's a pity that 'being a good person' was never translated into compassion at home, support for the family, understanding, listening - or just plain loving.

My mother's behaviour at home seemed only to involve, hitting, nagging, punishing, blackmailing, degrading and complaining, all wrapped up in a nice little parcel of guilt, which she handed out with extreme generosity.

My mother was the archetypal hypocrite.

If there was a neighbour, a relative, or especially a member of the Kirk in the vicinity, she could instantly transform herself into 'Agnes the pious martyr'. It was an amazing transformation to witness.

From all of this self-indulgence, you could be forgiven for assuming that I hated my mum.

You would be wrong.

This was just normal life on my housing estate. These were the average levels of parenting skills utilized within my community and I, like most little boys, loved my mum.

I wanted to please her. I treasured her and often stood in awe of her. I cuddled into her warmth whenever I could and I retreated into guilt whenever my presence drew her wrath.

No matter what - she was my mum.

Even throughout the violent dramas that I experienced far too often at home - when I was alone in the dark with my head hurting, when I was very afraid and I knew that my temporary sanctuary in the cupboard would not save me - even then, I loved my mum.

I don't deny these feelings even as I recognize the motivation of that wee boy I once was - it was a desperate need to love and to be loved - and it was no less real for its grounding in despair.

My love was a silent scream from inside the hall cupboard.

Love.

Love mum.

Cupboard love.

CHAPTER IV
Snick, click

'It's scary here.
Everybody shouts. Mum cries and says that I'm always bad and that if I'm not good I'll go back to the home. The home sounds scary. Maybe it's like the place where these Barnardo's boys from the church live. They always get hit. I don't want to go there.
Why does dad get drunk?
Why do I always get hit? Maggie gets hit too. Maybe we could both run away and Maggie could look after us.
It's always scary here.
I don't want to be scared any more.'

++++++++

What does a wee boy do when he feels threatened every day? When he knows that he is so bad that punishment is always just a small step away and that, no matter what he does, something bad will happen to him that day.

Some children rebel. They become so tough on the outside that people see them as a little scary themselves. Some children crumble and cower; they become nervous, withdrawn - jumping at shadows. Some become cunning, learning to manipulate and to minimize their trauma with a little misdirection. Other children learn a pattern of behaviour that they take into the world as their 'norm' for survival - they become dangerous.

All seek escape. Escape in hiding. Escape in aggression. Escape into fantasy.

All children clothe themselves in whatever armour they can develop, either consciously or unconsciously.

Leslie Ronald Smith developed his own armour...

++++++++

Dad: 'Agnes, will ye look at that! The wee bugger's spilt milk on the carpet again! Come here, ya wee nuisance, and stop yer crying - I've no' even hit ye yet!'

Agnes: 'He's nothing but trouble, Pat. Leslie - do ye want tae go back tae that home then, eh? Eh?' Whack! 'And ye can stop yer crying - ye deserved that. And you can stop tae, Maggie - do you want some of the same?'

Maggie: 'Stop hitting him, mum. He didn't mean it - please, mum!'

Agnes: 'You're' whack 'just' whack 'as bad' whack. Here - don't you run away from me, girl, or I'll really give you something to cry about.'

++++++++

Snick, click.

Maybe it was the many westerns I watched on our tiny black and white television, in a room dominated by the stale scent of my dad's pipe and the musty smell of second-hand furniture and old carpet, which started the development of my psychological armament.

Western justice. Wherever and whenever someone was oppressed, a John Wayne type of character would ride up, cock his rifle or gun and put the world to rights in a blaze of glory.

Perhaps it was the influence of the war films my dad so loved to watch, or simply the violence of my home and surrounding environment - but snick, click became little Leslie Smith's inner anthem.

By the age of seven I was a strong, sullen, withdrawn, curly-haired little boy. I took very little pleasure in anything. Why bother when it wouldn't last? Sooner or later I would commit some wrong or other and be condemned, beaten and reminded of my place as a burden on my family - and an ungrateful one at that.

But that was all on the outside.

Deep inside myself I had weapons undreamed of, revenge unimagined by my weak, confused and uneducated parents.

Whenever life got bad - snick, click, and a bullet slipped into the breech. The barrel of my deadly weapon pointed carefully, almost delicately, at the head of my parental antagonist. My mental finger softly squeezed, and in my mind their head would disappear into a black void. No mess, no screams, no pain, no retribution. Just the sweet snick, click of my weapon - then they were gone and a calm feeling would descend.

On the outside no one knew. People would comment on the 'expressionless face' on such a wee lad. People who didn't know me at all would say I was a quiet and moody wee boy.

But on the inside...

Snick, click - Leslie was strong and calm.

Snick, click - Leslie was smiling.

I was an instrument of vengeance and a mighty killing machine. I raged against the storm of my oppression and I destroyed all who came against me.

On the outside I may have had the weakness of a child, but inside...

Snick, click!

++++++++

You may now believe that this book is a story that should be entitled 'Diary of a Budding Psychopath'. Snick, click - oh, oh! Well, I guess it very easily could have been. You just need to look at the environment around the child who was Leslie Ronald Smith. Look closely at his surroundings and his peers, many of whom were hosting a similar catalogue of abuse - or much, much worse injustices. If someone ever wanted to create the perfect environment to breed a group of psychopathic nutters, then he need look no further than the tiny world of Leslie Ronald Smith.

Violence administered with complete conviction and justification. Self-worth flayed to bloody threads on a daily basis. Emotional blackmail delivered by the people charged with his protection but who used their parental privilege to vent their own frustration about the world and their place in it. He was shown daily images of violence and, moreover, had the constant knowledge from talking to his peers that the 'nice people' his parents associated with, or looked up to, were similar monsters within their own homes.

Snick, click had a lot of potential.

But this little seven-year-old boy, who had hidden his soul deep within and was trying to survive, simply used the 'John Wayne sounds of justice riding in' to bolster his courage and - for a brief moment - win! This was payback time at the OK Corral, or an evil Nazi dictator stopped by a bullet from the gun of a silent hero.

25

This was the meagre protection of fantasy.

Snick, click - it isn't happening.

Snick, click - you're dead.

Snick, click - brother and sister are safe.

For a short while I could protect my sanity with imaginary notions of revenge. For a brief moment I could load my imaginary gun and keep the pain at bay.

I would have plenty of time later to nurse the cuts and bruises of my latest beating.

Snick! Click!

SONG 4 - BORN INTO BLUES (2)

So Lord, keep him safe now
Look on him with grace
Oh please keep a smile on
His tender little face
And if he is tearful
With sadness not with joy
Please send him my love, Lord
My lovely little boy

CHAPTER V
Irony, Ignorance and Selfishness

Betsy: 'She won't let us have him.' Sob. 'What can we do? We've tried the authorities, we've tried the Kirk, we've tried everything!' Sob.

Husband: 'Don't cry, love. The boy is probably settled where he is and we're going to have a new baby very soon. There's nothing we can do now...'

Betsy could not stop sobbing. 'But he's ours! Sob. 'You know I'd never have given him up if I'd known that you would come back and we'd be married. I wish I'd never listened to them and just held on.' Sob. 'It's not fair!' Sob, sob. 'Why does she want to keep our wee boy..?'

Husband: 'Hush now, love. We'll try again. Just keep thinking that at least the boy has a home and he's safe...'

++++++++

Irony: I was desperately unhappy in my new home; my adoptive parents were also unhappy and had no way to relate to their adopted son. Betsy had put me up for adoption on the basis that I would be happier and better looked after with two parents, but Betsy had now married my father, and they had a comfortable life together and they desperately wanted me back.

Ignorance: Agnes, with all her deep-rooted prejudices, believed that a child going into a mixed-blood family was much worse off, even though that child was of mixed blood himself! Agnes never acknowledged my roots. I was white enough to pass, and so she never felt that she had to acknowledge my racially mixed heritage. I didn't even notice any difference myself until I went to school.

Selfishness: Agnes and Pat wouldn't have known what to say to neighbours, relatives and members of the Kirk (who always praised

CHAPTER VI

Subjugating a Demon

Snick, click!

I was beginning to develop some armour.

With my armour in place, with my defences entrenched, I had killed a demon - at least a little bit. I had overcome some of my little-boy fears and I was becoming equipped to deal with the harshness of my surroundings.

Snick, click!

And I was no longer afraid.

Snick, click!

The bullet slid delicately into the chamber, the sights of my rifle pointed at the head of my oppressor, and I had a weapon to use against the intimidation being visited on me.

Snick, click!

I was armoured and safe, but was the demon really dead?

Snick, click!

And the demon of childhood fear was subjugated, harried and imprisoned deep inside me.

Snick, click!

This trauma was buried deep, but demons tend to breed and now my childhood fear had created a deadly partner - one that I eagerly fed. I had found some measure of protection, but I would eventually come to see that this protection was in itself yet another demon.

Snick, click!

I was still just a little boy, far from being free, with a darkness born from fear growing deep inside.

SONG 5 - HARD TO CARE

Sometimes this boy, he reads like an open book
You'll see him if you just look
Past his anger and pain
He won't cry, there's no tears - the well's run dry
He knows what he'll get and why
If he lets himself go

So he waits
He knows
It ain't forever and it's just too hard
Too hard to care
To care
Hard to care
Care

PART TWO
Boyhood, School Rules, all the Rough and Tumble - Demons

CHAPTER VII
Snick, click, bang!

Snick, click!

The transition was subtle, but eventually little Leslie Smith realized that it wasn't enough to point the gun and threaten - the trigger had to be pulled.

Snick, click!

At home I could deal with the now familiar forms of domestic violence. I could hide inside myself, recite my Snick, click mantra, and then step behind the safety of my armour. My parents would eventually stop the abuse and, anyway, Maggie was always there for me.

But outside...

Snick, click!

It never stopped. School, streets, playground, even the Kirk. Layer upon layer of intimidation, prejudice, power plays, competition, injustice, ignorance, attack, attack, attack - always a never-ending backdrop of violence. From a constant background companion, the violence of my surroundings built to a horrifying crescendo and just screamed for some release.

Snick, click!

It was the perpetual violence of my surroundings - sometimes verbal, sometimes psychological, but mostly physical - that finally forced the transition. At home, and with authorities in school or at the Kirk, I could be hit at any time and I had no form of defence that would not result in even more punishment. But whenever and wherever I could...

Snick, click, bang!

I'd make sure that I was no longer the whipping boy.

Snick! I'd recite my mantra, slowly levelling the barrel of the gun between the eyes of my antagonist.

Click! I'd send a bullet into the breech, relax and slip my finger onto the (oh, so) comforting trigger - and then...

Bang! I would launch a counter-attack, so ferocious, so determined, so malicious, with my fears completely drowned out by the violence of my inner scream - that I would totally destroy my aggressor.

Snick, click, bang!

Like the cowboy western heroes on TV, I would outwardly fear nothing. I would not let myself be intimidated by anybody.

Snick, click, bang!

Like my fantasy heroes, I would never start the aggression, but - cloaked in righteous retribution - I would deal with an aggressor without conscience or mercy.

Snick, click, bang!

By the tender age of eight, my peers learned to fear me - and most of them learned the hard way...

++++++++

School bully: 'Hey, it's the white darkie! Hey, Smith - you're just a white darkie! Boys - let's get him. Are ye scared, Smith? Are ye?'

I stop playing and stand - impassive. My wee friends stand a little apart, looking afraid. Alan might cry. I hope that, for his sake, he doesn't present himself as a new target by running away. Bullies like people to run.

School bully: 'Ye'd better run, Smith. We're goin' tae get ye, ya wee golliwog!' (The thug's friends gather round and laugh, waiting for me to react.)

Snick!

School bully, getting close: 'I told ye tae run, Smith. Do ye want a doin', then. Eh, boys - the darkie wants a doin'!'

Click!

Time slows around the scene in my mind. I hear the cackling laughter from this small group of bullies. I sense my friends' distress and their fear, not knowing what to do, not knowing how to react. I focus on the eyes of the bully confronting me and I know that this guy is about to strike.

As the bully pulls back his head, just about to deliver a painful head-butt...

Bang!

I explode with fury into him. All thought gone - except to focus on and destroy this bastard confronting me. Everything is action. My world is reduced to a berserk dance.

Bang!

Pummelling, head-butting, biting and kicking, my arms and legs strike and flail, delivering punishment as hard and as fast as I can. I become a maelstrom of pure and focused violence.

Bang!

Time ceases to exist until the culmination of my attack and the destruction of my enemy. No space except for the space between blows. I may also have been struck, but I have absorbed any pain into the storm. Pain feeds the storm, increases the volume of the scream and adds force to my retribution.

And inside, from the centre of this storm - I am strong, calm, centred and harder than steel. I am as indestructible as my television heroes, as I right the wrong and deliver my revenge untouched and unmoved by the consequences of my actions.

Bang!

The bully has no chance at all. The unexpected ferocity that is Leslie Smith immediately overwhelms him. He has no defence. He is beaten and beaten and beaten until...

Click!

It stops. The barrel is empty. I have run out of energy and my opponent is vanquished - thoroughly.

I return to the world of the playground, as if from a deep, dark sleep. I find that I am being restrained by the strong arms of the school janitor, assisted by several of the older boys in our school. I notice that I am still kicking, still snarling, still trying to punch and bite and gouge - but there is no longer a target, and so I stop.

I feel exhausted.

I feel disorientated.

Click!

The storm passes.

I look down at the bloodied and battered body of the bully lying on the ground before me, being ministered to by one of the female teachers, and my inner calm dissolves into a fatalistic knowledge of the retribution to come. I have a knot in my stomach. But I know that I was right, even as I mentally hand over my gun and put up my hands in surrender to the school authorities.

It is strangely silent around me. The only noises I hear are the sobs of the defeated bully, the small exclamations from the teacher as she ministers to him, the heavy breathing of the school janitor and the older boys, and a general playground murmur - strangely subdued. The angry janitor continues to restrain me, even though I have long since ceased to struggle.

Within that partial silence I hear something else.

Fear.

Fear - an emotion that has become so very tangible from being a constant companion in my young life.

Fear.

And something else too...

As I survey the crowd of children surrounding this playground incident, I can see other emotions clearly etched on their faces - awe, respect.

From days and nights of inner cowering, from a lonely battle against intimidation, I move into a new realm of feeling, as I taste the heady nectar of power for the very first time.

This bully had been known as a 'wee hard man' at school. He had many daily victims, but he had now been beaten by 'the white darkie', although from now on I wouldn't often hear that particular chant in the playground.

The bully and by association his cronies had now moved into the 'can be beaten' category in my mind, and in the minds of those who had watched this small drama. These guys would not find such easy pickings in the future. I could sense that I, on the other hand, had just moved into the 'wee hard man' category and would not find so many kids willing to try and attack or intimidate me.

Except that there would always be those kids in the playground who would challenge me to try and prove a point to their peers - either one-on-one, or more likely with the backup of team-mates. This would be a status challenge. If they could beat me, then they were a step up the anti-social ladder. They would come just that bit closer to being recognized as one of the hardest kids in the school: an accolade strongly coveted.

I would deal with that later, though. I would deal with the challenges to come. I knew that the other kids would forget what had happened today and - Snick, click, bang! - I would have to remind them.

It didn't really matter.

At eight years old, as I awaited trial and punishment for dealing with an unprovoked attack from a known thug, I instinctively knew that I had given myself a layer of armour. I had moved one step away from being a victim and, within one facet of my young life, I had escaped a prison of fear and had learned how to wield powerful weapons.

Snick, click, bang!

Fear, respect, power.

I would remain impassive.

I would look at my antagonists from within my armoured cloak and I would let them see the unholy intent shining from my eyes. I would let them know that I was fully prepared to take on any move towards aggression all the way.

I would say nothing - just paint the most destructive picture that I could muster deep within my soul and then project that image with my eyes.

And if that didn't work, there was always...

Snick, click, bang!

CHAPTER VIII

Cawder Primary

08:30 and it was time to go to school. Out of the house, down the stairs and out into the street. Turn left to walk past the row of small front gardens that the downstairs flats of the tenements enjoyed, and which allowed mum to believe that she was living a higher standard of life than her relatives still stuck in the 'room and kitchen' apartments of their Merryhill tenement homes.

Such apartments consisted of one main living room with: a small kitchen or cooking area in one corner; a fireplace (at one time every house had a range, but this was before even my mother's generation); and a pull-down double bed in a recess at the side of the room opposite the cooking area. Separated from the main room by a tiny hallway was the second room. This additional living space was nothing more than a small, square and - usually damp - box, containing a built-in bed-recess on one wall. More often than not the main room would act as the parents' bedroom, while the second room would sleep as many as ten children.

In addition to these less than salubrious accommodations, each room and kitchen was given a coal cellar, accessible through a small door in the tiny hallway and also accessible from the staircase outside via a hatch. In this way the coalman could deliver his load, without dropping coal or making black sooty marks on the worn linoleum flooring of the hall.

Within each four-level tenement block, there would be three such 'room-and-kitchen' apartments on each level of the building - as you can imagine, when family sizes so often went into double figures, each block had a sizeable population.

Without doubt, the biggest curse of this hive structure was the shared outside toilets. There was one toilet per three apartments on each landing. You certainly never wanted to have a dose of 'the runs' in that situation! Besides the wait (which often meant that the chamber pot was the favoured option), there was the smell and the damage to these disrespected places - nobody ever really wants to share a toilet seat with that many other people. I well remember the first time I visited my aunt in her room-and-kitchen and had to use the loo - she carefully measured out a number of pieces of very hard and shiny toilet paper, handed them to me and then said, 'Oh, an' ye'll need this, son,' as she reached behind her armchair for the family wooden toilet seat!

No wonder, really, that my mother was so proud to have moved up the social ladder to our little council house - complete with an inside loo!

At the corner, as I continued my journey to school, I would then turn left and walk down the hill to Cawder primary.

This was my morning ritual.

I always left just enough time to saunter through this route without being late for school. I deliberately tried to avoid leaving extra time for the playground survival games that greeted most of the kids attending my school. I would see and acknowledge friends and acquaintances, but I'd never allow my face to smile or my body language to display any outward signs of relaxation - I'd learned to remain impassive at all times.

I'd learned that, if you let anyone get too close, they would only let you down. I'd learned that if someone got too close to me then I would only have someone else to protect and I wasn't that strong yet.

No, I'd just saunter along, timing my entrance with precision, and only going at all because at this stage of my young life I had learned the severe limitations of my choices. It was school and I had to go.

Cawder primary school hosted children from the whole of the Cawder estate. It was a fairly modern school, built about the same time as the housing scheme itself. It was built on two levels, with an upper playground and upper classrooms for the first intake of kids and an L-shaped lower playground containing another building to house the older kids.

The playground was bordered by a big green playing field on two sides, which had a fence along one end, separating the school boundary from the railway line.

It also contained some bike sheds; obligatory, it seems, in any school - although leaving a bicycle unattended in our school was tantamount to giving the bike away. You might as well have left a can of spray paint along with it to save the thief's dad from the bother of having to steal a can themselves, so that they could transform your bike with another colour. A minor attempt at covering up the theft, but there were plenty of families who wouldn't even bother with the respray - they'd just dare you to ask for your bike back or tell the police. They knew that the latter would never happen - telling the police was itself considered the gravest of crimes on our housing estate.

The bike sheds, useless as a secure area to put your bike during class-time, instead provided a haven for smokers, a hidden den for card games, a favourite area for bullying and extortion, or a place to take a girl if she could be persuaded to give any of the boys a 'feel' at break times or after school.

The classrooms looked out onto the playgrounds, and these views of playground, fields and distant railway line provided a welcome vista for 'wool-gatherers' to concentrate their thoughts and stares on during lessons. I discovered, at an early age, that wool-gathering was a welcome reprieve from dealing with either the bullying which accompanied teaching in the classroom, or the bullying of the playground, which in our school passed as sibling fun. My mind was one place where I could weave a magical world of fantasy, untarnished by the realities of my surroundings. Cawder primary did nothing to bring light into my life.

Neither did the teachers.

They were mainly young to middle-aged women who taught in a school full of infants, a high percentage of whom were already budding psychopaths. They also had to deal with a majority of uneducated parents, whose sense of values was based around survival of the fittest and who had a deep-rooted hatred of what they saw as 'oppressive' authority. The people of my estate saw anyone with a job that involved some measure of responsibility as stuck-up and oppressive authority figures - so teachers fitted right into that group. The only thing that never ceased to amaze me, though, was that all adults on the estate assumed that teachers were never wrong and would punish only when necessary. It was almost as if everyone over 21 had given up the right to challenge an authority figure over any issue, and so expected the same from their kids.

No help there, then.

The Cawder primary school group of educators had long since abandoned any idealism that they might have had. They had given up all attempts at child development and had fallen back on corporal punishment as a means of maintaining authority within the classroom. They were quick to judge and even quicker to punish, sparing no time for reasons. If there was some breach of classroom protocol, the teacher cared only to know whose fault it was before punishment, usually corporal, was meted out.

Intelligent child or not, because of the aggression I had displayed in the playground I was just another psychopathic little thug in the eyes of these teachers. They spared no time to look into the reasons for my behaviour. I was just one of the many little nightmares that they had to deal with and they treated me accordingly.

To date I had escaped expulsion for my acts of playground violence, but only because I always had playground witnesses or the incident had been witnessed by a teacher or the janitor, and it had been proven that I was defending myself instead of initiating the fight. The establishment hated me, though. They hated the extent of the damage that I could inflict. They saw me as malicious and dangerous and they were just biding their time. They reckoned that I had been lucky to escape the ultimate sanction of expulsion or police trouble, but they were confident that, one day, they could ensure I got what I deserved.

School was tough. I had won some battles in the playground, only to enter a bigger war in the classroom. I knew that I couldn't win against the authorities - but I could survive.

School was just somewhere I had to be, so I rolled with the punches and strengthened my armour.

Snick, click!

++++++++

'Smith! Smith! Are you looking out of the window again? I told you to finish your work!'

'I've finished, Miss.'

'What do you mean, you've finished? You can't have finished it yet; let me take a look at that paper. See! I knew you couldn't have finished it properly - look at that awful writing.'

'But...'

'Never mind 'but'! I've told you a thousand times not to rush and to make your work neater. Do you want the belt, Smith?'

I knew by now that actually admitting that I didn't want the belt was the swiftest way to have the hated leather strap administered. My teacher seemed to take great pleasure in smacking her belt with great force across palms and wrists, especially on cold winter mornings.

I decided to say nothing.

'Nothing to say for yourself, Smith?'

'No, Miss.'

Rip, rip, rip.

'Well, you can just start again and make sure that you do the exercise neater next time. You think you're smart, Smith, but just remember that I'm a lot smarter than you are and I won't take any of your cheek. If I see one wrong line on your paper, you know what you'll get.'

'Yes, Miss.'

'And don't 'yes, Miss' me with that face, either, or you'll get the strap regardless!'

It seemed that teachers didn't need to make any more sense than parents.

At this point I'd always know that the strap was inevitable, and so I'd start to warm my hands up between the backs of my knees. The old witch, who would assume that I was playing to the gallery, was noting the sly smiles and glances directed towards me by my peers. I knew that I had no power here. All I could do was repeat my work, slowly, glowering at anyone who looked in my direction and await the inevitable strapping. My sadistic teacher was going to use me as an example once again.

It had been years since I thought: why me? It just seemed so normal now. If my teacher was in a bad mood, or felt that the class was getting out of hand, or for any other tiny reason she was not happy - then I became the whipping boy.

I finished my work for the second time that day.

When she noticed that I was no longer writing, she came over to inspect my work. Obviously to save time, she carried the three-pronged leather strap with her this time.

'You're not writing, Smith. Let me see that work!'

She gave my work a cursory glance. We both knew that it was as neat as I could ever manage.

'Look at that mess you call 'finished'! What did I tell you..?'

Snick, click!

Thankfully I had warmed up my hands and, as I went to the front of the class to be my teacher's example of the day, I remembered to pull my sleeves down as far as I could over my wrists. I was given the strap with all of the frustrated vigour that my teacher could muster. The result was just pain, a minor swelling on my hands and a couple of strap marks and bruises on my wrists where my shirtsleeves had failed to protect me.

I'd learned not to pull my hands away as the strap descended - many moons ago. That kind of defiance only resulted in a greater quantity of full-blooded strikes with the strap. After all - who could I complain to? Certainly not my parents. That would result only in further punishment to 'back up the poor teacher' who had to deal with me every day.

As my parents would say, 'After all, teachers don't hit kids for nothing - do they?'

Not a question worth answering from my point of view.

In the classroom I was powerless, so I bowed to the inevitable every time such victimization happened.

Snick, click! Face impassive, I would inwardly glower at my teacher and imagine dire retribution.

Snick, click! My mantra of revenge would slowly steal away the ache in my hands and my wrists. It would fill my mind with nothing but hatred for the 'witch' - and dreams of sweet, sweet revenge.

Snick, click! My armour solidified with each undeserved stroke of the strap. Heaven help any playground bully who decided to challenge me that day!

CHAPTER IX

Knowledge hurts

It was always like that. Schoolwork was easy. There was never really a challenge in it. It was just another thing that I had to do to survive. Teachers didn't have to make the classroom interesting, they just tried to make sure that you did the work they handed out and kept quiet while you were doing it. No one expected a new Einstein to appear from within the folds of Cawder primary school. In the eyes of the teaching staff, it was a bunch of budding thieves they were dealing with; soon to be unemployed alcoholics, gamblers and wife-beaters - even future murderers and rapists. After all, this was the general profile of many of the adults who populated our estate. Sadly, many of the kids at Cawder primary were well on their way to fulfilling some of these roles already.

Classroom survival was hard. The intimidation was constant and exhausting. Any attention or appraisal seemed to be a precursor to punishment. Contribution was dangerous. If you seemed to be participating in class activities with any enthusiasm, you lit a beacon that announced a flaw in your armour that teachers could use for appraisal and peers could use for intimidation.

I would plough through each day and hold out for my favourite classroom activity: library time. A time when the row upon row of children facing the stern countenance of their rounded, middle-aged teacher from hell would simply melt away. A time when an alternative existence could be found within the warmth of knowledge, or an escape could be found within pages of pure fantasy.

Of course, it wouldn't have done for me to announce such a passion. In my school, being bookish equalled being regularly beaten up, or at least having daily fights in the playground or on the streets. It was better and safer to suppress any outward display of excitement about library time.

Teachers have the advantage of adult insight, however, and it didn't take my teacher long to discover my love of books and to use this fact as another tool in her punishment box. I had to be extra careful not to rouse her ire on library days, or this escape would be forbidden, and instead of the sanctuary of paper I would be tasked with copying some nonsense lines from the blackboard - in my best writing! - which in practice gave me only a temporary respite before I was given the strap for not being neat enough.

When the fantasy series The Borrowers was released, the school library started to collect a set. I loved the hours when I could immerse myself in this rich fantasy world. When library time came around, I would make a quick move for a copy of this text and would submerge myself in a world of colourful fantasy. The Borrowers were my new-found wee friends. They gave me a time when I could drift into a fantastic world, away from classroom dictatorship, unjust punishments and constant, belittling attacks on my confidence.

Apart from my many, many copies of the Bible, given to me as Christmas presents, or won at Bible school, I had only the complete Gulliver's Travels to read at home. I read and reread that book, but I positively inhaled the school library, with all its richness and variety.

If there was any time that I could recall enjoying school - it was definitely library time.

But I had to keep it quiet.

My early love of literature hadn't removed my street-sense. To my peers, I was still 'impassive, dangerous Leslie'. Not someone to mess with. I was someone labelled 'thug' by the teachers. I was someone who could and would fight. I wasn't a bookish victim - I was one of them!

I made sure that my love of books never became a chink in my armour, and I scowled with the rest whenever library time was announced.

Secretly I was overjoyed, but in my school openly seeking knowledge put you in the 'victim' category. It was a lesson that I could see being played out around me on a daily basis, visited on those poor kids with a weaker sense of survival, but perhaps more raw courage since they never let the bullying sway them from continuing to try. To survive unscathed you really had to learn that there was potential pain in anything good you did, and therefore learn to disguise it at least.

In our school - knowledge hurt.

CHAPTER X

Woody Hard-head

Woody was a nutter. Not that he could fight, but he had developed his own peculiar method of surviving in the playground. Woody proclaimed that he had the hardest head in the school and regularly invited other kids to head-butt him and try to knock him out.

Woody: 'Hey, Leslie. See if you can knock me oot!'

Leslie: 'Don't be mental, Woody!'

Woody: 'Go on, Leslie. Nae offence an' that - see if ye can knock me oot. Go on!'

Other lad, standing with his entourage of friends: 'Ah'll knock ye oot, Woody. Come over here.' His friends are all laughing.

Leslie: 'Stay here wi' us, Woody. They're just goin' tae take the pish. Don't dae it.'

Woody: 'It's a' right, Leslie. Ah don't mind - honest. Ma heid's as hard as stane! Ah'll prove it.'

Off Woody would saunter towards a group of the school 'nasties'. With the rest of the group looking on, they would take turns to nut Woody on the forehead, bang his head off a wall, or in some other way inflict damage to the poor sod's skull.

Woody would take it all stoically, and I always had to remind myself that he had, in fact, invited the assaults. This crazy test of endurance would continue until: the group got bored; they made way for another group; playtime would end; or Woody would actually pass out! At the time I could never understand him. I always saw him as just another one of the many nutters that we had in school, and I thought this particular nutter was on total self-destruct, in order to prove himself hard.

When I look back now, though, I can see how the poor, fat kid was making a misguided but brave attempt at survival in a harsh world.

Woody was known. He entertained the nastiest elements in our school. He had a hard head, as attested to by the guys who frequently nutted him for sadistic pleasure and then told everyone how hard his head really was. The boy had notoriety for his hard head, but he also had some strange measure of safety. There was no point in picking on him, as all you had to do was ask him and he'd let you nut him. Lesser bullies feared his reputed hard head. You could nut him and he apparently wouldn't feel it. That, of course, meant that, in a fight, these weasels might have to take some punishment themselves - bullies don't favour that option.

Woody Hard-head had found a unique and painfully sad way to survive his early childhood.

If he is alive, well and happy today, and if he doesn't have brain damage, then perhaps his method of survival wasn't quite as crazy as it seemed. Who knows? At Cawder primary school, I certainly witnessed far sadder acts carried out in the name of survival.

CHAPTER XI

Gammy Jenny

Jenny seemed to inherit her method of survival from her older sisters and - if my dad and his cronies were to be believed - her mother too. Maybe it was just a trait that had been deeply imbedded in their genes. A leaning towards empathy or compassion perhaps, a naturally affectionate nature twisted into a harsh tool of survival. Who knows? But, by the time she was 11 years old, Jenny had definitely become a victim of this personality trait and all of her childhood innocence was buried under a sweaty, groping fog of male testosterone.

Jenny lived on a road very close to the school. She, like her two big sisters and her mum, were all adorned with fiery red hair. I used to admire Jenny's hair. It cascaded down her long, straight back and framed a pretty and freckled face, which by age 11 was far too mature for its young existence. You would guess that in a primary school all of the children would be fresh-faced and innocent. Unfortunately this was not true for many of my schoolboy peers, and it was certainly not true for Jenny.

Jenny was in my class at school. She was always a bright kid. Good at her lessons and unchallenged by the basic knowledge that was served up to us each dreary day. I think that academic intelligence was also a common gene in her family pool.

In fact, the girls in her family were very similar in nature. I knew one of Jenny's sisters, who was not much older than us, and she had the same type of red hair, a nicely freckled face and the same aptitude for her schoolwork.

Jenny's sister was also one of the girls at school who was popular with the lads.

I guess I fancied Jenny. Sometimes I would look at her and wish that she were my girlfriend. I had very little understanding of her predicament, other than that the older lads could be overheard talking about her and her sisters in terms still foreign to my pre-pubescent mind. I could only imagine holding her hand, or walking home from school with her. Somewhere, deep down, I guess my romantic nature was beginning to develop. As showing such feelings would have been a chink in my armour, I - of course - buried such inclinations deep down and only imagined what it would be like to have a soft, freckle-faced and smiling girlfriend of my own.

Maybe, if I hadn't been such a coward and had succeeded in making Jenny my school sweetheart, she might have escaped the vile abuse she received from the older boys.

I had heard my dad and one of his cronies talking about Jenny's mum with some distain once. My mum was knitting and half listening, with that 'down-the-nose' look on her face that always indicated that the person being discussed was not in the 'good Christian' league. The men were saying something about Jenny's dad being a 'mug tae pit up wi' it', and how, if it was them, she'd have her marching orders by now. But something in the 'smirky' way that they were talking seemed to hint a little bit at jealousy somehow. Even I could see that Jenny's mum was a good-looking woman, who seemed stronger and not as downtrodden as the majority of mums on the housing scheme. I think both my dad and his crony were secretly wishing that they had the option of finding out why Jenny's dad never gave her mum her marching orders! As if they had a chance. I'm pretty sure that Jenny's mum would have had my dad's measure in 30 seconds, would have had him dangling on a string in 45 seconds, and slinking off to my mum in under a minute. The lady did have a problem with drink, though. I saw her drunk in the afternoon too many times for her to be able to pretend that she did not have a serious problem.

Of the fact that Jenny's mum had been popular at school, there was no doubt. I'd already learned that only good looks and popularity drew the kind of venomous remarks that my mum and her fellowship of witches handed out to other women. Remarks such as: 'Who did she think she was, anyway - dressin' like that for her shopping. She must think she's some kinda model or somethin'. Trying tae get all the men tae chase her - that's aw'. Mutton dressed as lamb. That's all she is - mutton dressed as lamb' prevailed whenever the extended coven would meet up for a cup of tea and a bitch. Actually, those were some of the nicest comments.

As for Jenny's big sisters... Well, even a pre-pubescent wee primary school boy got the picture, when he overheard the big lads talking about them.

'Does a turn 'n that. Great diddies - eh? Ah wis right in there - wur you? Let's take her up the canal the night - eh? It's my turn for a gammy!'

Derogatory, disgusting, ignorant, violent, violating rhetoric, reserved for the popular girls that the young thugs took it as their right to molest. Talk kept for the girls who had given into male peer pressure and had used their blossoming sexuality as a means of being a part of the scene. They joined the scene, but it seemed that the lads around them would protect them from everything except themselves. The thugs used these filthy words to describe the girls who, in their minds, had no way back because, after all, 'They did it once, so they must want it all the time.' Testosterone-charged filth used to describe some of the saddest young victims living on our estate.

Shunned by 'the good girls'; desired but held in contempt by the decent lads; abused by their own peer group; with their first act of sub-mission, these lassies had unfortunately chiselled their own sad stories in granite.

Jenny's mum, Jenny's sisters - and now it was Jenny's turn.

In retrospect, I don't think she really had a chance. Her older siblings had at least marked her as a possibility in the mindless depths of the sewers that passed for these guys, heads. To minds such as these - if one did, then chances were that they all did. Perhaps this is even how it began for each of her sisters as well - maybe the role of their mother and the abuse of our fathers had marked them all.

Jenny survived for nine years as an innocent, but eventually one of the most sordid sides of our school caught up with her.

Lad, at playtime: 'Hey, Jenny, comin' over tae the sheds wi' us, 'n that?'

Jenny, smiling and looking at her counterparts with an 'it's me the big lads are talking to' look: 'I don't know.'

Other lad: 'You're Senga's sister - eh?'

Jenny: 'Aye, so what?'

Lad, smirking: 'Come on, then; we want tae show you something.'

Jenny was ten years old and the boys who were 'courting' her were the 11-years-plus lads. No respecters of childhood innocence these. Just a bunch of musky thugs, looking for some playtime abuse to pass off as fun and to use to gain some petty status with the rest of their team.

Jenny acquiesced, of course.

I can't say for sure what happened on that first 'visit to the sheds', but such visits soon became a common occurrence and Jenny's name quickly became yet another noun to the filthy adjectives popular amongst the bigger lads.

Jenny changed.

The teachers saw her change in attitude. She became cocky. She was no longer interested in group participation within the classroom. She no longer cared about the quality of her work. She would often be sullen and miserable in class, but no one ever investigated why the poor kid had almost overnight lost her innocent spark and become so disturbed. To the faculty Jenny was just another problem kid among many, and as such she was either punished, ignored or both. That was the way things were done at my school, and unfortunately this wasn't going to change for poor Jenny.

I still liked Jenny, though. I even still fancied her, but her proximity to the local thugs meant that, in my mind, the chances of her ever being my girlfriend had become so slim as to be an impossible fantasy. I always worked hard to maintain a steady distance from that scene and now poor Jenny was a part of it - so she was off-limits to me.

I was around Jenny through most of my schooling. Very little changed in her life during that time. Like me she got a bit harder. Like me she got a reputation. But where my reputation was armour against the thugs, Jenny's reputation was an invitation to the kind of boys who only caused her more pain.

She became less popular over time. Like a well-worn shoe, the very lads who had originally taken her in were quick to discard her. The thug mentality dictated a 'who wants to have Jenny? - she's anybody's' atti-tude. Unless, of course, it was a night when the lads had had a few pints and were looking for some easy action. At times like these poor Jenny was still a target.

Jenny ventured beyond the thug scene of our housing estate eventually, looking for the pseudo-respect that she had originally had with the Cawder thugs. Other gangs would want her around, but only for a while. For brief moments she'd be flattered by the gang and roughly courted, then - once she had been passed round the team - she was once again 'the old boot nobody wanted'. She was destined to carry the stigma of being the girl that nobody would admit to having as their girlfriend, because all of the other guys in the gang had been there as well.

Poor popular Jenny.

I wonder what happened to that red-haired girl from Cawder. I'd love to think that, with the sexual liberation of women in the 1960s and 1970s, Jenny would have been able to shrug off her beginnings and any associated guilt or stigma. I'd like to think that she finished her education, travelled, met good and interesting people and grew as a person. I hope she did. I hope she became JENNY - a woman respected, with no filthy stories or degradation attached to her name.

I hope that she escaped.

I really hope so.

Jenny's mum.

Jenny's sisters.

Jenny...

I hope that there were no more Jennies after that.

CHAPTER XII

Happy Times

If one thing about television was the bane of the Cawder primary school-teachers' life, it was the advert for HP Baked Beans. It was an advert that started with a child in the playground singing 'HP Baked Beans, they're the beans for me'. He sang it over and over as he marched around the playground, with children joining in and marching behind him, until the whole school was singing and marching.

This song became a Cawder primary school anthem for weeks. One kid, or a group of kids, would start it off and others would join them, until the whole school was marching and singing in accord. Our anthem had no care for the limits of playtime, or the appeals and threats of janitors or teachers. It just kept going and going - around and around the playground. It wound its way in and out of the sheds, across the fields, even out of the upper school gates, down the street and back in through the lower school gates. It was a rousing song that, once started, had a life of its own.

There were no leaders, although being at the front of the line was desirable and the bigger kids would always join the parade from the front. But nobody really cared. It was the singing and the marching and the stamping and the laughing that really mattered. Kids would march round for what seemed like hours, just being a part of this big 'thing' going on.

There were assembly lectures to try and deter us and a futile ban was put on singing in the playground - but we were unmoved by any such authoritarian protests. We were the 'HP Baked Beans kids'. For a brief, joyous moment in time, we were not a bunch of surviving savages - we were a team. For a short magical period each day we were together, alive, bursting with life and song.

It is one of my happiest memories of Cawder primary school. One that I treasure.

It is a memory that stands out and shouts - CHILDHOOD.

I can't remember when or why it stopped. Perhaps something else came along and the 'HP' song became old. I'm glad it happened, though. For a brief time I remember being a child and happiness was...

'HP Baked Beans, they're the beans for me...'

CHAPTER XIII

Virgin Snow

The only time to be at school early was in winter, after a heavy fall of snow. Particularly on a Monday morning, if the snow had been falling all weekend.

Dave and I ran down the hill. 'It's snowing!' was written all over our faces, and our feet hardly touched the ground as we zipped over the still-locked school gates at 08:00 on a beautifully snowy winter morning.

We were first!

Soft crisp snow greeted our eyes. Everywhere we looked, there was nothing but pristine whiteness. The landscape was flattened under a blanket of beautiful, cold, virginal white snow.

We were at school first and the world was our oyster!

Dave: 'The field! Let's take the back of the field afore anybody else comes!'

Leslie: 'OK, but let's roll one frae the start o' the field and it'll be huge by the time we get over tae the back!'

We raced down the steps that paralleled the infant classrooms, being just careful enough to avoid slipping on the treacherous ice. We leapt over the tiny wall separating the concrete of the playground with the now-white playing field and stopped, gasping and laughing at our good fortune. First! We were first! We could build a snowman, erect a barrier and collect enough snowballs to be major players in the inevitable snowball fights to come this morning! Our thoughts tumbled as we comprehended our good fortune, and with one accord we made small snowballs and started to roll!

Dave said, 'I'll go this way, Les; you go that way, and we'll get all the snow!'

I agreed, and we wound our way up and down the field, creating parallel lines of green, as we gathered masses of snow onto our giant snowballs.

We had a limited time to get set up and we knew it. Any minute now, the school would start to throng with kids, all vying for the precious white stuff. We knew that the older boys would start making their snowball ammunition near the gates, all the better for pounding kids and teachers alike, who would begin to arrive very shortly. That was in our favour as the bigger kids were going to be our most aggressive rivals, but there were plenty of other kids like us who would want to set up their snowmen and barricades on the field.

We hurried.

With panting breath, we met again in the middle of the field, after many ups and downs while collecting snow onto our now-sizeable snowballs.

Dave: 'Mine's huge, Les; so's yours! Ah'll no' be able tae push it mysel' soon.'

Leslie: 'Let's roll mine over to the fence tae make a heid for the snow-man, Dave, an' we'll keep rolling yours for the body.'

With the clock ticking, we rolled my snowball carefully over to the fence and started to enlarge Dave's snowball. Eventually we were satis-fied with the size of our snowball body, and rolled Dave's over to the fence too. With a massive effort, we managed to lift the head onto the body with only minor and easily repairable damage.

The snowman was set.

Kids were starting to arrive. We now had to guard our earlier work, while we erected a snow barricade and made a supply of snowballs. I was hoping that Al or Kev would arrive soon to bolster our side. Already the other kids were looking at our stash with envy, and I knew that we would soon have a struggle to keep our stockpile intact.

In the distance, we could hear the shrieks of the younger kids, being pounded by snowballs from the bigger kids as they arrived at school. Teachers were arriving too and we could also hear threats and the occasional entreaty, as volleys of cold wet snow were launched at them from behind the school fence as they arrived for work.

Time was running out.

I spotted Al and Kev running towards us.

Kev: 'Brilliant, boys! Is this oors? Let's get the barrier up, that big lot'll be doon here soon.'

He referred to the older boys. Very soon they would run out of victims at the gates and would be heading towards the field to commandeer barriers, destroy snowmen or decorate them with the gloves, scarves and hats from our better turned-out kids. They would requisition stockpiles of snowballs to use against us and bury some arbitrarily chosen victims in the snow. We were in the second oldest year group, and if we were quick enough to get up our barriers and store our own snowy weapons we had little to fear. The height and strength of our barrier was extremely important, though, because Crazy and a few other lads were known for burying stones inside their snowballs, despite the regular snow-time assembly lectures on 'taking out people's eyes'.

We worked like things possessed. Snowballs were rolled to a decent size and packed into a barricade by Dave, Kev and me, while Al and John, who had recently appeared, built up a stockpile of snowball ammunition. Other kids, especially the wee ones, seeing our massive start and the industry we were putting into our work and with the sad knowledge of previous annihilations by the bigger boys, drifted over and asked if they could help us. Normally our team would stick together and accept no visitors. It was a dog-eat-snow kind of thing, and survival of the fittest ruled the day. But for some reason, I looked at the others, they looked at me, and with the authority of our unspoken agreement I turned to the surrounding kids and yelled, 'Anyb'dy who wants to be on oor side, start helpin' wi' the barrier or start makin' us some weapons!'

I guess it was my first taste of taking command - something pretty alien to my normally solitary demeanour. But, on this wonderful snow-day, we were all high and I wanted everyone to be a part of this thing we were doing. Our younger helpers worked like demons to add to our protection and the munitions supply. Pretty soon we had the best barricade I had ever seen at the school and an enormous mass of ammunition.

But our time for preparation was almost over.

Kid: 'They're coming, Leslie; they're coming!'

The wee kids started to panic and I saw more than one kid stuff his mittens, scarf or hat into his pockets or schoolbag to leave nothing obvious for the big lads to plunder. Nerves started to fray as the bigger lads were seen pounding across the playground, intent on a new snow massacre at our expense. I yelled, 'Everybody grab some weapons. Get behind the barrier. Quick, boys - they're comin'!'

I looked around and was amazed at the size and length of our snow barrier and by the numbers of kids who had come onto our side!

Wow!

We were an army!

With Dave at my side, I stood in front of our army, who were mostly ensconced behind the massive snow-wall we had built.

The bigger lads slowed to a walk as they approached us. Most of them had snowballs in their hands, ready to attack. Some disdained collecting their own snowballs, of course, as they fully expected to wrest control of our stockpile in a few moments and pound everyone with them.

Big Lad: 'Move, Smith, we're taking over this wa'.'

I didn't move.

'Ye'd better get oot of oor way noo, boys."

Much to the big lad's frustration, Dave and I stood our ground.

'I told ye tae move, Smith!'

I continued to stand my ground. I had my army behind me and, with a soaring heart, I knew we couldn't be beaten. Dave and I faced down the big lads, and we anchored ourselves to the front line.

We had a few deserters in those first moments of confrontation. Some of the kids could see a very familiar threat starting to turn ugly, and so they ran away from the barricade to distance themselves from what was to follow. Who could blame them? They were the cannon fodder of the school. The ones whose hats, scarves, gloves and even coats would normally be starting to adorn purloined snowmen by now. They were the lads who knew what it felt like to wear a pair of trousers full of snow, or a cold, sodden shirt, as the older boys packed their clothes with the white stuff and tried to transform them into living snowmen.

On a day like this - let them go. I was sure that it was destined to be our day anyway!

It was time for us to attack.

I felt like a Roman conqueror as I raised my hand, took aim, and sent the first snowball flying towards the leader of the pack opposing us. Before the big lads could respond, a hail of missiles, thrown from behind the safety of our snow barrier, pounded into them. Our victims started to move forward, their faces red with anger at this abnormal turn of events. But it was too late. Heartened by the obvious surprise on the faces of many of the big lads, and bolstered by my impassive stance and Dave's and my perpetual point-blank barrage of snowballs from in front of the barricade, my army arose!

It was a complete rout.

We depleted our stockpile of snowballs in a fast and furious attack on these boys from the top year. Kids ran round the barrier with armfuls of snowballs and smashed them into our enemy at point-blank range. More and more of the youngest ones came forward to attack and the bigger lads - soaked, battered, defeated - turned tail and ran.

It was fantastic. My blood was pounding with joy as I saw them turn tail and I shouted to my troops, 'Come on, boys - charge!'

And we hared after the departing top dogs.

We chased them around the playground, some of us occasionally stopping to quickly make another snowball or two. Even the weakest and youngest kids joined in, carried along on a tide of righteous revenge, fear of retribution temporarily banished from their minds. This was payback day and they all wanted a part of it.

The school bell rang and still we chased them, till, with the big lads yelling curses, threats and promises of future retribution and us yelling insults and shrieking with laughter, we chased them right out of the gate in the bottom playground and pounded them from the perimeter fence as they glared at us from the road!

We'd won the day! We'd beaten the big lads!

Panting, exhausted, elated, we allowed ourselves to be herded back to the school doors, where we would all line up in our neat little rows, as the teachers and janitor rounded us up and finally began to take control.

Dave, Kev, Al and John stood beside me. I positively beamed with joy and I could see equal joy reflected in each of their faces.

We'd won!

Nobody cared about the forthcoming punishment of being made to stay in class and work at break-time. Such punishment was completely trivial set against our wondrous victory over the big lads.

We'd won!

It is the only snow-day I can remember that we actually held the field and temporarily reversed the hierarchy of power at Cawder primary school. But it was so, so special. For weeks afterwards, kids would come up to me and say, 'Do ye remember the battle, Leslie? Do ye? It was dead brilliant - eh?' I'd just smile and garner warmth from the memory.

During later snow-days I'd saunter around the playground and play-ing fields, seeing snowmen adorned with coats, gloves, hats and scarves. I knew that the owners of these garments were huddling somewhere, trying to remove snow from wet underpants or shirts, but I'd smile. Instead of pitying the poor sods in sodden underwear, I'd remember the day of our glorious snow battle and think: never mind, boys - we had our day!

...And what a day it was!

SONG 6 - BORN INTO BLUES (3)

How cruel can this life be
My lovely little boy

CHAPTER XIV

Lost Chances

How do I feel about it? Well, I guess it could have been different, but, once again, I fall back on the maxim that 'if anything had changed, then Leslie Ronald Smith would not have been here today'. As I'm happy about where I am today, then I guess I only wonder occasionally how my lost relatives are all doing. Just once in a while I ponder what my unknown brother and sisters have made of their lives. Not much more, really...

++++++++

Betsy was both excited and anxious. This was a MEGA-change. For a woman who had never even been abroad before, the thought of moving to the other side of the world filled her with a mixture of dread and excitement.

How would she live? What would the people be like? How would the children fit into this strange new environment? What about the weather, the clothes and the food? It was all going to be very strange.

But Betsy was a trouper. She had already endured some of the worst lows in life and this was, after all, a step-up for the whole family. This adventure would bring a new job for her man and a chance for the whole family to improve their circumstances. Betsy would dig in and - as she always had - she would make the best of it.

As she prepared to leave the country of her birth only one thing remained to nag at her conscience. 'What will we do?' she sobbed. 'They're still not prepared to give him up. I thought that, with this new opportunity, they'd give in. We can give him the chance to spend his life with his brother and sisters. It's not fair; I thought that she might finally let us have him.'

Husband: 'We have to let it go now, Betsy. We've tried...'

Betsy: 'I know, but...'

Husband: 'We have to let it go, Betsy...'

Unknown to Leslie Ronald Smith, his parents and siblings moved out of reach of his life forever. His father has been given a new and high-powered job overseas and, after a final attempt at reclaiming their first son, they packed up their home in Scotland and travelled across the world.

And so, as I waited out my childhood, praying for the day that I could finally leave the madness of my adopted home behind me...the door to an alternative life that I did not even know existed - finally closed forever.

SONG 7 - ON THE STREETS

There's no rocking horse behind me, no security at home
There's no magic to remember, once again I am alone
I just walk around observing, life controlled by fists and feet
Escape the prison of my family, to live the prison of the streets
All the gangsters form a circle, leave devastation all the time
They look at me with open hatred, they have a club that I won't join
Instead I've built myself some armour and weapons that they cannot fight
On the outside they see danger; I'm glad that they can't see inside

Feed the fire, make me angry, I won't take it and you know
I know you can see, there's hate inside me
Don't come near me, you're right to fear me, avoid the anger in my soul

They swagger round like '30s gangsters, they have a language all their own
They think that no one can see through them, they really fear to be alone
They're scared the team will turn against them, they fear the other gangs as well
They try to act like they are heroes, while they create a living hell
I see them battle with each other, with weapons they fight each other's feuds
And always they will have a champion, anointed with his victim's blood
A local champion called Malcolm, was bright enough to get away
He gave it up to be a hero, to guys who knew no other way

Feed the fire, make me angry, I won't take it and you know
Can you feel the heat, of life on these streets?
Don't come near me, you're right to fear me, avoid the anger in my soul

CHAPTER XV

From CYT to the Cross

The streets used to be meaner, to hear my dad bore on. In his day the boys were hard, the razors were as sharp as the second-hand suits, and nobody messed with him and his boys.

Complete pish, dad! How could the streets be any meaner?

From the graveyard that marked the boundary of Cawder-land to the end of Merryhill Road there were more gangs than fleas on a dog. BIG fleas, who bit hard and with unmerciful regularity.

For example, if you were one of these rare lads of a pacifist, non-fighting, non-gang-member persuasion, how would you get from the Cawder estate to your school in North Kintyre?

There was only one way - you would run!

First leg of the journey: through the land of the dominant gang in the area the Cawder Young Team, commonly feared as the CYT. It was sub-divided, of course, into the Tiny Cawder Young Team, made up of kids

66

still in primary school; the almost-secondary-school kids which banded together as the Young Cawder Young Team; and the kids of secondary school age and upwards, which made up the Big Cawder Young Team, simply called The Cawder Young Team. There were also the female branches of these gangs as well. Like the sharpened-steel-comb-wielding group of vicious Cawder Young Team girls, who styled themselves (spot the anomaly) - The Lady CYT.

But why would you fear your own housing estate gang?

Well, you only had a few options that could protect you.

You could be in the gang and known and/or respected.

You could be outside the gang and tough enough to be at least slightly feared - but for this to work you would have had to build up your own hard-man reputation.

You could be connected to the gang through your family or by having a friendship with someone who had a big enough reputation to give you some kind of an umbrella of protection.

If none of the above options prevailed, then you were prey.

So, on the first leg of his journey to school, even although this part was within his own housing estate, one of these rare lads of a pacifist, non-fighting, non-gang-member persuasion could not feel safe. In fact, he should feel less safe than he would outside the estate, as all the local hoodlums knew exactly where to find him and had a precise picture of his lowly position within the pecking order!

There were two exits from the Cawder housing scheme on the way to school, neither of which were sanctuaries.

Second leg - exit 1: through Possil Park and past the hunting grounds of the weaker (in my time) Possil Young Team, which had bred such notorieties as the now literary Jimmy Boyle. There were a few other minor YTs past that estate and, if you avoided the Ruchill or Barnes Road Teams, then you could make it to North Kintyre with only the remnants of The Roland Street and other surrounding gangs to worry about. Not much worry there, as these houses were being demolished and the inhabitants relocated into new schemes. With this relocation, these gangs had been fairly well diminished.

There was a two-bus change going this way, and it was by far the longest route to school. But the bus changeover took place on fairly tame gang territory, so this was the favoured exit route by those most afraid, or by those who had bad enemies scattered across the other route.

Second leg - exit 2: up the hill past the Cutter Inn, where a small YT had their land. This team was fairly subservient to the Cawder Young Team, whose territory bordered theirs. You then walked down a long and poorly maintained street into Merryhill Road, which had a YT at almost every corner, most notably the Merryhill Fleet.

The Fleet were considered the second top gang, next to the Cawder Young Team of this era. It wasn't smart to mess with this lot, as they still dreamed of past glories as the number one gang and were prepared to perform any crazy act to get the top spot back.

Next to the Fleet lived the Gairbraid gang. I always found it amusing that the Gairbraid Young Team managed to coexist with the local police station, which it was right alongside. They had a prime place for causing mayhem, as their 'land' was at the main changeover stop on bus routes from and to Cawder. Their proximity to the rule of law seemed to do nothing to deter them from acts of pain and chaos. In the scheme of getting to school unmolested, this lot were small enough and underpopulated enough not to figure in desperate evasion plans - although I do remember that their spate of stilettos-into-the-back-of-passing-strangers gained them some minor notoriety for a while.

Third and final leg: this involved crossing the 100 yards between the bus stop and school. You may think that this was an insignificant part of the journey in the overall scheme of things, but, for a lad of a pacifist, non-fighting, non-gang-member persuasion, this was still a major ordeal.

Let me explain the lay of the land around our school.

North Kintyre was a senior secondary school. You were only able to go there if you attained a certain grade in your eleven-plus or had a high score from primary school IQ tests. Those who did not make the grade for NK (as it was known) went to a junior secondary close by. There was a lot of resentment directed towards NK school kids from the junior school lot.

NK also had a Catholic school in the neighbourhood. In these days it was still considered acceptable to segregate children by their parents' religion. This, of course, was madness and served only to perpetuate sectarianism across the city. Our attitude was no different from many other Protestant schools, in that the local Catholic school was seen as a sworn enemy of NK. Bloody wars would break out between the schools and you could never be sure when the next battle was likely to begin.

Add to the above rivalries a number of little thugs who either didn't go to school, or had just left school but who hung around outside the school gates looking for easy prey, and you may begin to see how that 100-yard crossing could easily become a 100-yard dash!

In my time the last 100 yards was not so traumatic for most of the kids from the Cawder estate. Cawder's gangs ruled the NK playground as well as the streets at this time, so for some of us there was a small umbrella of protection on the final leg into school. Unfortunately for them, this umbrella did not cover kids who had no status on the streets of Cawder.

Finally: once they had arrived at school, all of our rare lads of a pacifist, non-fighting, non-gang-member persuasion had to survive in the playground till the bell rang and they could enter the frail and temporary sanctuary of the classroom. No easy task in itself.

Using the frequent bus service from the estate to NK, kids could travel the above routes to school in some safety. There was an alternative mode of travel, however, often used by people such as me. We would sell our free bus pass in order to fund our smoking habit and we would walk these routes to school.

This was not an advisable alternative for softies.

I can't imagine a soft lad braving the walk through the estate and along Merryhill Road in a pristine school uniform - that would be like hanging out a sign asking the local thugs to mug him.

I also know that a weaker kid would never take the short cut along the smelly rat-infested canal to Ruchill and then walk the remainder of his route to school along Merryhill Road. The canal was a very quiet and hidden route and, in a land of opportunist thugs, it gave far too many opportunities to passing or loitering crazies for mugging or torture. Soft lads might as well have announced their intent before they set off, painted a target on their school bags and waited patiently to give all their valuables away. For softies this route was suicide.

Still, no matter how arduous the journey, these were the ways to get from the Cawder housing estate to NK school. No matter how hard or soft a person was, they had to make this journey each day and hope that they could get to and from the place unmolested.

Believe it or not, there were a few rare lads of a pacifist, non-fighting, non-gang-member persuasion on our estate. My hat goes off to them. In terms of being hard men, I really believe that they were the hardest on our estate. You would have to be pretty hard to endure the same mental and physical torture each day and yet still keep going. Regardless of their fears, they still went to school, still did their best to work hard and tried to make something of their lives. These brave lads just kept bouncing back after beatings, muggings, threats and constant humiliation.

They were the real hard men at school.

They were not always the brainiest kids, either. Sometimes they were downright borderline academics in class, but something in their make-up or upbringing kept them trying, and they never changed no matter how much aggravation they were subjected to.

My hat comes off to you, boys!

This was just one aspect of life within the Cawder housing estate. A survival zone which was appropriately bordered on one side by the biggest graveyard in Glasgow and by violence and trouble all around it.

The streets were much meaner in your day, dad? Absolute pish!

From CYT to the street gang who named themselves the Cross, the streets were a Glasgow equivalent of the untamed American Wild West that our law enforcement service was impotent to restrain.

Believe me, living in this war zone was no easy option - these were mean streets.

CHAPTER XVI

Mental Malkie

As I write this book and think about the old Cawder Young Team, I get a laugh imagining that a now much older Mental Malkie, renowned CYT gang member and one-time 'leader-off' (gang leader), has read these words and is talking to his mate Wee Jimmy in the Cutter Bar.

The dialogue might go something like this:

Malkie: 'Hey, Jimmy, did ye see that book Full Circle by that cunt Smith? He's goat uz boys in there. Did ye see that, Jim? The cunt's talkin' aboot the CYT 'n 'at'. If eh' ever comes back here, ah'm goana' huv that cunt. He's dead if he ever comes back tae this scheme.'

Jimmy: 'Fuckin' bastard's slaggin' us aff? We shid find oot where that bastard lives...'

Malkie would growl these words at the ears of an outwardly enthusiastic, but generally uninterested, Wee Jimmy. Jimmy, of course, never needed to be interested to want to find out where somebody lived and - well - give the bastard a 'Malkie'! (Malkie was such a 'famous' local thug that dealing out a horrendous near-death-or-worse beating was now synonymous with his name - this was Malkie's biggest source of pride.)

Malkie would display the appropriate disdain, shoulders stationary, head moving, to emphasize his words in the proper Glasgow fashion. As he spoke to Jimmy, his guttural voice would project the promise of violence and CYT revenge, but, if you were to look closely, deep in his eyes you would see the pride of recognition. In reading my words, written about the CYT, calling them the 'top team' of my era, calling him the top thug - the heady flame of notoriety would burn brightly at the centre of this wee hard man's eyes.

I doubt if he'd really understand the depth of contempt I have for him and his kind.

Malkie was never big. Like most Glaswegians he never reached the six-foot mark. He always looked big, though. He projected big! He had a big reputation. Malkie's not just a Glasgow hard man, you understand. In his day he was the hard man. Even now that he's gone into semi-retirement, he's a forty-something that people don't ever mess with. You only have to look at Malkie's face to know that somebody might beat him in a battle, but the only way to survive the war would be to kill him.

Malkie stands about five foot ten in his worn-out shoes. He generally wears the half-rumpled suit jacket of a regular visitor to the Cutter Bar (usually in fashionably faded brown). He'll either be wearing an ordinary pair of not-too-stained trousers, belted tightly, or a pair of faded denim jeans. Even in his legendary heyday he was never a slave to fashion and was always happy in a stout pair of fighting boots, a pair of rumpled trousers and a T-shirt or short-sleeved shirt that displayed to best effect his ugly collection of tattoos - particularly the Bar-L dots, which denoted the time he had spent as a guest of the Barlinnie Young Offenders' Institution.

Malkie was never good-looking in any sense of the word. He always had the scrawny body of a 1930s prizefighter, which served only to accentuate the solid muscles in his arms. He has mousy brown hair, which started receding by the time he was 18 years old. He wears a few second-prize scars across his face, but in Malkie's case you really don't want to see the state of the other feller.

You might have looked at Malkie and thought: scrawny runt (if you'd ever said it to his face, of course, you wouldn't have survived to read this story). You might have been right about his scrawny appearance, but it would have been suicidal to ever mistake that thin look for physical or mental weakness. I've seen Malkie take boys the size of a WWF wrestler and turn them into a writhing mass of bloody, violated agony within a few scant minutes.

Malkie could fight.

Malkie could really fight.

Very, very few could hate and hurt like Mental Malkie.

He definitely earned both the fear he instilled and the fear that he always kept locked within the depths of his dwindling humanity. He'd slashed more than a few faces. He'd kicked fuck out of more than a few friends, foes and incidental strangers. He'd violated his share of girls. He'd stabbed, ripped, nutted, tortured and dehumanized his way into the annals of local Cawder history.

He did all of this in the interest of gaining and maintaining his CYT gold bars. I doubt if Malkie really cared enough about anyone in particular to actually hate them, but he was prepared, at the slightest provocation, to turn unfettered, maniacal rage on anyone. This was one boy who was determined to remain as the top dog.

If there was ever a need for a hard-man curriculum vitae, Malkie's would display: 'has knocked off stuff from shops; has knocked off and burned out cars; has fought with and damaged policemen; has terrorized Pakistanis and other ethnic-looking punters; has served time in the Barlinnie Young Offenders' Institution; has taken lives; has degraded, tortured and abused many members of the public; and has both given and received battle scars; willing to do it all again with maximum enthusiasm and without any provocation whatsoever.'

Malkie was a thief by profession. Probably the only thing that he had never taken or attempted to take by the age of 21 - was a prisoner. No, if you got in Malkie's way, it meant damage. You would be subjected to an incident of violence and degradation as dreadful and as permanent as the circumstances allowed.

Malkie was a nutter - he was king of the nutters.

There have been many bodies, scarred by knives and half eaten by rats, lying at the bottom of the canal between Cawder and Merryhill. More than a few were particular works of sadism wholly attributable to Malkie, with his head full of the favoured local beverage 'Special Brew' as he 'performed for the boys'. There would always be a supporting cast for his performances, you understand. The hangers-on and the Malkie-admirers, who would egg him on, glad to be on the winning side of his evil temper and hoping that association with Mental Malkie would offer them some general protection on the streets. Some of these guys might even have spared an occasional sympathetic thought for the victims of Malkie's ire, but they would never risk their own status or security by offering him anything other than encouragement during his antics, no matter how painful these atrocities were to witness.

As for any of his cronies telling the police? That was real suicide. Grassing was the ultimate crime in this world. Once you were known to have grassed, you were excommunicated. You were free prey to any and every Young Team in the area - and they all wanted a piece of you. Even if your information had led to Malkie being incarcerated for one of his crimes, the process of law being what it was you had the inevitability of knowing that, one day, he would be back and, no matter what horrors your imagination conjured up - believe me - the final retribution would be much worse. Such retribution would not just be visited on you, it would be dealt out to your whole family and anyone associated with you.

So Malkie kept surviving his crimes and, with each heinous act, his reputation just kept growing.

He did serve time occasionally. The police obviously had him marked and, whenever possible, they would haul him in and throw him in jail for some offence or other. Far from acting as a deterrent, however, this time in prison served both to enhance his reputation and to encourage him on to bigger, more extravagant acts of mayhem. You see, prison was a school to people like Mental Malkie. In prison you learned new tricks and met new 'hoods'. Prison had its own pecking order and if you rose to the top 'inside', as Malkie did, then your reputation spread outside the bounds of your home ganglands and into the wider expanse of the city. Prison was an opportunity to develop new criminal skills and to build an even bigger reputation. Through new associations formed in jail, people like Mental Malkie could even get a chance to be a part of better paying crimes.

I always thought that he'd eventually go too far and commit a crime too big to hide. I imagined that he'd get caught and that the authorities would lock him up and throw away the key (or, like Jimmy Boyle, that he'd get an education in prison, paint pictures, write a best-selling book and then get released to a life of comfort and social notoriety). It never happened in my time, though. Malkie was never chained for long; in fact he just kept getting bigger.

I could go on to give the madman his full CV. I could describe many nights like the night when the CYT, led by the mental guy himself, destroyed the local Merryhill Fleet. The night when Malkie gained special battle honours, by actually chopping off one downed opponent's hand with his well sharpened kindling axe, known as his 'chib'. (He'd actually borrowed the weapon from his granny's coal cellar that night in anticipation of the melee to follow.) After the bloodbath, the chasing, the (always belated) intervention of the beleaguered police force, his escape, the new T-shirt to get rid of the blood, Mental Malkie celebrated victory by nailing the newly dissected limb to the door of the Fleet's local pub in the wee hours of the night - as a warning.

I think the life of his mutilated victim was saved, but I can't really remember. Nobody talked much about the long-term fate of a loser in these street wars. All the street talk was saved for the exploits of the winners.

Unfortunately, such violence was commonplace in my teenage world.

It wasn't the violence of this 'nutter' that burned his image into my memories of life in Cawder; it was something else that made him unforgettable. You see, although the story I have just told would indicate otherwise, Malkie wasn't actually stupid.

I remember him as a wee boy at school. I remember his good school marks, the big numbers from his IQ tests and his obvious comprehension.

I also remember the pains he took to hide his intelligence from the teachers.

I remember the victory and defeat mixed in his eyes, when Miss McClaren told the whole school at assembly that Malkie McBain was 'just an evil child who would never know anything other than crime and violence'. She pointed at him and said, 'You're nothing, McBain; nothing.' If you looked closely at McBain you could have just glimpsed a little bit of hurt, but that was quickly hidden - to the general school population, Malkie crowed that day. I remember it well and I'm pretty sure that this was the day he finally gave in and accepted the life other people expected him to follow. That was the day at the crossroads of Malcolm McBain's choices. I guess it was the day that Malcolm McBain died and we saw the birth of Mental Malkie.

He was only nine years old.

It was also a day that launched my determination to escape one day and never become a Mental Malkie. I knew that I wasn't nothing, no matter what my teachers thought.

Malcolm McBain knew that he was considered nothing and was prepared to do anything to make sure that he was noticed. They might think that he was nothing, but Malkie would make sure that they never forgot him! He'd never needed Miss McClaren to tell him what they thought he was. Perhaps he could have risen above it, even though in our world that was a long shot, but instead he just took their judgement and chose to make himself something as Mental Malkie. Something that nobody would mess with, somebody who would make them keep their mouths shut!

He created a monster and, although he knew what an offence his existence as Mental Malkie was to the 'normal' world, he didn't care. I wonder what he did to avoid glimmers of truth about what he was becoming seeping through his mental armour and into his conscience? I wonder if he really cared? Or maybe I'm just dreaming and seeing Malkie in a way that I would perceive myself in his circumstances. Who knows? I never got close enough to Malcolm McBain to find out, but there is no doubt in my mind that, if evil exists, it found a patch of willing soil to bury its roots inside the soul of Mental Malkie.

As we grew up on the estate, Malkie always hated me. I think in his eyes I had somehow escaped, and he didn't like people getting away. I never got sucked into his 'team' or his darkness. I fought, as fearlessly and as viciously as I needed to, but I never gave in and joined his team. I think he saw me as a traitor somehow.

But Malkie never challenged me with anything other than a look. Like a few other kids on the estate I had my armour, and there were too many easy victims around for him to bother messing with my demons. He had little to say to me and I had nothing to say to him.

I wonder what I would say to Malkie if I was to meet him today?

I think it would be: 'Don't mistake anything in this story for admiration of you and yours, McBain. You were even less of a human being than the rest of your tribe. You at least were intelligent and made conscious choices, while some of the kids were driven into 'nutterhood' through fear of folk like you.

'I was never one of 'your boys', Malkie, and you would have done anything to prevent my escape and turn me into somebody like you, because if we weren't 'yours' we were the enemy.

'You were and probably still are an evil bastard, McBain, and only significant as a sad example of one of life's perversions that should be avoided at all cost and destroyed whenever possible. So, take your meaningless life and suffer, as I saw and heard you make others suffer.

'An eye for an eye, Malkie? I've heard you use these words to justify some brutality or other, as I walked by and never challenged your bragging or your brutality. I've wished many times I'd 'done' you for your acts of atrocity, McBain, but then I'd have just been like you and I guess you'd have won.

'But look at you now - down-at-heel, has-been, going-nowhere McBain. Even if you're not in jail where you belong, in your case nobody had to perform an act of revenge on behalf of society to beat you. In your case - the eye for an eye's an own goal!'

I hope you do read this, Malkie...

CHAPTER XVII

Hide your Daughters

There were many nights on the canal bank, commonly known as 'the nolly', when some member of the CYT would bring a poor female victim up for sex (she thinking it was a date) and then, after he had had his way, the rest of the young team would appear. What followed, under the certain threat of extreme violence, would divest the poor wee lassie of any shred of dignity she would ever possess, either then or at any other time in her now easy-to-predict future. You see, once she had submitted for the first time, she never had no as a viable option.

Punchy was famous for this trick. Up in court for rape three times - no convictions. These poor girls and their families had to live in the housing schemes without protection and there were never witnesses to be found so that a perpetrator could be convicted. Occasionally the wrong girl would be raped or molested and some bloody family vengeance would follow. Vigilante retribution was the real rule of law on our estate, as grassing to the police was never considered as an option.

I remember being within earshot of Punchy's arrogant voice at school one day, when he and some of his sycophants were laughing and insulting Marlene to her face about the previous Saturday night. Marlene was sobbing and pleading with the boys not to tell anyone at school. Punchy promised they'd all shut up, if they got 'seconds' up on the canal bank at dinnertime.

I walked away and never heard poor Marlene's answer.

I do remember how that poor girl changed, though. She just seemed to wither. Belatedly her parents took her out of our school and moved somewhere else. One of the girls in school that I often spoke to told me that, after Marlene had gone, she was consumed with guilt for what had happened on that first night. She somehow saw the incident as her own fault and it was killing her. Her parents had eventually managed to move her to another school in a different area. They finally noticed the depth of her pain and, fearing what she would do to herself, tried to solve the problem with a slight change in her environment.

Marlene went willingly into hiding, but she never moved far enough out of the area and so failed to escape being prey. The stories about her continued to circulate within the estate and she never went to the police about her attacks. A new school a few miles from ours wasn't quite enough to save her.

Bits of Marlene died every day. In her mind, she was already soiled. In her poor young mind, she had lost her worth.

Marlene, Marlene, how could you think you'd done wrong? You were living in a zoo, a gentle prey to obscenely perverted animals. I hated them for you, Marlene; I cried inside for you, but it didn't help, did it? When I heard that you'd married one of them, many years later, I could have wept. Marlene, Marlene, beautiful, gentle Marlene; what did these bastards do to you, to make you give up so completely?

In Cawder, if you had a daughter, you either should have hoped that she was never pretty enough to attract the attention of these animals, or you should have hired her a bodyguard. I don't know about locking up your daughters, but in our jungle they definitely needed to be guarded.

Marlene wasn't the only one to suffer.

Street survival was hard on the lassies.

CHAPTER XVIII

CYT Ya Bas

There were several ways into the housing scheme and the CYT made sure that they were all covered. If a stranger, police car, on-foot police-man (however unlikely!) or anyone without a home, connections or rep-utation on the estate tried to come into CYT Land, they could be bom-barded by stones, broken bottles or any other handy missile, from the top of the canal bridge at the border of one side of the estate. If they came on foot from any other direction, including across the graveyard, or through the fields, they could be met and chased by well-armed Young Team patrols. If they tried to enter by bus (the most foolhardy option for any of these prospective victims), they could easily be trapped on that bus and open to 'abuse at leisure' from the thug pack through-out their journey - not a happy scenario.

I remember hearing, one day, that team members were being assigned different routes to guard by Mental Malkie. That was the start of organ-ized thug patrols. Eventually it just became the norm for one group or another to roam a particular area within the housing scheme, and the CYT fell into a solid routine of guard duty.

Team members, assigned to guard against territorial violation, would ride the bus for free within the boundaries of the scheme. Bus conduc-tors, usually given the route because they came from the estate, would not have the courage to actually ask for fares, and fearful bus inspectors knew when to cut their losses and save their skin by not bothering to check on these passengers.

It was an unspoken law, one of the gang's inviolate laws - 'no strangers get to roam the estate with impunity'. It was considered every CYT member's duty to enforce this law.

Territorial incursions were always punished hard. Team members learned the finer points of dehumanization, mutilation and violation, while keeping the housing estate clear of outsiders. Occasionally, when drink or circumstances dictated, they would also go too far and learn how to administer the ultimate sanction. Killing was never common, but it happened occasionally.

In Mental Malkie's day, with the gang protected through outsiders' fear of the main man himself, even small kids were well blooded and were almost certain to generate their own legendary stories of violence in the future.

Almost every kid in Cawder was an integral part of the 'Young Team'. Lads and girls of all ages aspired to be the hardest, the most feared and therefore the most respected of the pack. There was very little that a kid wouldn't do to prove himself or herself to their peers, and as a result many potentially bright futures were subjugated at a very early age. All over the estate the banner was portrayed in colourfully spray-painted signs: 'CYT Ya Bas'.

Acting like heroes, yet creating a living hell. Cawder Young Team - you certainly were a bunch of wee bastards!

CHAPTER XIX

Wee Jimmy

Most Saturday afternoons outside the Cutter Bar, in striking contrast to his pal Mental Malkie, would stand Wee Jimmy. He is very small in stature and is permanently battle-scarred (some of these scars were presents from his best mate - Malkie). He assumes that the facial scars make him look a bit harder and Jimmy wears his hard man image with pride.

Although Jimmy is small, he makes up for his diminutive size by sheer, raw aggression. He is always at the forefront of the charge, always ready to pounce on an opportunity to attack, hurt or maim - Jimmy has always maintained his reputation by being fearless. I'd simply call it stupidity and bravado - this boy has no brains at all!

Part of his lack of intelligence may, of course, be down to the severity of his gang-fight injuries. He will always wear a steel plate in his head from the night he charged into a battle with the Tong, only to discover that Soft-Man had talked Malkie into holding back the troops a wee bit for a laugh. Jimmy charged in, determined to show no fear - and he got massacred. By the time his laughing, screaming mates arrived to fight back the opposing savages and drag his barely living remains to safety, he was so badly damaged that he needed to spend two months in intensive care and have a steel plate welded onto his skull.

For most people, such an incident would be a definite indication to change their lifestyle; not for Jimmy, though. Jimmy thought he'd made it that night, with: his two months' intensive care; the steel plate; his nearly constant twitch; his limp; and the nine months' imprisonment in the Barlinnie Young Offenders' Institution (the police were always quick to arrest the bleeding bodies after a big gang fight). I imagine that he'd consider the trouble a bargain, because it had also earned him: full acceptance as a major nutter in the CYT; his hero Malkie's recognition and protection; and a licence to carry out spontaneous violence on any-one he felt like - after all, who'd mess with such a madman. After the night he was 'betrayed for a laugh', Jimmy now generated fear on and off of the housing estate.

What would I say to Jimmy if I met him now? I think it might be: 'Well played, Jimmy; you're definitely a real nutter now - ya poor wee halfwit!' But I'm sure he'd miss the point. Jimmy would never really remember the pain of that fateful night, as he was always too busy bask-ing in the notoriety it bought him.

In fact, sad Wee Jimmy only remembered four things: to perform vio-lent acts whenever he could; the people who owed him money or drinks; his place in the pecking order, which he judged as being just under Malkie; and revenge. Love had never graced Jimmy's life. Compassion was an alien concept - but not revenge, particularly violent revenge. That thought made Jimmy's eyes shine, and almost put lustre into his receding, shoulder-length, 1960s-style haircut.

I'm sure that Jimmy still remembers that he owes me some revenge, even after all this time. If he ever discussed me with Malkie, I could imagine him saying something like: 'Aye, Malkie, I hope that bastard comes back here one day, because I've goat a wee message fur that cunt!'

As I've said, Wee Jimmy was known to be fearless. But he was fear-less because he had the backing of his team and knew his place in the pecking order. Even Jimmy wouldn't challenge some people. He had been given too many bad beatings on his 'way up'. No, there were peo-ple that Jimmy knew he could beat only with his team adding their intimidation or muscle. I was eventually one of these people, but the crazy wee hard man had needed a sharp reminder.

It's a reminder that I'm betting will still grate on the wee man.

Within the scope of confrontation on our estate, it was a pretty small incident. I was walking through the scheme (housing estate), on my way to the youth club for a game of badminton - my sporting passion at the time. I was the top player in our area, and on my way - I hoped - to becoming a top Scottish player. I was fanatical about improving my game and would not be deterred from my goal by the fact that the youth club where I practiced also doubled as the Cawder Young Team's primary meeting place.

This night Jimmy and about 20 of the Young Team members were hanging about on the corner outside the youth club. As I passed them, nodding to some, ignoring most, Jimmy stepped in front of me.

'Where dae ye think yer goin', Smith? Gie's that bat and I'll let ye past.'

Jimmy had a smirk on his face that I knew meant: 'I'm going to show off at your expense, Smith, and if you don't take it, me and the team are going to sort you out.'

I stopped, put on a stony face, said nothing and...

Snick, click.

I waited, staring him out.

I saw a brief change in Jimmy's eyes and I could see that he had just remembered my reputation, but he quickly covered it up, as the girls who were hanging out with the gang started to taunt him.

'What's up, Jimmy? Are ye scared or somethin'? Can ye no' handle badminton boy?'

Damn! Jimmy's hard man reputation was now firmly on the line. Unfortunately, so was mine - if he started, I had to finish.

Snick, click.

I stood waiting, knowing that any movement forward on my part would start things off and I'd probably have to deal with the whole gang. I waited, solid, face still impassive, and looked for Wee Jimmy's inevitable move.

The rest of the gang had formed a semicircle behind Jimmy. Mental Malkie was looking on with a half frown, probably wondering why I wasn't displaying the usual fear that the gang had come to expect from such incidents. The girls looked anxiously between Jimmy, Malkie and me, awaiting the action and their next opportunity to goad us into violence.

Snick, click.

Jimmy was getting restless. He glanced behind; gathering courage from the team arrayed at his back, especially Mental Malkie's presence, and with a confident smirk, he made a grab for my badminton racket.

Snick, click.

I had been holding my badminton racket under my arm and, as he made his move, I grabbed the handle with my right hand, pulled the racket down to my right side and sidestepped Jimmy's forward lunge.

Snick, click, bang!

As Jimmy, now overbalancing from missing his lunge for my racket, stumbled towards me, I grabbed his left wrist with my left hand, held the pressure point on his wrist between my thumb and my fingers and twisted hard. My other passion at this time was martial arts and I was getting pretty fast and fairly confident.

Jimmy kept falling and landed on his right side, while I twisted his arm with my left hand. He squealed and cursed me. I was pushing his arm back against the joint and I knew that he must be in agony.

'Let go, Smith, ya bastard! Let go or I'll kill ye, ah'm no' kidding. Aaaawww! LET GO! Malkie! Handers, Malkie'

This was the customary pitiful cry of a team member, used to gain the overwhelming support from his gang in a fight that he was losing. 'Handers' they would cry, and the rest of the team would pile into the other lad, giving him no chance whatsoever of surviving the contest.

Snick, click, bang!

Expecting the worst, I pushed Wee Jimmy harder into the ground and, while still holding onto his wrist, put my right foot on his left side for leverage. If I was 'getting it', Jimmy's arm was coming right off! I looked up, just as I was about to throw my weight forward against his arm and...

Mental Malkie had his arm across the chest of one of the other boys, stopping him from moving into the fray. The rest of the gang were poised to join in, but were looking to their leader for a signal. The girls were shifting nervously, hunched forward to goad and stick a pointy shoe into my face or body when the guys brought me down.

But at that moment the tableau was frozen.

Face still impassive, I looked straight into Mental Malkie's eyes and held his gaze.

Snick, click.

I eased my finger off the mental trigger of my illusionary rifle, but allowed my eyes to fill with warning, so that he knew - if it starts - he'd be next and it'd be worse than a lost arm if I could help it. The exchange was probably over in seconds, but - for me - time seemed to slip by like treacle dripping off of a spoon. I waited, and in my mind everybody disappeared except me and the leader of the pack.

Then Malkie spoke. 'You started it, Jimmy. I'm fed up bailing you oot - you take 'im. Go on, ya wee hard man - let's see ye take 'im.'

I knew then that I had won.

Malkie was smart. He knew I wasn't an easy kill and he knew what my reputation meant: if a battle started, then it wouldn't be over until at least one of us was unable to walk; even if they beat me today, he would have a challenger at his back, one who was just as capable of doing the business as he was; if there was a knock on the door at his house, it could be me waiting there with an iron bar. Mental Malkie didn't flinch from a direct challenge, but I hadn't challenged him. It was Jimmy's problem. Malkie had no pride on the line and he could afford not to get involved.

Malkie addressed his pack. 'Stand back, you lot; they're baith Cawder boys - let them huv a square go!'

At their leader's command, the pack backed off, and, although they resumed their glowering stance, they made no overt moves towards me. I could see, written across their faces, that they didn't like it, and they certainly didn't like me, but Malkie's word was law. His decree constituted a line that they wouldn't dare cross.

I looked down at Jimmy, still lying in agony on the ground.

'He's breaking ma arm, Malkie! The bastard's breakin' ma arm! Get him aff, somebody!'

Snick, click.

The sights of my 'comforter' moved away from Malkie's head and focused on the wee hard man at my feet. I moved myself around till I was standing at Jimmy's head, still holding onto his arm and twisting it further back, the movement sending excruciating shafts of agony into the joint of his shoulder. Whatever happened now, Jimmy's fighting days were definitely postponed for a while. I used my foot and forced the right side of his face down into the tarmac. He squealed even louder as he was pinned and, with sweat joining the tears in his eyes, he pleaded with me to stop.

'So, you want a square go, Jimmy?' I said. 'Nae bother. I'd like tae see how a one-armed man gies me a do'in! What d'ye say, Jimmy? Dae ye want a square go or no?'

I took the pressure off his arm a little to ease the pain - just enough so that he could answer me without having to scream.

'I'll get ye, ya' bastard! When I get up I'll fuckin' kill ye!'

Bad answer.

Snick, click, bang!

I put the pressure back onto his arm - hard! We all heard Jimmy's socket pop, and his squeals even made the hardened Young Team members blanche a little.

'Nae bother, Jimmy,' I said above his shrieks. 'I don't mind rippin' both yer arms aff.'

I wanted this to be a lesson. Not just to the too-stupid-to-surrender Jimmy, but to the rest of the gang as well. I knew that, by tomorrow evening, the whole of the gang and everybody at school would have heard of this incident. I would use it to reinforce my position as one of the 'untouchables' on the estate.

I let go of Jimmy's arm and stood back.

'Get up, Jimmy. I thought ye wanted a square go?'

Jimmy writhed in agony, with his arm twisted at a sickening angle halfway behind his back. He stared at me with wide open and agonized eyes as he squealed pitifully and tried to roll away. I casually stepped towards him.

'NO! Naw, Smith. I gie in. Honest, I gie in - honest, please...'

The message had been delivered.

I kept my face impassive, shrugged my shoulders, put my badminton racket back under my arm and dismissed Wee Jimmy with a look.

'No' much of a fighter, boys,' I said as I sauntered past the now-silent onlookers. 'Cannae take the pain - eh? Just as well fur him that I'm late for ma game. He'll keep till ah've goat mair time - eh?'

Programmed to be on the winning side, most of the team nodded in agreement, casting disparaging looks at the luckless Wee Jimmy, who was still rolling in agony on the pavement in front of them. They looked at me with grudging respect. This was a survival lesson and one that they had leaned pretty thoroughly. None of them wanted to be Jimmy - or worse. As I strolled nonchalantly away, I heard Malkie dismiss the incident: 'come oan, boys, let's go. An' you, Jimmy - get up, ya saft wee bastard, and get that arm fixed -fucking loser.'

I went to my badminton class that night feeling that my armour had grown a little bit stronger around me.

There were other similar nights, but thankfully not too many, when I had to battle for survival on the estate. But this is the night that must still burn deep in Wee Jimmy's memory. It was quite a while before he used that arm again. He learned nothing more from the incident, though, than to pick easier victims or to ensure that the gang was in on the kill before he started an attack. He quickly made up the loss of face by picking on a series of guys he knew he could beat and then damaging them atrociously.

Because of nights like this I was also known as a nutter in some quarters; but I didn't care - I knew I was leaving one day. People such as Wee Jimmy would never escape; the damage was too deep. The conversion from human being to an evil thug living a life of wasteful brutality was permanent.

As I look back and remember some of the characters from my childhood, I value that escape from the streets of Glasgow more and more.

I remember you, Jimmy.

There, but for the grace of God...

SONG 8 - SCHOOLBOY BLUES

Here I am (I'm here) I'm stuck in school (I wanna be cool)
I want to learn, but I'm alone, so I act the fool
(misunderstood now)
They've got me pegged now, as trouble - not as cool
(I'm a troubled boy) (he's trouble)

What's the matter now, my marks are good (top of the class)
No chance of recognition though, because I break the rules
(can't help it, teacher)
Two types of people here, the victims and the hoods
(I wanna be strong)

Have not long to go (you should go), last term in this place
(I'll get away)
School's gone psychedelic - new game, same old face
(still the elite boys)
At least it's cool now, to find yourself some peace
(give peace a chance)

Chorus
Here it goes again (again) drives me round the bend
(right round the bend)
I can't be good, I know I should - maybe I'm insane
(I'm losing my mind here)
I'll try to do better, if you'll just let me explain
(I wanna be good)

CHAPTER XX

NK

Hope wasn't something that experience had helped nurture inside me. Hope had not been inherited from those adults with whom I had shared my existence. And yet North Kintyre, at the age of 11, symbolized that very thing - hope. I can still remember the primary school leaving-talks from my teacher.

'This is an opportunity for you, children. It's a chance to make something of yourselves. If you perform well at NK, then you can give yourself an opportunity for a bright future. But if you mess around, you will be expelled and transferred to the junior school and you will have given up any chance of making something better of yourselves.'

(Obviously the kids going on to a junior school were well screwed!)

'Remember that you are only going to NK because of your IQ results and your eleven-plus marks. You can very easily be taken out of there. There are plenty of places at the junior secondary.'

And the teacher had a little personal barb for me.

'Especially you, Smith! If I had my way, you would not be going to NK at all!'

I listened with excitement, undeterred by the personal reference and the obvious loathing in my teacher's voice when she had singled me out. In fact, her venom served only to encourage me. 'If she didn't want me to go to NK, it must be a great place to go.'

Perhaps this was my chance. Perhaps, from now on, I could shed my armour and take open enjoyment in my education and school life. Perhaps I would make new friends of a like mind and we would learn together, have fun together and forever banish both solitude and aggression.

Perhaps pigs in frilly petticoats would jump over the moon...

I was soon disabused of these fairy-tale notions.

How can I ever forget my very first day at NK? I arrived, another pristinely uniformed 11-year-old boy, ready to start his initial six months in 'prep'.

In these days a 'classic' education was still taught at secondary school. Children were streamed by ability, each group getting a designation that started at A and went to F. If you were in the A stream, then you were in the most academic group and you were given the classic subjects, such as Latin and Greek. If you were in the F group, you were given much more metalwork, woodwork and sports in your curriculum than your more elite peers.

'Prep' was the school's way of both inducting children and finding out their abilities. During this period you would get a wide range of subjects and your aptitude for each would be assessed. It seemed a good system to me and I was primed and eager to use this time to make my mark. I swore to myself that, no matter what happened, I would avoid trouble and troublemakers. Davy, my friend from primary, was of the same mind, and together we were looking forward to starting out on the road to that 'bright future' we'd been told about in our exit propaganda speech at primary school.

My first impression of NK school was that it was old. It had two buildings, separated by a lane that ran between them and accessible by parallel roads running down each side of the buildings. The bottom building was called the 'old' school and the upper building was called the 'new' school, although I could not see what was 'new' about any part of these constructions. The buildings were grey from the city pollution that they had gathered over time. They still had outside toilets, which regularly froze each winter and smelled so bad that they made the shared Glasgow tenement toilets of the time seem like luxury.

The top building was the location for new children to gather on their first day. This building was built on two levels. It had an upper and a lower playground, with the actual school building thrusting up from the bottom playground to tower over the top playground. It was a big structure and I remember feeling dwarfed by it at the time.

Davy and I arrived bright and early for our first day at school and we waited, with many of the other confused-looking new intake, in the bottom playground. We hung around, feeling a mixture of excitement and trepidation, waiting for the bell to ring and for someone to shepherd us to our first lesson.

'Hey, you!'

I was facing the road when I heard the voice. Davy was facing the upper playground and so must have seen the speaker. I looked at Davy's face, not wanting to turn around or to engage in any movement or eye contact with this guy. I just hoped that he was not talking to us, but, by the transformation taking place on Davy's face, it didn't look hopeful. Davy, like me, had learned how to be impassive. His face was turning to stone - not a good sign.

'Hey, you! Curly heid! Are you some kind of Paki or somethin'? You, first year, turn 'roon'!'

My heart sank. Obviously my pristine uniform had marked me as a new boy and, as usual, my curly hair and half-caste looks had made me stand out to this troublemaker. Obviously there was an element in this environment that saw certain kids as prey. I hoped that he was an exception and not the rule.

Davy and I looked at each other, neither of us wanting to look at this boy, or confront our worst fears about this 'brave new start' we had supposedly been given.

Even my mental comforter was silent. I must have subconsciously buried my weapons, hoping against hope that I would not need them here. I decided to walk away. Nodding to Davy that he should go in a different direction, which we hoped would show that we were not a 'team' looking for trouble, just wee boys, scared enough to walk away and prepared to accept this verbal taunting. I walked towards the other side of the playground.

'Where the fuck dae ye think you're goin', pal? Did ah say ye could walk away frae me?'

Davy and I just kept walking in separate directions across the playground. Neither of us looked back at the antagonist or across at each other. We wanted no confrontation - not today - not a blot on our bright new futures.

I listened, straining my ears for some salvation. When was that bell going to ring?

It wasn't to be. I felt a hand on my shoulder.

'Hey! Hey, you - darkie-boy!'

He spun me around, making my escape impossible. I stopped and assessed this threat to my freedom from violence.

I learned later that his name was Jakey. Probably he'd been christened Jacob, but had adopted Jakey as a cooler description to have on the streets. The parents who had christened Jacob probably wouldn't recognise this snarling little bully-boy who was trying to intimidate the newest and, by definition, the weakest members of the school hierarchy. I'm sure they thought that he was a nice wee boy.

He wasn't.

Jakey was not much taller than me. I had grown in a big surge just before I left primary school and was then only about one inch shorter than my eventual height of five foot eleven in my socks.

Jakey's uniform was scruffy, his shoes were scraped and unpolished, and his tie was rumpled and skewed. He had a long face to match his skinny body, framed at the top with a mop of dirty brown hair that looked as if it had been greased with chip fat. He had more than the usual amount of teenage acne all over his face and he had a long and pointy nose. His thin-lipped mouth wore the type of sneer I had seen on 100 other would-be hard men.

'Where the fuck dae ye think you're goin', darkie-boy? What's in that bag - eh? Huv ye got any money, boy?'

Snick, click!

Reluctantly I levelled my mental pacifier at his head. I knew what was coming. This was an old story in my young mind. Here was another predator and he had picked me out as his prey. I had nowhere to run and experience had taught me that there were no guardian angels waiting to sort these people out. Jakey was a third-year, I was a 'preppy', and Jakey felt that this meant that he could prey on me whenever he felt like it.

Snick, click!

Jakey continued to snarl.

'Gie's that bag and I'll huv a look mysel'. You just get yer money oot yer pockets and ye'll no get hurt, pal!'

You may say that, perhaps my school life would have been different if I'd just let Jakey have his way, took it on the chin and walked away. Perhaps in some environments that would have been true. I could have taken the punishment, walked away, maybe even reported the mugging to some authority and been given back my stuff. Unfortunately, in this environment, all it would have meant was weakness. I'd have been a target for constant future intimidation; prey to anyone who wanted to show off or flex his muscles.

I wouldn't go there.

Snick, click!

I stood impassive, letting the stone countenance of my armour cover my stance and my features.

Snick, click!

I tried to lock Jakey's eyes, but he was too far gone with his intimidation and too confident in his status as a third-year to take any notice.

I wasn't obeying and Jakey was getting impatient. With a final snarl, he reached for the brand new school bag tucked under my arm.

Snick, click!

Perhaps it was born of the disappointment I felt, finding that the same street rules that I was used to on the estate of Cawder were prevalent in NK; perhaps it was these years of frustration that I had tried to suppress, so that I could really make something of this new start, that acted to fuel the power of my response.

I don't know what gave me the strength, but it became one of the ugliest moments of retribution I ever delivered.

Snick, click, bang!

As Jakey's hand moved towards me, I pulled back my head and butted him with all the strength I could muster. His nose exploded in a fountain of blood and his hands made a belated attempt to cover his shocked face.

Snick, click, bang!

I went berserk. I pinned Jakey's neck with my left arm and punched and punched and punched into his ruined face with my right fist till I had knocked him to the ground.

Then I started kicking him with all the strength I could marshall.

A crowd had gathered, forming the traditional circle around us, and the kids were baying for blood, but none of this reached my enraged senses. I continued to kick Jakey with my new-start, well-polished school shoes. I battered him mercilessly.

In retrospect, I might have actually killed him if not for Davy. Somewhere in my subconscious I heard the words: 'He's finished, Les. Ye'd better let him up afore the teachers come.'

I felt a hand on my arm and just managed to stop myself from delivering a reflexive head-butt as I recognized my friend Davy standing beside me.

I took a few deep breaths, ignoring the agonized cries of a badly beaten Jakey lying curled up before me. The crowd of kids had gone silent. Many of them were not from my background and I could see the shock on their faces as their first exposure to extreme violence began to register.

'Don't ever try to pick on me or my mates again, ya bastard. D'ye hear me, pal!'

I growled these few words at Jakey, picked up my school bag and walked away, once again under control, with my features masked in stone. I could already feel the darkness of a horrible inevitability creeping up inside me.

Jakey pulled himself to his feet. His sobs were subsiding, as he attempted to regain some measure of composure in front of what he had considered his 'prey'.

As I walked away he shouted at me. 'You think ye won, ya bastard. But you just messed wi' the CYT! You're dead, pal!'

My glare was enough to deter him from any further elaboration. I looked around at the crowd, and my face was sufficient to tell the rest that it was time to break it up and go away into small huddles and gossip about what they had just witnessed.

I stopped to watch Jakey limp away, and I heard another kid say to him: 'That's Smith, Jakey. Ye know - Smith frae Cawder. The CYT'll no' touch him.'

With a sinking heart, I watched the recognition of my name dawn on his face. My reputation was once again on my back, and I'd have to carry it into this chapter of my life with me.

Poor Jakey. The CYT were the dominant gang in this school and, although he wasn't from our estate, he had bonded with them, but now he knew where I came from and he had obviously heard about my street reputation. I could see the awareness of his mistake starting to dawn on his face. He knew that he had just humiliated himself further, by delivering an empty threat.

Back in control of myself, I turned away. Davy was standing to one side of me, and as I looked over at him he just shrugged; he knew what this meant for my brave new start.

My heart sank further.

With my armour firmly in place and my mental weapons adjusted, I awaited the school bell with a feeling much less than the hope I had cherished at the beginning of this day.

A bright new future? No chance.

Snick, click.

CHAPTER XXI

The A Stream

I was in the A stream at school. Despite my chequered beginnings, despite the reputation that had followed me to this new place, via my primary school report, despite my first-day-at-school incident in prep, despite it all - I was in the A stream. Something was going right. I wasn't completely happy, though; I knew that my status in the top group at school was not quite solid, when my French teacher asked me to stay behind on the first day and said: 'Smith, you have to remember that, if you do something wrong, it stays with you for a long time. If you do something good, then the recognition is fleeting, but do something wrong...' She paused. 'I hope you make it, Smith. I really do. Just keep remembering what I told you.'

I can't even remember her name. She was an older lady and she retired that year. She had the significance of being the first adult from within the system that I could ever remember taking the time to talk to me, let alone try to help me. I wish I could remember her name.

'Yes, Miss. I understand.'

And I did. I knew the dangers inherent in being judged, categorized and written off. I really didn't want that. I really wanted to make it at this school and to use this time to learn and grow. I understood quite clearly that education was a strong weapon in my armoury - one that I was eager to acquire - and I understood that with good qualifications it would be far easier to make an escape from my current environment.

Thanks, Miss whoever-you-were; I understood you and - believe me

- I actually tried to follow your advice!

++++++++

The A-stream class consisted of a mixed-sex group within our mixed-sex school. The B stream was a girls' class and the C stream was a boys' class. This was the second academic tier, and the splitting of the sexes always indicated to me that the establishment felt that kids of lesser academic ability would not be able handle their hormones and study at the same time. Perhaps they thought that this was a bit like rubbing your stomach and simultaneously patting your head - a feat that perhaps could be mastered only by the top tier of students.

D and E were also single-sex groups of children, whilst F (which was always assumed to mean the failures - half a step away from being junior secondary) was once again mixed-sex. I don't know the logic for this. Perhaps the authorities expected the F stream to be thinking of nothing but breeding anyway and saw no reason for going through the bother of trying to keep their out-of-control adolescent hormones separated.

There must have been something in it. I remember a big to-do because one of the younger female teachers in the English department couldn't seem to stop one of the 3F boys from masturbating under his desk during lessons. No amount of 'getting the belt', or other popular punishments, seemed to deter 'Wee Handy'. Of course, the other boys in the class constantly encouraged him, even though he shared his double desk at the front of the class with no one but himself. Eventually 'Wee Handy' was expelled. He's probably a (one-handed) cameraman for one of the sex channels by now...

But I digress.

I was in the A stream and I felt as though I had made it!

I would have to distance myself from my top group peers, however. Just looking around the class, on that first day of registration, I knew this group was going to have big playground-survival problems. I wondered just how many of these kids would actually make it to the fourth year without being battered senseless.

NK had traditionally been a school of proud academic achievement. It had all the trappings of a higher education establishment built into its form. It boasted a classic education through its curriculum. It had the tradition of male and female prefects in every year, overseen by a head prefect; their duty to the school was to maintain discipline in the playground and to show a good example through their behaviour. It had proud teachers who saw themselves as student educators and expected to be shown respect. It had science laboratories, music laboratories, classrooms and gymnasiums with a long tradition of discipline and learning engraved into their uncomfortable wooden seats and hard wooden benches.

NK had a proud past, but things were changing even as I joined this school.

The government of the time, in its wisdom, was set to abolish the eleven-plus examinations, as being unfair to those children who could not perform well in single tests. Although they were still able to stomach sectarian divisions in schools, the government had lost its taste for senior and junior schools, believing that all children should be given an equal chance of competing within a standard curriculum.

This decision resulted in an educational fiasco. In later years, poor kids who would have been perfectly happy to be given a vocational education well suited to their needs were thrust into inadequacy by being made to try and learn languages, arts and sciences that were well beyond their particular abilities. Children who would have thrived under a purely academic criterion were forced to share classrooms with others who were both academically clueless and very disruptive. Of course, as with most of the things I experienced at this time, the worst elements always rose to supremacy and the good kids quickly became cannon fodder.

Government policy was about to ruin schools such as North Kintyre.

That I joined NK during this transition was evident in both the violence of the playground and the rowdiness of the classroom. Many of the older teachers were retiring and it was getting increasingly difficult for the school to recruit replacements of a high calibre. When NK had taken in a more elite group of pupils, the school would always have drawn the best teachers into its ranks. Violence was also increasing in the playground. At the time this movement towards mayhem was lead by class 3E, which was almost a school-based arm of the CYT. Disruptive behaviour was increasing in the classroom, and the prefect discipline and punishment system was breaking down completely. I was discovering that this was just the wrong era to have been awarded the honour of a place at NK!

Given my school environment, I discovered a new battle - a battle to simultaneously survive in the playground and yet still try to learn. I had not given up hope of achieving something at this stage, but I knew that it would be a hard road and I knew that my class would have 'victim' stamped on it by the lower academic tiers. I couldn't see this A group banding together to establish a ring of protection around itself!

My A-class student peers were academically clever. Some were survivors from estates like mine, but most of them were kids from nicer homes and environments - obvious cannon fodder. There was also a sprinkling of the clever-but-vicious amongst our group. These were kids similar to Malkie, who had a good brain but had no intention of letting that fact stand in the way of them earning a reputation for being hard. This was the worst threat to our ability to achieve good results in the classroom. These were the kids who would always make the grades and achieve the basic results required, but in the process would be as disruptive as possible in class. They would seek to become the 'kingpins' of the playground, and use every opportunity that they got to prey on their fellow classmates or anyone else in the school that they perceived to be weaker than them.

We had people such as Roxborough, Preston and Horsborough in our class: children of high academic ability from homes and parents who cared for and supported them; children whose parents would have been proud the first time that they saw their young children go off to school in their bright new uniforms, completely unaware of the horrors that awaited them.

I'm sure my softer peers would eventually have left school and captured careers of some importance. When they escaped the trials of the playground, they could then bury their darkest school time demons, but on that first day in 1A, with one look at these weak wee boys and girls, I could already see the sad saga of bullying and intimidation that was to follow.

I wasn't wrong with my observations.

CHAPTER XXII

Roxborough, Preston and Horsborough

'Right, you three, I've had enough of it. You're goin' tae learn how tae fight.'

This in the playground, one balmy autumn day, when I had just about had enough of watching these lads fall victim, not just to the tough guys, but even to the more vicious of the softies in our class. I couldn't watch the degradation a moment longer, without at least trying to do something, and so Roxborough, Preston Horsborough and I were standing in the upper playground this lunchtime and I was trying to show them how to fight.

Drawing both on my martial arts hobby and my own street-survival knowledge, I thought it would be best to start by showing these weaklings how to punch. The kind of reprobates who picked on them were mostly the vicious little snakes from within their own A class. My guys had mastered the art of becoming invisible to the bigger monsters in the den, but they couldn't escape the notice of these weaker denizens, as they shared the same classes each day.

I knew these bullying freaks well; they would spend equal parts of their mean existence kowtowing to the tougher lads, quietly sharing inane pseudo-intellectual humour at someone's expense, and picking on those kids who were brighter but weaker than they were themselves. If Roxborough, Preston and Horsborough managed to learn even a little defensive work, I knew that the rubbish that hounded them would quickly back down and seek easier prey. I couldn't protect the whole school, but in my year I was king and I could at least try to protect these three softies.

'This is how tae make a fist. Try it, boys!'

I was rewarded with limp-wristed efforts for my troubles.

'No' like that - like this. You couldnae bust a wet paper bag like that!'

I received cheesy grins from boys who were glad to be getting playground attention that didn't divest them of their dignity or administer any pain. But the boys made genuine attempts to mimic my actions even though their physical strength and fighting prowess hardly matched that even of the tougher 'preppy' girls.

They were useless but they tried.

I sighed. 'Boys, you're a smart bunch o' lads. Ye know that if ye kin learn tae punch, then they rats'll be too scared tae jump ye. Learn tae punch, stick together and eventually thae wee thugs'll leave ye alane.'

Roxborough, Preston and Horsborough each turned a slightly whiter shade of pale at the mere mention of a possible confrontation. Preston's eyes started to dart about nervously, probably as he prayed that the aforementioned petty thugs were well out of earshot. These guys were smart and they knew that any outward show of aggression on their part now would, if seen by the wrong people, result only in challenges they could not win. But I was on my crusade and was determined that, somehow, these guys would learn to fight back. It hadn't occurred to me that these poor boys were only standing in front of me in this cold corner of the playground because they were too scared to refuse my offer of martial training. In reality they didn't really want to fight back - they just didn't want to be fought with.

I persevered.

'Right, boys, let's try some punches now...'

Poor lads. I persisted right through our lunch break, except for a ten-minute interlude for me, when I told them to wait where they were and went into the toilets for a cigarette. When I got back my pupils hadn't moved an inch. I ignored these signs of terror and continued with their martial training.

Eventually the school bell rang, summoning us back to our classes. Roxborough and Horsborough were in my class for Latin, Preston was joining his language section for French. I gave them some bad advice, which at the time I felt was sound, to send them on their way. 'Right, boys! Remember what I teld ye. You boys stick together and, if some of thae wide boys try it on, ye just stare them oot. If they make a grab fur ye, ye punch them hard like I showed you. Don't worry, they'll soon back aff - got it?'

I must have been crazy.

They nodded agreement and we went off to our classes.

As usual, when we arrived in class, there was a short period of settling in while we awaited the arrival of our teacher. This was one of the most vulnerable class times for the softies. It was during periods like this that they would be cornered and victimized by the lowlifes. I took my usual seat and watched as my martial arts pupils took theirs, side by side. They seemed a bit more determined. So far so good, I thought.

Enter Hopkins and Tyne.

I watched them saunter into the room and begin to make their way to their seats at the back of the class. Then Hopkins spotted my lads, smirked something into the sadistic Tyne's ear, and they changed direction to come up behind my trainees.

As usual, Hopkins started the trouble.

'What were you two poofs doin' at lunchtime, then? Hanging out wi' the tough guys - eh? Think you're tough guys now - eh?'

Our lessons had obviously been observed and noted by the undesirables.

I sat back and just watched; my face was stony but I was curious as to how my boys would handle their first confrontation since my wee lesson at break time. Hopkins spotted me watching them and elbowed Tyne in the ribs.

'No offence tae you, Les,' grovelled Tyne.

'Naw, no offence, mate,' stuttered Hopkins, the weaker of the snakes. 'It's just them wee turds - eh?'

I said nothing.

By this time, the rest of the class had entered. We still had no teacher but our peers were unusually silent, watching this minor classroom drama unfold.

The snakes took my silence as acquiescence and, with a last cheesy grin in my direction, they turned back to continue to taunt Roxborough and Horsborough (unfortunately nicknamed Horsey).

'Leave us alone, you two. We don't have to put up with your bullying -do we, Horsey?'

'Nnnnno,' stuttered poor Horsborough, who looked very capable of both vomiting and filling the seat of his trousers at that moment in time.

I sighed inwardly. This was not going to plan.

'Ha, ha, ha!' chortled Tyne. 'Do ye hear that? These boys think they're tough now. Ha, ha, ha! This calls for some torture, don't ye think, Hopkins?'

Hopkins, himself doubled over with laughter at the weak attempts of my boys to stand their ground, slapped the back of Roxborough's head in answer and nodded vigorously at Tyne through his tears of mirth.

My boys were terrified. Tyne and Hopkins each grabbed one of the poor lads round the neck, throttling them.

I had seen enough.

Snick, click!

'Enough!'

I bellowed my command and bounded out of my seat to stand in front of the now completely silent classroom. Hopkins was the first of the snakes to respond. He immediately let go of his victim's neck, eyes wide, and said: 'What's up, Les? No offence, mate...'

Snick, click!

'Enough! Ah've had enough o' this. From noo on, these boys are ma mates and, if anyone even speaks to them the wrang way, they'll have to speak tae me as well. Are we clear aboot that, shitface - eh? Are we?'

Such was the venom in my tirade I actually think the whole class nodded with Hopkins and Tyne. Hierarchy, once established, was pretty much set in stone at our school and no one wanted to push on the boundary. I think the girls even nodded in agreement.

Hopkins and Tyne nodded with the greatest vigour. Hopkins even tried a: 'God, I'm sorry, Les. We didn't know they were wi' you - did we, Tyne? Honest, Les, we didnae know...'

His appeals didn't matter to me. It mattered only that Tyne had now also taken his arm from around my lad's neck as if it was on fire, and that both of them were shuffling away to their accustomed places in the class.

Snakes!

Then I remembered Preston, alone in his French class, and I realized that, if this was the treatment that these two could expect while together to bolster each other's courage, poor Preston could be in deep trouble.

Shit!

I hurtled out of the room, just as my Latin teacher arrived.

'Smith, where do you think you're going? Get back in this class!'

'Can't, Sir - toilet,' and I continued my rush with 'You're in trouble, Smith' echoing down the corridor behind me.

I ran along the corridor and up two flights of stairs. If I was quick enough, I could catch Preston's class before their teacher arrived. Either way, I was determined to deliver my message to anybody who thought that Preston was easy prey.

Enough was enough.

Panting down the corridor (must give up the fags) to the classroom that housed the French class, I could hear 2A before I saw them. Obviously Miss McQuaid hadn't turned up yet. I skidded through the open door and - sure enough - the sight that greeted me bore out my worst fears.

Preston was on the ground, almost in tears, with Motson, one of Hopkins' and Tyne's cronies, straddling his chest. I stalked towards them.

Motson, who was facing the door, saw my approach and with a smile said: 'Hey, Les; this wee cunt just tried to punch me when I asked him for his homework tae copy. Can ye believe it, Les; Preston finally got some balls - eh, Preston?'

And with a smirk he reached behind, grabbed and twisted the aforementioned balls, revelling in the pain instantly displayed across Preston's face. He should have paid attention to my face instead.

Snick, click, bang!

I stalked towards the pair on the floor, bent down and launched a punch into Motson's chin from roughly floor level. He went flying backwards to land on his back.

I gave a hand to the now sobbing Preston, pulled him to his feet and told him to go and sit at his desk.

Then I made my general announcement, snarling at the whole class. 'This is the deal. Roxborough, Preston and Horsborough are under ma wing noo. Nobody, but nobody, messes wi' them. Do you cretins understan' that?'

Nods all round and surprised sobs from Motson, who was a coward that could never take a punch and would never have picked on anyone further up the tough-guy hierarchy than poor Preston. I turned to this prick, who was just getting up onto shaky legs. I thought he might need a further little warning.

Enter Miss McQuaid.

'Smith! What are you doing here, Smith? And what's going on? Have you been fighting again? Right, that's it - I'm just going to make an example of you!'

I could see Preston begin to raise his hand. I discreetly signalled him to stop. I'd have to teach him the rule about grassing if he was to survive. It was good of him to want to stand up for me, but he would be better saving his energy to stand up for himself. Miss McQuaid hated me and wouldn't have let the truth deter her from punishing me anyway. The most my lad would have achieved would have been dual punishment for both Motson and me. I was perfectly capable of making sure Motson got his share at lunchtime.

I took my punishment - the usual six of the belt - and then returned to the same fate in my Latin class for running out when the teacher had just arrived.

Ah, well; just another day at school, I suppose.

I heard later on in the week, from some of the boys who liked to foment trouble, that the talk in the playground covered three alternatives: that the three softies were 'my bum boys'; that I was getting paid protection money by them; or that they were doing my schoolwork for me. I ignored it all. Nobody in NK could ever have accepted that a supposed hard man had developed altruistic tendencies. People looked after themselves in NK, or formed packs to look after each other. Nobody looked after the prey.

Roxborough, Preston and Horsborough were actually hard work. It was like having three shadows a lot of the time, and we really had nothing in common.

But somehow I felt better for taking them under my wing.

At least for the remaining 14 months of my NK life I would not have to watch them being dehumanized.

They had 14 months' grace.

Although I shudder to think what happened after I left...

CHAPTER XXIII

Winter Science

Winter, and the toilet pans were frozen as usual. It was a bloody liberty! You could use the urinals, because they just consisted of a long trough dug in the ground, placed along the walls of an unroofed building, which was positioned at the edge of the playground. The urinal drains might get iced up, but, as the drains were usually blocked with cigarette ends anyway, winter did not make much of a change to either the smell or the sluice.

Heaven help you if you were either a girl (similar outside arrangement), or if you were in dire need of a dump. On many a winter's morning, the toilet pans in the cubicles of the outside toilets were frozen solid.

They were completely unusable.

Of course, taking a dump had its hazards in normal weather conditions as well. For a start, you had to hold your foot against the door, as there were no locks left on the cubicles. You also had to be quick and hope that none of the smokers generally hanging out in this smelly den would take it into their head to kick open your door and embarrass you - or worse. I think that most people either had a dump at home, or when classes were under way, and the usual suspects were too occupied to prey on anybody.

Yes, it was a bloody liberty that the pupils in this school had to put up with these lousy outside toilets in the winter. We, the pupils, felt hard done by, and on this occasion the Midge, an inventive lad in 2A so-called because of his diminutive stature, had a bright idea.

We were ensconced in a science lab when the idea of such injustice hit home. These labs were archaic places filled with the horrible smell of gas from Bunsen burners and smelly vapours from jars of chemical compounds and class experiments. The Midge was complaining about how we should have been sent home because the toilets were frozen again. The establishment's answer to this problem, given to us during assembly, had been to declare that we could use the unfrozen toilets in the bottom building if we really had to, and that the upper toilets would have thawed out by lunchtime. As we all wanted the day off, we righteous pupils were not happy with such an easy answer.

After a vigorous round of inter-class moaning and suggestions about how we should really smash up the toilet pans or rip off the cisterns, the Midge, who had been mulling things over, looked up and, wearing his typical cunning grin, declared: 'I know - let's blow the bastards up!'

His suggestion was greeted with smiles and agreement all around.

Under other circumstances, and in other schools, this would probably just be another schoolboy fantasy, in the same league as: burning hated teachers at the stake; being given a years' holiday from school; or having that young lady teacher everyone fancied take you back to her place. But, in NK, in the well-provisioned science lab, with a resourceful wee man such as the Midge, blowing up the toilets was all too possible.

There were no dissenters. Even the softies didn't seem to baulk (although I knew that they would never be the ones to execute the final plan).

Whispered discussions ensued around our desks, while our oblivious teacher worked up at the front of the class, concentrating on setting up some meaningless experiment or other.

Eventually we decided that a good quantity of sulphur and phosphorous on top of the iced-up toilet pans ought to do the trick. We all remembered fondly the day that the suck-up idiot Brown had dropped tiny quantities of the same into one of the lab sinks, while trying to clean up a lab bench to impress 'Sir'. The resulting flash and small explosion had caused endless days of laughter, especially when suck-up Brown was seen trying to do something with his bandaged hands, such as taking a pee at the urinals. Needless to say, no one volunteered to help Brown, but many willing hands pushed him in the back while he was peeing no-handed, causing him to wet his trousers and shoes so often that eventually his parents kept him away from school till the bandages could be taken off.

We'd experienced foiled attempts at creating lab explosions in the past. Leaving the gas taps in the lab turned on, shutting the windows and doors and then exiting the room, hoping that someone would come in and light a match before the smell was noticed. This trick seemed to be an old school favourite for most year groups. A teacher always stopped the fun by evacuating the kids, turning off the gas and opening the windows to clear the air. The sulphur and phosphorous bomb idea was a new one, however, and - inquisitive wee children that we were - we were just dying to try it out.

Stage one: we had to get the teacher out of the classroom, so that we could nick enough of our explosive components to do the trick. Nicking the stuff was not a problem for our class. The Midge had a set of keys for every classroom and cupboard in the school, which he had stolen ages ago from the janitor. He had copied them and then left the originals lying around to be 'found' again. Unsuspecting, the school didn't change a single lock. This gave the wee man carte blanche to: steal exam papers for previews; steal dinner tickets and bus passes for resale; generally steal anything he fancied that was not nailed down (even if some object of desire had been nailed down, I'm sure that the inventive Midge would have been able to acquire it).

We couldn't wait for lunchtime or after school to acquire our chemicals. We wanted to do this thing at lunchtime today, and so we would need to get the teacher out of the way for a while and have the 'stuff' secreted before he got back.

Strangely, it was softie Roxborough who suggested that: one of us should pretend to go to the toilet, instead go and get a boy from class 2B by pretending that our 'Sir' wanted to see him, then brief this boy to pretend that a teacher in the bottom building needed to see our 'Sir' urgently. That way, we would get rid of our teacher for the short while we needed to steal our supplies.

Not bad for a softie such as Roxborough.

The Midge said that whoever did this would obviously be remembered by teachers and would automatically be in the frame when our 'prank' went off, so he suggested that, if we just forged a note and left it on the teacher's desk, then someone could draw his attention to it (preferably one of the girls) and say that it had just been delivered. It was a big classroom and our ageing teacher was not known for his observation of anything but the results of his stupid experiments.

The plan was agreed.

The Midge forged a note and we got one of the more brazen girls to slip it onto 'Sir's' desk unnoticed, go back to her seat, wait till the teacher was well into his experiment and then say, 'Sir, what about the note?'

'What note, girl?'

'The note that boy delivered earlier, Sir. When you were plugging in the van de Graaff generator at the back, Sir. It's on your desk.'

A puzzled teacher went over to his desk, read the note and declared: 'OK, 2A; I want you to sit quietly and get on with your work. I'll be back shortly and Mr McGulligen next door will be listening out for any bad behaviour. And DON'T play with the gas taps!'

Off he went, discarding the note in the waste-paper bin. The Midge retrieved and destroyed this note, leaving no evidence for any later tribunals.

The game was afoot!

Several lads made straight for the chemicals cupboard, duly locked against 'accidents'. The Midge produced the appropriate key after a bit of fiddling about in his school bag. The cupboard was opened up and the chemicals were ours. There was an air of high excitement in the classroom.

'Right, boys,' said the Midge, 'We'd better get this stuff intae beakers and hidden doon in the toilets. Who's wi' me?'

A couple of lads were picked to accompany our prank-leader, and all three soldiers filled beakers with the components of our potential explosives.

Off they went to the toilets.

Our lab overlooked the toilets. This was, of course, another bone of contention. Anyone in the high-up top classrooms of the old building could watch someone peeing at the far wall of the urinals, or see the tops of people's bodies through the gaps at the top of the cubicle doors. It was another bone of contention ignored by the establishment. Their toi-

110

lets were cosy, warm and private inside jobs! Well, now we'd get to see how they felt about our toilets after lunchtime!

The majority of our class leaned out the window to watch the progress of our 2A guerrillas hiding the contraband in the 'lavvy'. In due time the deed was done, and our boys returned to the class with big grins on their faces. One more period of science and one of history - then we could look forward to an explosive lunchtime!

This was shaping up to be a very good day.

Everyone was sworn to silence under threat of death and the Midge pointed out that, 'As co-conspirators in the theft of the chemicals, no one in 2A would be considered blameless if the plot got out.' This statement whitened the faces of many of the girls in the class and, of course, the softies baulked, but the Midge had been smart giving such an address and silence was assured.

I seem to remember that giggles, smiles and a feeling of expectation punctuated the rest of that morning. Nobody wanted to miss out on the lunchtime show, by being kept behind after our history class, so this class was remarkably well behaved. Our history teacher even congratulated us on good work and on our good behaviour that day.

'Well done, 2A. I hope that you can be as well behaved in all of our classes in the future as you have been today. I can see that you are actually starting to mature.' He glowered, 'Except for a few giggling girls, that is!' He smiled again. 'Well done.'

We all laughed. Little did he know!

Quite frankly, he is partly to blame for what followed. No teacher from our school who saw a sudden change in the temperament of a class, even an A class, should have let it pass unchallenged. No teacher in his right mind who saw an eager bunch of pupils, smiling, working so as not to be disruptive, but exchanging happy glances, should have let that go without a thorough investigation. He was pleased when he should have been terrified!

I hope you're reading this, Mr McLean!

Lunchtime dragged round, and we exited our school building for the playground. The girls were not allowed in the boys' playground, where the game was to go off. They had to make do with crowding along the fence in the adjoining girls' playground, or standing outside our playground in the street and craning their necks to see what would happen.

They'd be able to see nothing but the outside of the toilet wall and the reaction of the boys when it went down. But they were mostly satisfied with that; most of the girls wouldn't have wanted to be too close to the action, anyway. The more brazen girls hung about just inside the playground at the gate, ready to bolt if a teacher came along. These few ladies would get a closer look.

While the girls clamoured for a view, and most of the 2A boys hung around outside the toilets, a small crew of three (the same lads who had stolen and stashed our chemical weapon) retrieved the contraband and were preparing to do damage to our outside toilets.

Inside the toilets, Captain Midge was running the show. 'They've got tae mix tae dae the most damage, boys,' he said in authoritative fashion.

The boys had six glass flasks: three containing sulphur, and three containing phosphorous in oil. The Midge was directing them to place one phosphorous and one sulphur glass jar side by side on top of the ice that covered each of the three targeted toilet pans. They placed the substances as instructed and left the cubicle doors ajar.

'That's it, boys. Noo, get yer bricks, and when everybody's back tae here (he stood against the furthest wall, in line with the cubicle doors) just lob your bricks onto thae beakers. Just lob them though. We want tae break the glass, we're no wantin' tae knock them aff!'

They got into position.

'Right, boys. Throw them - noo...RUN!'

With military precision and timing, three 2A lads lobbed substantial bricks onto the glass beakers containing the purloined chemicals. Outside, the gathered throng heard the crash of broken glass as the lads who had carried out the prank beat a hasty retreat to join the now sizeable crowd gathered outside our toilets. At first, nothing happened; then, as the chemicals mixed together and merged into the iced H_2O on top of the toilet pans...

KABOOOOOM!

It was magic!

Children roared with pleasure. They could hear fragments of porcelain ricocheting off the toilet walls as 'the breaking of the shit-pits' (as it was later dubbed) came to an ecstatic conclusion. They were truly impressed. Remember that these kids, living in Glasgow's violent estates, were used to destruction in all of its most vivid forms - but this was special. This was anarchy, rebellion, smoke, noise - and it was all happening in school. This was us against them, and - to a pupil - they were proud!

I could even hear the shrill cheers from the girls' playground as they watched the action. I imagine that they could smell the rancid smell of the sulphur (added bonus) from wherever they stood. All around me were cheering - laughing, ecstatic children. The noise didn't even die down as janitor and teachers, including the headmaster himself, came out to investigate the noise. The volume of cheers was in fact raised several decibels at each successive shriek or exclamation of horror from a teacher.

It was great!

The atmosphere of carnival just continued to intensify as teachers tried impotently to sift through the crowd for culprits and vainly tried to restore order to the playground.

It was brilliant, and it was a 2A prank - a prank by the class who were considered among the geeks of the school.

What a day!

As you can imagine, for weeks afterwards we were lectured at assembly on safety, responsibility and on criminal behaviour. Such lectures at first raised gouts of laughter, as the kids happily remembered 'the breaking of the shit-pits'. In an attempt at making us take these lectures seriously, noise-related punishments were meted out, and after several assemblies the cheers subsided to smirks, the occasional giggle or an individual 'hooray'. Even the visit from our community policemen did nothing to dampen our pride whenever this glorious day was mentioned.

As for the wee man, the Midge - he, as always, remained cool. Everyone knew by now that he had been responsible, but nobody grassed him to the authorities. Even the establishment was sure that he had masterminded the whole thing, but, as there was no proof, he got off scot-free. All of 2A were questioned, as the chemicals were traced to our science lab and we were one of two classes under suspicion of the theft. But even the softies stayed silent.

It was all just too good!

The Midge swaggered around the playground for a month or two, accepting the smiles, winks or more verbal accolades, as was his due. He stood tall, in spite of his diminutive stature, and nobody ever thought of him as a 'wee man' after that day. The Midge was smart and he used his brains to dream up further mayhem on successive occasions, to keep up his 'No. 1 prankster' profile - much to the angst of the school establishment.

Like many, the Midge was a survivor. He had carved out his own way to survive, by always being one con and several steps ahead of the school authorities. At 13 years old, he was a quick thief and a smooth conman - considered an artist by his peers. He made all of us laugh long and loud on many occasions and everyone wanted to be his pal. Almost everyone wanted to feature in one of his future games.

Good on you, Midge. He caused no permanent damage and far less harm than most of the survivors in NK. I kind of like the way he survived.

The toilets were duly repaired in time. We never got the nice cosy inside jobs that we had wanted, but by then nobody cared as spring was approaching and we had other school beefs to occupy our minds. The toilet pans were never blown up again, though for a while the janitor was tasked with keeping a special vigil over this area at break times. This period of observation didn't last too long and the toilets were soon once again the main province of our smokers.

2A didn't carry out many school pranks as a group, but the winter science experiment was definitely our high point.

Even today - it still makes me laugh.

CHAPTER XXIV

Today's your Birthday

At NK you never wanted to let anyone know that it was your birthday. A birthday should be a time when, as a child, you looked forward to parties and presents, being the centre of attention and being generally spoiled. In my world, there was a minimal bit of that at home - but at school...

Adjoining the toilets and the back wall of the upper school playground were our school sheds. I don't know if the original intent of these sheds had been to park pupils' bikes, but as this was a really stupid thing to do - with the only possible result being a stolen bike - they were never used as such in my time at NK. Instead, the sheds were usually a place for football at playtime and lunchtime, a place to shelter and have a smoke when it was raining, or as goalposts during our infrequent playground PE sessions.

These sheds consisted of walls on three sides topped by a flat roof, with a single iron pole, used to support the roof, in the middle of the open side facing the playground. Kids would think of many things to do in these sheds, especially on rainy days. They would often house gamblers playing cards or dice for money; or child thieves and their customers, who would regularly deal in stolen dinner tickets, bus passes, cigarettes, comics or sweets. It was a part of our way of life, and no one paid any real attention to the activities in the sheds - unless it was some poor unfortunate's birthday.

If you were a school celebrity like the Midge, or if you were either considered hard or well protected, then you were all right. But, if you were none of these things, you really didn't want anybody at school to remember your birthday.

Being given a birthday present at our school was never funny. I remember the first time that I saw one being delivered. I cringed and felt so, so sorry for the victim.

I was still in prep when I first witnessed a birthday being celebrated in the sheds.

On this particular day I strolled out to the playground at break time with Davy, as usual. We saw a crowd over at the shed and wandered down to see what was happening. There was a lot of noise going on, and over the top of the general mayhem we could distinctly hear pleading.

'Naw! Oh Naw. Dinnae dae it, boys! Please!'

Intrigued, we wandered closer.

What we saw, as we got close enough to the front of the crowd, was to make us sweat and would put us off ever reminding anyone at NK that it was our birthday.

A thin-looking third-year, in clothing that was now well dishevelled, was struggling futilely in the grip of some of his peers. He was suspended horizontally off the ground. Several boys had a hold on his shoulders and arms and there was a lad holding each of his legs.

'One, two, three!'

On the word 'three', the group of victimizers ran at the pole in the centre of the shed, carting their victim between them. By this time they had parted the poor boy's legs. They gained speed, spreading his legs wide enough to go one on either side of the shed pole, and rammed the poor wee lad's testicles against that solid mast of iron.

Everybody in the watching crowd winced.

The laughing perpetrators dumped the screaming boy at their feet, where he curled up into a ball and wept deserved tears. Then, strolling off with smiles on their faces, the sadistic celebrants sang, 'Happy birthday to you ...'

116

Bizarre.

This was another bizarre and barbaric NK custom, which prevailed during my whole time at that school.

The girls didn't escape birthdays unscathed, either. At the beginning their 'birthday treat' was to be tied to the fence adjoining the boys' playground, with their skirt pulled up and their school blouse loosened, thereafter to be groped by any passing boy who fancied doing so. There were always plenty of perverted little volunteers.

Of course, these poor girls were humiliated and degraded by this and, quite rightly, after much parental protest and a visit or two from the police, the school managed to stop this birthday celebration from being carried out. The girls resorted then to other means, such as water-filled balloons lobbed into a birthday girl's cubicle as she had a pee.

The authorities never stopped the ball-crushing, though.

Bizarre.

After witnessing the 'nutcracker suite' that first time, I determined that, whether I was considered hard or not, nobody would ever know when it was my birthday.

I wonder if many of these birthday victims actually went on to have children in later life..?

CHAPTER XXV

Classroom High Jinks

Who'd be a teacher at NK? Don't get me wrong. I was far from being an angel myself. Within this 'them or us' environment I did my share of teacher-taunting and created my own share of teacher misery.

In those days I thought that they deserved it.

Some of them did.

Take the time a mad English teacher whacked both me and a girl in the row of seats beside me across the face with his leather strap. We had been talking when we were not supposed to - but this guy had gone too far.

I retaliated by leaping out of my seat, grabbing a long window pole and breaking it over his head. I knew I was in trouble, so I left him half conscious on the floor and went straight to the headmaster's office. I showed him the red welts on my face and told him what I had done.

Our headmaster at this time was a chain-smoking, depressed, ex go-getter. I remember that he had come to NK with all sorts of progressive ideas. Between pupils, parents and teachers he was quickly disabused of those notions; he was now a mere nub of the man he had been.

With a cigarette between his lips and a still-smouldering stub in the ashtray on his desk, he told me he was sorry, but that I'd better go home, as he would have to suspend me till he found out the full story.

I went home and avoided letting my parents know by pretending to have got out of school early that day. I was supposed to bring my parents in with me the following day to discuss matters, but I planned to go in on my own and say that they were working. Parental interest in school activities was so rare at our school that I was sure I would not be found out.

I was lucky. The abused girl in question had a mum who kicked up such a fuss about the weals on her daughter's face that I was reinstated the next day without punishment. It turned out that the excuse given to the complaining mum for the English teacher's violent act was that he had been a prisoner in a Japanese prisoner-of-war camp, and occasionally had lapses...

Think about it. What was a guy with deep mental scars from torture in a prisoner-of-war camp doing teaching kids in the first place? At least he ended up being retired - and I was reinstated. Believe it or not, the girl's mum swallowed this excuse and didn't press charges with the police as she had promised.

It was a lucky break for me too - that time.

I was no angel at school, but, even in my very partisan view, some of the wee NK demons went a bit too far.

There were many teachers driven to early retirement in my time. There were loads of teachers who looked like complete nervous wrecks, and I wondered where they got the courage from to turn up each day. Many were driven out of the school or out of education entirely, to be replaced by gym-teacher-looking maths teachers, or ex-commando-looking English teachers.

None of these exchanges benefited the quality of education at our school, but what could the pupils really expect? The French exchange teacher 'thing' was cancelled, as no French teacher would come near us. The German equivalent had been driven out of our school with third world war taunts by a previous generation of NK kids.

Sometimes - in fact, most of the time - I didn't care, but sometimes the teacher-torture was just too much for me to stand back and watch.

I had no love for teachers, and I definitely had no respect for authority, but I must have had just a wee bit of human compassion because, on one particular day, my mental armour went into top gear in protection of a teacher - our hated enemy.

'Soft' subject teachers, such as art teachers and music teachers, had the worst time of it at school. Then, in the hierarchy of teacher-torture, language teachers, science teachers and - eventually - maths teachers were victimized (most people wanted to get half decent results in maths).

The teachers who had the most influence on me during school were Mr B (maths), Ms W (English), and a music teacher whose name I can't even remember. These were great teachers, who never failed to make their lessons interesting, and whom I protected from the worst behaviour that our class was capable of. Everyone knew that I didn't want any of these lessons to be spoiled. Maybe I should have set this tenure up for the rest, but, as I said, it was a 'them against us' culture most of the time.

I really loved music classes. We were often given music appreciation and I always looked forward to slumping forward with my head on the desk and listening to previously unheard-of classical marvels. Music soothes the heart of the savage beast, they say... Unfortunately for the music department, I seem to have been the only savage beast affected by its charms.

On the day I turned temporary hero, I was looking forward to my music period and hoping we would get more Mozart to listen to. I was coming towards the doors that opened into the main (top) building of our school, and, as I approached them, one of the second-year kids shouted to me: 'Hey, Les! Huv ye heard about Mrs Parker?'

'What aboot her?' I said, only slightly interested because she was going to be my teacher for music in a minute.

'It's 3E,' the lad said. 'They've got her pinned in the classroom wi' an airgun. What a laugh - eh?'

Wait a minute - I was looking forward to my music lesson with Mrs Parker! I'd spent my lunchtime at the park and so had missed the news of any school incidents. I already wasn't pleased.

'What dae ye mean - pinned?' I asked.

'Pinned, Les. Pinned! She cannae get oot o' the classroom. They keep firin' darts and pellets. They've had hur pinned aw lunchtime and the teachers cannae get them tae stop! It's great - honest, Les! We've aw been kicked oot the buildin' by the jannie [janitor], though - so ye cannae go in, Les.'

Snick, click!

This was bloody typical of our school. Thugs could attack a teacher, and the headmaster never wanted to call the police. He was always more interested in avoiding even more bad publicity for him and the school. He was also a genuinely liberal guy and was most loved by our worst elements for writing fantastic character references for them whenever they were called up to court. I knew that he'd be trying to reason with the thugs in that pathetic wee voice of his and that he'd be urging some poor school teacher to attempt to disarm them - fat chance! If I knew 3E, it'd take more than some weedy schoolteacher to dig them out.

I was pretty pissed off. This was my music lesson, and I had been looking forward to it. My temper was beginning to snap.

Snick, click!

I strode into the school building like an avenging angel, stiff-backed and furious with everything and everybody. It was so bloody unjust, I kept thinking to myself. That weak twat of a headmaster and those stupid wee thugs were going to spoil the only bloody lesson that I was looking forward to. I pounded up the stairs to the floor that housed the music room and pushed my way through the throng of teachers, hiding just out of sight of the gun-wielders.

'Smith! Where do you think you're going, Smith! Come back here - now!'

I ignored the teacher's protests and barged on.

Snick, click!

Their futile words fell on deaf ears, as I turned the corner and saw the scene of the incident with my own eyes.

It wasn't untypical.

Five 3E boys, the worst five as far as I could tell, were armed with two airguns and a seemingly endless supply of pellets and darts. They were holed up in a classroom across the passage from my music room, with the door open and overturned desks in front of them to form a barrier. The music-room door had a glass panel on the front of it and I could see that the cowering teacher inside had pushed her blackboard on wheels in front of the door. The wooden part of the music-room door had a couple of darts sticking into it and repeated rounds of pellets had cracked the glass panelling.

The would-be 3E hard men were jeering at the crowd of teacher onlookers and the headmaster. They were probably drunk - again not unusual for this lot - and they were firing the occasional warning shot at the establishment, daring them to approach.

I took in all of this in a moment.

I could also hear Mrs Parker sobbing behind the door. It was just too much.

Snick, click!

Madder than hell, I strode towards the pellet-gun-wielding thugs. When they saw me coming, they must have imagined that I was joining them as a reinforcement.

'Come oan, Les! Quick! We've got the old bitch shitting hersel', an' these...' he waved to indicate the establishment '...fuckers cannae stoap us! Come oan!'

I came on.

Snick, click!

As I reached the barricade where the thugs were holed up, I grabbed the barrel of the nearest thug's airgun and yanked it out of his hand.

'Hey, Les, ye kin huv a shot, mate. Nae bother. Don't break ma fucking arm,' he whined.

Snick, click, bang!

I smashed him in the face with the butt of the gun, reached forward and grabbed the other gun from the hands of a second, now stunned, thug.

'What the fuck?'

I wasn't in any mood. Moving past the classroom containing the now disarmed bunch, who definitely smelled as if they'd been drinking, I marched up to the also stunned-looking headmaster, thrust the weapons into his hands and said: 'Kin you no keep any sort ah order in this place, ya useless cunt?'

I was SO pissed off. This place was getting worse by the day and I couldn't wait to get out.

'Leslie, I don't know if you should have...' the headmaster started to say.

'Shut it!'

I stormed down the stairs, out of the school and gave myself the rest of the day off. I was mad as hell and needed to calm down.

What a day! I'd sided with a teacher, I'd started an inevitable war with the thugs in 3E, and I'd missed my music lesson.

What a bloody day!

The upshot of all this was that: the thugs were given a month's suspension and then allowed back into the school; I was secretly thanked by a few teachers and openly chastised by others; the headmaster took me into his office and tried to talk me into becoming a prefect; and I had an ugly fight with 3E, which I survived and - as far as you can with these things - won.

Who would be a teacher at NK? Nobody who had any sense, I suppose.

Who would be a prefect, or a protector of the weak and innocent? Nobody who had any sense, I suppose.

Knowing that what I did didn't solve the underlying school violence problem with those or any other kids; knowing that I just made trouble for myself and that the music teacher left the school shortly afterwards anyway; knowing all that, I can imagine you'd believe I wish I hadn't got involved at all.

You'd be wrong, though.

As I look back on my chequered school time, I am so glad that, even though I wasn't an angel, on that day I tried. On that one day - I actually saved somebody, and I stopped an ugly and violent incident from continuing.

If I was to live it all over again, I think I'd take that prefect job and try to do more of the same. I might even try to work out a way to reverse the trend. I didn't take the job, though, and just continued to live out my time in NK and survive as best I could.

If I'd had more courage, maybe I could have made a difference.

Who knows? But at least, on that day, I tried!

CHAPTER XXVI

Football, Religion and the Kirk

During this phase in the life of Leslie Ronald Smith, the Kirk, or Church, was a big, big feature. Of course, as usual, there were complications in the Smith household.

My dad was born in Ireland and was of the Catholic faith - originally. My mum was born in Glasgow, into the Protestant faith. Both were living testimonies to a lack of understanding of their faith and to the prevalent orthodox practice of - hypocrisy.

To understand this part of the tale fully, you must first appreciate both the strength and influence of the Catholic and the Protestant Churches, and the overwhelming sectarianism common in Glasgow at the time, particularly among the working classes.

Football: you either shot with your left foot (Catholic) or your right foot (Protestant); you either supported Glasgow Rangers (Protestant) or Glasgow Celtic (Catholic).

School: you either went to a Protestant school, a Catholic school, or sometimes - as in my case - you had parents of mixed religion who made the choice.

Youth Organizations: you joined the Boys' Brigade, which was run by the Protestant church, or you joined the Cubs, who took in either Catholic or Protestant kids.

The street: you lived in a predominantly Protestant or predominantly Catholic street, which meant that you had to hide your Rangers or Celtic football scarf if you were badly outnumbered (the areas around each of the football grounds being the worst segregated areas).

Friendship: there were few inter-religion friendships in my day.

Faith: you worshiped in your own religion's building. You would not be welcome in another congregation unless you were a hated 'turncoat' and were changing from one religion to the other. You might then be accepted, but you would always be viewed with suspicion and would be derided behind your back. I got a bird's-eye view of this from my father's experiences.

Work: early on in the first day at a new job, someone would approach and ask questions such as: 'What team dae ye support then?' (Rangers or Celtic defined your religion, and Partick Thistle defined your lack of interest in the sport!); 'How're ye hangin', then?' (left side meant Catholic and right side meant Protestant. I don't know what the girls were asked.); 'What school did ye go tae, then?'...and so on.

All questions were designed to segregate you from your fellow man.

Although legislated against now, it was just as common to be asked any of the above questions when you went for a job interview in Glasgow, particularly if the foreman, manager or interviewer was a member of the Orange Order.

Religion was indeed a big feature of life in Glasgow at the time, and an enormous feature in the Smith household.

My father had converted.

To appease my fanatical mother, who seemed to think that Catholicism was synonymous with 'evil', my dad had joined the Church of Scotland and immersed himself in the activities of the Church to such an extent that he was now a Church Elder.

I often wonder how my mother and father ever got together. They were brought up in an area where prejudice and religious segregation were rife. My aunt had even married a man who boasted a high position in the Orange Order. My mother's family were far from open-minded, and my mother herself was a closed book on religious freedom. It can only have been love that brought them together, I guess; although there was certainly no indication of that love displayed within our household.

To be fair, my father's family never seemed to display any tendencies towards religious bigotry at all. They just didn't seem to care about religion, and on this issue they were refreshing to be around. Their lack of faith served only as a beacon to my mother, however, who ignored them for years - as being beneath her - then tried for years to convert one of my only two 'nice' aunts to the Protestant faith. She failed, but she never stopped trying for as long as I can remember.

I think it was this 'nice' aunt and 'fun' uncle, plus the fact that I was sick to the teeth of the religious bigotry I saw displayed by the Protestant religion at home, in school and on the streets, that made me decide to become a Celtic supporter, regardless of my schooling, home location or 'religious boot-camp' training.

Being a Celtic supporter in my school and street had its dangers, though.

'Hey, Smith! What are ye wearin' that thing fur?' Wully exclaimed, as I walked down our street towards the sweet shop. I was an 11-year-old wee boy with a strong Celtic attitude.

'Shut yer mooth, Wully! Ah'll wear what ah like - see!'

That was a typical exchange at the beginning of my Celtic-football-team era (although, even with the attitude gone, I am still an ardent fan). Even my dad, an ex-Catholic, was nonplussed by my choice of football team.

'Ye want tae go an' see the Jags (Partick Thistle) this Saturday, son? They're playing Motherwell - should be a good game.'

'Naw! That lot are useless!'

'Ye're better aff wi' the Jags, son - better fitba' tae watch.'

Which was complete rubbish!

I guess, as an ex-Catholic, my dad had no choice but to turn to the hopeless Jags as a football team. Glasgow Rangers fans were uncompromising in their hatred of Catholics - and my dad wasn't ex-Catholic enough to go to that level. But, having converted to the Church of Scotland, he would not feel that he could support Celtic any more.

That's how stupid the whole thing was.

I was sticking with Celtic. It meant a few fights, but what were a few more fights, anyway? It meant a bit of isolation, as I was the only Celtic supporter in my street or at my school, but isolation suited my deepening sense of distance from anything within my environment. I could cope with the looks, answer back the jibes, and fight whenever I had to. Celtic was my team, regardless of my force-fed Protestant education and schooling.

The whole sectarian thing was crazy to me, so I was going to be crazier - as usual.

It was a great time to be a 'hoops' supporter and strut about proudly in my traditional Celtic green shirt, banded with white hoops. Celtic was the top team in Scotland under Jock Stein's management, and during this period they also became number one in Europe. As a result I had plenty more jibes to give than to receive. Folk quickly learned to leave me alone, but I could see how much it stung them to watch me parade about with my Celtic scarf on, and I loved it! I was also proud that Glasgow Celtic refused to be a part of the sectarian game and would take both Catholics and Protestants into their team, while Rangers would employ only Protestants. I felt that it was poetic justice that Rangers were doing so badly against Celtic.

I was a righteous football supporter - a dangerous concept.

I guess, too, that my Celtic supporter status didn't help me gain much acceptance at my weekly Church of Scotland boot-camp sessions.

++++++++

As a youth, religion meant that a significant part of my week was spent in tedious study, sanctimonious oppression and wasted time. This would be a typical week's schedule.

Sunday involved: getting up early and putting on my Sunday best, so that I could take the long walk to the kirk and sit on a hard wooden pew listening to values which completely contradicted my circumstances and personal experience. It meant sucking a Mint Imperial to keep me quiet, and singing (I enjoyed the singing) hymns of praise, with people I knew to be less than Christian in their daily lives. It also meant being herded off halfway through the proceedings to Sunday school, where I was forced to study the Bible, memorize scriptures and neither fidget nor talk out of turn, for fear of being slapped on the leg, getting pinched or having my short-trousered leg painfully squeezed by the Bible-class teacher.

The only high points of Sunday were the occasional opportunity to nick a few glasses of communion wine; or the times that I would sneak back into the main hall while the posh-hatted and best-suited adults were exchanging false smiles and cheerios, there to quietly play with the massive church valve organ, pushing pedals and keys, while trying to knock out a hymn - this was my only Sunday ecstasy!

I'm sure that the minister knew about my musical interludes, but, for a period at the kirk, we had a great man called Mr Ferguson as our man in charge. He didn't stay with our kirk long, but he stands out in my mind as a man of real Christian values, and he was always a kind friend to me. I imagine the local hypocrisy was why he left our wee den for a new life in America. It's a pity, as he brought a piece of sanity into my life for a brief period, by actually listening to me and occasionally intervening with my parents.

He also ignored my little forays into the organ playing area.

Mr Ferguson was OK in my book. When he espoused some Christian story or value, I could actually begin to believe it. During his period in charge I studied the Bible diligently and even started to enjoy the philosophy it contained. It didn't last, though. When he left, replaced by a popular fire-and-brimstone regular, my interest once again died and I couldn't help feeling that Christianity was more about the singer than the song. I had no doubt that Jesus Christ and many of his apostles as described in the Bible were men of sound character and belief, but as for his latter-day saints...

Only later did I discover that, like all religions, the Christian faith contained the tenets of a worthwhile philosophy, but that very few people ever attempted to live by them.

With the departure of Mr Ferguson, Sundays turned once again to mud!

Monday - Wednesday: these were days without any formal religious training, except for the occasional period of RE at school. In the Smith household, however, a day rarely passed without my mother taking the opportunity to espouse some Christian value or other - usually whilst I was being chastised.

Thursday: this was Bible-class night. Another night when I was dressed, scrubbed and sent off with my sister, to partake in more religious education, which was probably thrown at us just to get us out of the house for a while. These were nights of further tedium and study. Both my sister and I seemed to excel in these classes and could therefore look forward to our just reward in heaven - plus, of course, the many versions of the Bible that we received as prizes over the years. Unfortunately, in each version, the story was always the same, so sitting down to read a prize had a certain air of predictability to it.

Somehow, walking miles in the cold, wind and rain to gain this level of piety never felt like a fair trade-off.

Friday: this was Boys' Brigade night. My parents seemed to think that walking through gangland on a dark Friday night, dressed up as a target in my Boys' Brigade uniform, complete with stupid round hat, was a great character-builder. I don't know about character-building, but the miles-long journey certainly built fortitude and helped to hone my street-fighting abilities.

The Boys' Brigade was an organization that provided ample opportunity for abuse. We were supposed to learn discipline, comradeship, plus a host of useful skills, such as being able to tie a half hitch standing on one leg with a blindfold on. I have never found a practical use for a half hitch!

It was a little military-type organization, with great emphasis put on the appearance of your uniform and the shine on your shoes. There were levels within the organization, starting with the domineering officers at the top, through the ranks of bullying sergeants and corporals, to the lowly cannon fodder such as me. Religion was well woven into the fibre of this organization, of course, since the Church of Scotland sponsored the whole thing.

Each Friday I was handed more misunderstood Christian values, administered by pious and self-righteous people who gained grand church accolades through the selfless donation of their time.

It was the Barnardo's boys I felt the most pain for. They were carted off to the Boys' Brigade each week, as a special treat. The poor wee buggers must have been pretty stuck for a laugh, if the BB was their only social outlet. From the stories told me by these boys, they really didn't need the type of bullying and abuse that was such a common part of this boys' club - they got enough of that at home on a daily basis.

As usual within my world, there were the strongest, the strong, the hangers-on-to-the-strong and the victims at the BB. You would have thought that an organization run by the Church, with an emphasis on discipline and Christian values, would have acted to prevent such an unjust hierarchy developing. You would have been wrong. Complaining would mean only that you were branded 'a whiner', that you would be shunned by most of the other boys, and that the bullies would find some excuse to 'get you later'.

Although I really tried hard to avoid it, I had to endure some personal experience of the bullying behaviour that was typical within the BB. This is my most memorable experience.

We were leaving the church hall on a dark winter's night, at about 9:30 p.m.

'Smith! I hear ye think ye're hard - eh?'

This from a thin-looking boy a couple of years my senior, whose name I have now forgotten. He was standing in a group of older boys and was obviously looking to gain some infamy amongst his peers. If I remember correctly, he was always a fairly minor figure within the hierarchy, but was protected because he had a stronger older brother.

I stopped, took all emotion from my face, looked into his eyes and waited.

'Did ye hear me, Smith? I think ye're just a wanker. Dae ye want tae fight me, then - eh?'

Normally, at the BB, I would just have walked away and ignored his jibes. After all, it wasn't like the street or school. There was some measure of control at this club and I didn't really fear later reprisals from within this group.

My friend Al was standing nervously beside me, and I was about to walk away when the bully, taking courage from my silence and the encouragement of his peers, stepped in front of me, put his nose up close to mine, and said, 'Ah'm goin' tae have you, Smith. Hear me. Come oan, ya craw!'

'Craw' was the common slang for coward. I heard the words and understood the threat, but, for the life of me, when I looked at this guy and knew that it would be no contest, I couldn't bring myself to react to his threats. So, stupidly, I looked him straight in the eye and said, 'Just go home. I don't want tae hurt ye.'

Silence all round. Time seemed to stop and you could have heard a pin drop. The bully stepped back, face incredulous, and shared a look of pure incomprehension between the onlookers and me.

Here he was: older; bigger; surrounded by his friends; known to have a tough big brother. Here I was - alone, with a soft friend beside me, and yet I was saying that I didn't want to hurt him! It was a statement beyond his comprehension, and I might well have used the resulting confusion to make my escape, but for: 'Aw, just take him! Are you scared o' that wee shite, then?' from one of his entourage.

Now he had to do it. His peer standing was in peril. He had to make his move, and I knew that the time for reason had past.

Snick, click, bang!

With a sigh, I brought my head back and butted him full in the face, while he was just raising his fist for the first punch.

Snick, click, bang!

Before he could do more than flounder, I straight-armed him with the heel of my hand, and we all heard the crack as one or more of his ribs succumbed to the force of my blow. I grabbed his hair with my left hand, brought my fist back for the killing blow to his already damaged nose, and then - stopped!

I couldn't do it. This was no contest and he was not and would never be a real hard man. Even his BB mates had backed so far off that they would be communicating by phone any time soon. Something inside me knew how wrong it would be to add any more injury to this already beaten boy.

I pushed him away, shrugged my shoulders, said, 'sorry, mate - I tried tae warn ye,' and walked away.

I never had to fight at the BB again, although there was need for the occasional 'street-survival exercise' whilst travelling to and from the church hall.

Friday nights spent in Christian fellowship at the BB - what a fiasco.

Saturday: at least there was one part of Kirk activity I regularly enjoyed.

It ranked up there with secret organ playing and collecting for church jumble sales, where you could keep the best 'jumble' for yourself. Every Saturday afternoon I donned my white sandshoes, white shorts and white T-shirt, took up my borrowed wooden-shafted, gut-stringed badminton racket, and got the opportunity to play my favourite sport in the church leagues.

This was me in my element and at my best. I revelled in these afternoons of sweating, competing and honing my skills. The Kirk badminton league! No discipline instilled into you by old hypocrites, only the personal discipline required by your sport. No doctrine, no punishments, no tedium, no threats, no overwhelming odds. This was just two people or two couples completing on a level playing field, with nothing but their skills to aid them.

Saturday badminton - that was the best of the Kirk for me!

++++++++

As you will have gathered from the above description of my week-long religious education, for me it was balanced more towards torment than pleasure. Don't get me wrong. I deny no man his faith - no matter what it is. I applaud anyone who genuinely follows a set of values and codes of conduct that he truly believes in, and I grudge no one any kind of support network that really works for him or her.

...As for me and football, religion and the Kirk?

I have always stayed faithful to Celtic as my football team and I have never allowed myself to be drawn into sectarianism on the back of my sport. I have many friends who support the Celtic arch-rivals, Rangers. We enjoy the banter and deny any connection between sport and a religious belief - just as it should be!

In later years I studied a variety of religions.

I couldn't help knowing a lot about the Christian faith because of my upbringing, and I wanted to understand more about religion in general, so I read. I read books on various branches of varied religions, such as Buddhism - which was very popular in the 1970s. I also read about the Muslim and the Hindu faiths. I even read and listened to various cults, which seemed to pop up every other day during the 1970s. I read, I tried to understand and I formulated my own spiritual philosophy, gleaned from pieces of everything I came to understand or at least acknowledge.

I couldn't find anything wrong with any of the philosophies contained in other religions. It was always the day-to-day interpretations that seemed to fall short.

But I am still left with some spirituality today. A personal set of beliefs, which provide a solid foundation for my own day-to-day behaviour.

Perhaps it started within the Kirk, but it certainly didn't flower there.

During my early years, religion was just another demon that I had to learn to deal with.

CHAPTER XXVII

Fear

This was a strange and alien feeling that crept up on me unawares. I cannot easily place its beginning, only the symptoms of its beginning. I cannot say exactly how or what things had changed to allow this feeling to start and take root, but take root it did.

The symptoms were there when I was challenged to the fight outside the BB hall. I didn't want to go all the way. I saw my opponent as weaker than me and I didn't want to mete out full punishment.

The symptoms were creeping into my attitude on the streets. I no longer welcomed a challenge as a vehicle for 'showing them that they were crazy to mess with me'.

The steady change coming over me was manifest in my attitude towards my environment at school. I couldn't ignore the fact that, safe as I was, there were people such as Roxborough, Preston and Horsborough continually being tormented. That, no matter how distant I felt from the tenets of the school authorities, I could hardly stand to see the rogue behaviour of my peer group that was making their lives a daily hell and was responsible for ruining the chance of a good education at the school.

The daily violence and violation was getting too hard to bear. It came to a peak in my awareness when Fred came to join our school, in my last year at NK.

++++++++

'Hey, Smith!'

I halted my walk across the playground from the smoking den in the toilets to the doors leading into the school building. I looked across at Watson, who had addressed the remark to me. Watson was never my friend, but was conscious enough of the hierarchy to never make himself my enemy.

He was a nutter himself, of course. Watson used to brag about incidents such as the time he put the live cat through the hand-mincing machine, because it had scratched his wee brother. He used to smile that sick smile of his as he told the story. I really hope that he made it to an asylum for the criminally insane, before he caused too much harm to the general public. A mind such as Watson's was far too dangerous to be walking the streets as an adult.

Watson was smirking and standing with a boy about our age that I had never seen before. The new boy - Fred, as it turned out - looked over at me and said: 'Is that him, then? He disnae look so fucking hard!'

Snick, click!

This was a situation I could read in an instant. Fred was obviously a new boy out to make a name for himself. He had found out from Watson that I was the 'top dog' in NK and he was about to take that title for himself.

Unfortunately, I had seen it all before. Not long ago, a new English kid had picked on the Midge, mistaking his diminutive size for a lack of fighting prowess. The Midge was small, but he was very, very cunning - and he could fight. The English kid took one hell of a pasting. It was pretty ugly.

Here was another new boy, and he had decided to pick on me. He had probably picked Watson for potential back-up. Watson looked hard. Unknown to Fred, Watson was no threat to me on two counts, however. Count number one was that Watson had taken his shot in a previous year and could still feel the pain of that attempt. Count number two was that Watson was a wicked little bastard, who loved watching people getting 'done in'. He was definitely looking forward to watching this fight and would never do anything that might shorten the action or limit the carnage.

I turned to look at the new boy, face impassive, and sighed. Here we go again!

Snick, click!

'So, you're Smith - eh? Ye're nothin' tae me, ya bastard! Ah'm gonnae huv you!'

Talking himself up, as was often the way with these petty gangsters, Fred walked closer to me. As he got within striking distance he launched his forehead at my face, trying to 'nut' me.

Snick, click, bang!

It's scary, but this is one fight I can't remember the details of now, and couldn't remember just afterwards. I must have made some offensive move. I must have hit him, brought him down and pummelled, kicked, bit and gouged him for some time. The scary thing is, once it was over I remembered nothing about it.

One minute Fred was coming towards me, the next he was lying on the ground with a significantly sized circle of kids arrayed around us. There were screams, other excited playground noises and...

Fred was destroyed.

I couldn't believe it as I looked at him. I couldn't remember a thing about carrying out this destruction - but destruction it certainly was.

Fred was covered in blood. He was curled up in a ball, with both of his hands covering his face, and there was blood just pouring between his fingers. The backs of his hands were completely bloodied and his knuckles were obviously burst. He had lost teeth, as I could see one lying on the ground beside him. A clump of his hair was missing. His clothes were soaked in blood. He looked like a victim in the worst type of graphic horror movie. It was a truly awful sight.

I actually heard myself snarling - frothing at the mouth. I had completely lost it this time.

As awareness came back to me, I relaxed, straightened myself up and wiped the snarl, along with any other emotion, from my face. I looked around for my glasses, which must have flown off my face at some point during the fray, and saw Watson, still grinning, holding on to them. I retrieved my glasses from him, retrieved my school bag from the playground and walked through the crowd, which parted like the Red Sea to accommodate me.

There were kids actually sobbing in the crowd, with looks of horror on their faces. These were kids used to violence, used to brutality. What on earth had I done?

I looked over my shoulder and a still-grinning Watson was helping the new boy Fred to his feet. I could hear him saying:

'Don't worry aboot him, Fred; ye'll get him next time - eh?'

I had at least made Watson's day.

But I was a tortured soul. As I walked away, all I could see before me was the broken, brutally beaten body of the new boy, and I was suddenly and completely overwhelmed with...

FEAR!

I was so scared that I thought I might pass out. I had seen the monster under the bed. I had been to hell and seen the demons. I had visited a real-life horror movie and seen the monster from the pits - and it was me!

I took out a cigarette and, as I walked out through the school gates, I lit up and breathed deeply.

What had I become? One of the thugs in the street, like these losers in the CYT? One of the petty animals I despised so much? Before, I had only ever seen myself as an avenging angel. I was John Wayne fighting the bad guys. I was The Alliance defeating Hitler. I was bad, but I was only protecting myself - so I was good. That argument would not take hold in my mind, as I still visualized the broken body of Fred. It slipped easily from my grasp, like mercury through my fingers.

I sat on the steps of the tenement building, just across the road from NK, and thought.

What if it had been as bad before, but I had never noticed? How long had I been this monster? What had brought me to this awareness now? The beating had been horrible, but why could I not justify it as self-defence? After all, he had attacked me, not the other way around. But still it wouldn't stick. I couldn't find an answer.

The answer seems simple now.

You see, I had been growing in awareness without even realizing it. People that I had given no thought to had influenced me: Mr Ferguson, who had shown me nothing but kindness and whose genuine Christian values had found some root; the schoolteacher Mr B, who had always treated me fairly as he taught me mathematics and had opened a channel of logic inside me that I revelled in and still find compelling today; and Ms W, the English teacher, who had instilled a love of literature and writing in me and who had encouraged me to read the sorts of books that do change people. These were the sorts of stories and philosophies that made a difference.

I had also been reading the works of Aldous Huxley and Herman Hesse, and I loved them. I hadn't just read them - I had studied them, analysing their tenets and absorbing the magnificence of the possibilities they encompassed.

I had just discovered Kahlil Gibran, whose poetry in The Prophet and Journey to the East opened totally new doors in my mind, and its spirituality sang to some deep subconscious place inside me, providing light and a clear window into brand new possibilities.

Without consciously seeking it, I was maturing in ways that I had never expected or prepared for. I was becoming aware of who I was, what I did and of the consequences of my actions. I was becoming a human being at last.

If I had been growing in awareness, I can only guess that the reason I did not remember doing the damage to Fred was that, while my body went into automatic maximum defence mode when Fred attacked me, my mind had refused to accept it and had somehow shut itself off. I realised how very dangerous this was. I could never afford to let that happen again.

Later that day, the PE teacher cornered me and said:

'You were lucky, Smith. That wee bastard got transferred here after stabbing a teacher at his old school. He's a nasty piece of work and deserved all he got. But that was some kicking you gave him, son; you were lucky - very lucky.'

I didn't feel lucky; I felt sick.

I was afraid.

I was so, so afraid of myself and what I was capable of.

There was no escape.

I had to somehow stop being me.

I had to change.

I had to kill this demon of violence.

Fred never came back to our school again. The talk was that he had spent a considerable amount of time recuperating both in and out of hospital, but that he had never betrayed 'the code' and grassed on me. Even as he lay for days, unable to see through his swollen-closed eyes, unable to move without pain from cracked ribs and bandaged all over - Fred never grassed.

I guess I was lucky, as the PE teacher said, as I could have faced serious assault charges for that incident.

I know I was lucky, because, horrible as that fight was, it stopped the rot!

I was afraid.

There was no escape.

I had to stop being me.

I had to change.

But how..?

CHAPTER XXVIII

John and Yoko, Man

Our NK John and Yoko strolled through the playground in bare feet, smelling as if they had fallen into a vat of fragrant oils. John's hair was in the customary hippy style of unwashed grease and obligatory pony-tail. Yoko's straw-coloured hair was a little less greasy, but she had the uniform dying daisies placed on her head in a crown-like ring.

We thought they were amazing.

Hippy life had reached out from Woodstock to touch NK. Our own John and Yoko epitomized the times we were living in. They were a colourful notification that the world was changing, and that even the lives under development at NK could change right along with it.

This 'peace and love, man' couple had a bigger impact on my school class than most. John was the brother of one of my classmates and, as this lad worshiped everything about his older brother, he was the first of us to begin to mirror the cultural change. Yoko was the sister of another boy in our class and - as an added bonus - their dad was an artist! How cool was that?

This was as intoxicating as it got at NK and everyone wanted to be on the bandwagon.

As you will have gathered from previous chapters, 'peace and love' was not a philosophy that was easy to adopt at my school. But such was the power of the movement, through the media of television and - more importantly - the influence of music, and such was the allure of every-day examples like our own John and Yoko, that the culture took hold at an amazing rate. I don't want to mislead you by saying that, overnight, we became a school full of peace and love, where all cruel thoughts and violent actions were banished in a storm of patchouli oil and flowers. Unfortunately, this was not the case, but sudden and obvious changes were definitely happening.

The first thing to change was our language. A conversation during the new era would start like this:

'How're ye daein', man?'

'No' bad, man; how are you, man?'

'No' bad, man.'

'Cool, man.'

This could have been a greeting exchanged between two boys, two girls, or a girl and a boy - none of whom could have been mistaken for a 'man'.

The language continued to evolve. Lines from cool albums by artists such as Captain Beefheart, Frank Zappa or Pink Floyd were bandied about. It wasn't so important that anyone actually understood these words; it was only important to say them.

'Hey, man; how ur ye doin', man?'

'Safe as milk, man. Where are ye goin'?'

'Goin' tae Montana, man.'

'Cool, man; cool!'

A conversation that made absolutely no sense, but would certainly impress your peers! Because of the 'newness' of this esoteric rhetoric, very few kids, most of whom were aspiring hippies themselves, would ever challenge these strange statements. Non-aspiring hippies were considered so uncool, or straight, that any challenge from them held no water. So it was cool to talk gibberish now in the playground and on the streets of Glasgow and give yourself an aloof air of 'difference'.

Of course, during this time there were some hopelessly dangerous misinterpretations of lines from our rock-idols' albums. For instance, 'careful with that axe, Eugene', took on a whole new meaning when interpreted by an LSD-crazed member of the CYT!

Other changes took a quick hold.

It was cool to be seen carrying the latest and most off-the-wall album cover you could find. Kids would be seen sporting albums such as the incomprehensible 'In C' record, produced by Terry Riley. I can't believe that music written entirely with one note (C, as you might have guessed from the title) actually appealed to these kids, but it was a 'thing' and nobody disputed the 'coolness' of someone who owned that album. Also Asian-style music by bands such as Quintessence were very much in vogue, and, if the album cover you carried had a 'hash burn' on it - even cooler, man! Music had become a big thing, and, if you were not bleary-eyed from staying up late to watch the Old Grey Whistle Test, then you really had nothing to talk about the next day.

Personal appearance changed as well. There were no fashion rules except for the rule that you could not look 'straight'. No one saw this as a dichotomy at the time. 'People should be free to dress any way that they like' was the banner refrain, but if you liked to dress 'straight', in conventional clothing, you were ostracized and shunned. I even remember one poor fashion victim, who got into trouble from teachers at school for inserting a purple triangle into the bottom of the leg of his school trousers to turn them into 'cool flairs'. He looked like a dork, but 'hey, man, it was his thing!'

Education took a strange turn at school as well. Kids were reading more - voluntarily! All of a sudden, kids wanted to read Island and Brave New World. Kahlil Gibran grew in popularity and new authors such as Richard Neville, with his book Play Power, were in high demand. Hippy magazines such as Gandalf's Garden and the soon-to-be-banned Oz were regularly pored over during break times and lunchtimes, inserting more new language and concepts into the malleable minds of our impressionable teenagers.

The criminal activities in school were also affected. To meet the demands that 'hippydom' brought to NK, our entrepreneurial school thieves started stealing: albums; incense; hippy clothes; hippy magazines; fragrant oils; even books - the de luxe hardback edition of Lord Of The Rings, the hardback of Kahlil Gibran's The Prophet, and Richard Neville's Play Power were three of the most popular books to nick, I remember. Of course, these kids had missed a philosophical point in carrying out these crimes, but they were now 'anti-establishment' liberators, and as such our thieves had found a new status level within the hippy movement in Glasgow and were attaining a new level of respect and popularity. It was now considered pretty cool to steal from establishment 'fat cats'.

Later on in my life, when I was on the board of multinational companies and observed the business practices of many senior executives, I would be able to draw a strong comparison between the 'justified entrepreneurial behaviour' I was seeing and the 'anti-establishment liberation' I had witnessed at school in the 1970s. But that's a part of another story.

Our NK John and Yoko strolled through our playground, symbolizing all sorts of changes in the world around me - all sorts of possibilities. I've mentioned some of the changes that these times brought to my Glasgow existence, but the biggest was the one I've saved till last and the one that destroyed as many lives as it changed. It was, of course, the delight of choice for all hippies worth their kaftan: drugs.

CHAPTER XXIX

Jimmy the Pill

Jimmy the Pill was a temporary feature of NK, and he symbolized the change that drugs were to have on our life at school.

Imagine: here was an acned, worn-brown-suited, greasy-haired, late-twenties man, who hung around our school gates with impunity. None of the thugs painted a target on him. Nobody attacked or beat him up for having the audacity to enter our territory as an outsider.

Jimmy was always around. He would be there at break times, smoking in the toilets, and he would be there at lunchtime, talking to kids at our school gates. People would ask, 'have ye seen Jimmy, man?' and you knew that Jimmy the Pill had another convert in NK. But nobody moved to stop this wee parasite and his distribution of 'uppers' and 'downers' to NK adolescents.

The obscene wee man had nothing to offer but trouble and bad advice, but our kids seemed only too happy to purchase both. Jimmy used to say, 'If it says take two, three times a day, on the bottle of pills, then take six and wash it doon wi' vodka!'

Unfortunately, many impressionable children took his advice verbatim.

++++++++

'Hi, Jimmy!'
  'Hi, man; lookin' tae score?'
  'Aye, Jimmy. What huv ye goat?'
  'The usual, man; uppers an' downers.'
  'Goat' any 'Mandies', Jimmy?'
  'Aye, son; how many dae ye want?'
  'Couple o' quids' worth, man.'

Money would change hands and the transaction would be carried out.

This particular transaction would be for Mandrax sleeping pills, popular at the time amongst many of my peers. They were particularly popular with one boy, whose exploration of vodka and Mandrax earned him the nickname of 'Mandy'. It was a nickname that he hated but couldn't shake off.

Mandrax, or 'Mandies', was a drug taken in quantity, and washed down liberally with vodka, or any other strong spirit available. The pills quickly induced a state of severe drunkenness and incomprehensibility. It was a very dangerous concoction, which many lads never judged quite right and so ended up in hospital being stomach-pumped to save their lives. It was considered a notch up from sniffing glue, which had also become popular with a minority of school kids. I was never tempted into that particular deviance. It was enough to see Mandy staggering about the playground, streets, or occasionally the classroom in a sleazy stupor, to dissuade me from entering that particular realm of madness.

'Mandies' were a crazy drug of choice, but downers were cheap, so Jimmy the Pill had a ready customer base at NK.

I can't make up my mind if the school authorities of the time were stupid, blind, uncaring, or simply unable to stem the drug market, which grew at a furious pace each day. Because of 'the code', of course, there was little or no chance of anyone grassing Jimmy, but surely someone must have noticed the high percentage of wasted kids each day. By simply catching and incarcerating Jimmy the Pill, a lot of young lives could have been saved from tragedy.

Jimmy was also the first to introduce readily available 'hash', 'grass' and 'acid' into playground circulation. He was the first person that NK people knew who could supply their needs. He was the first, but it wasn't long before availability was widespread and commonplace.

Eventually everyone knew people who were dealing and many of the older kids at school had branched into dealing themselves. Knowing people became voguish and everyone wanted it to be known that they knew somebody, but, picking up on the paranoia prevalent within the drug scene, nobody wanted to share their contacts and nobody would break 'the code' and actually take a peer to a dealer's house. It 'just wasn't cool, man'.

Needless to say, the brothers of our own John and Yoko, along with their school cronies, were some of the first to embrace this new phenomenon. They quickly affected the language, dress and attitude of the hippy movement. They swiftly learned the philosophical words, and they were leaders in promoting the drug experience now widely on offer.

These were guys who couldn't fight and who had previously enjoyed only a minimal amount of protection as a pack at school. These were boys whom nobody was afraid of and who lived near the bottom of the hard man pecking order. In a world full of hard men, they were easy - and yet, all of a sudden, they became both cool and safe! Nobody picked on these boys. Nobody challenged their differences, or victimized them for existing within a world where they couldn't defend themselves.

Thugs didn't befriend them; instead, the thug scene looked upon them warily. These weirdoes, who affected the nickname of 'freaks', represented something that the thugs' violent culture had left them unprepared to deal with. They were symbols of a change that was sweeping across our small world and as such no one really knew how to deal with them. So, they were left pretty much to themselves and their scene.

For a while I watched this development with only a small amount of curiosity. These boys had never been close to me and I had little interest in either their movement or their fate. As time passed, and they gained strength and followers, I observed with more interest, awaiting the inevitable 'thug-land' challenges.

They never came.

My interest peaked, and I started to get closer to this group to try and understand what they had that kept them so well protected.

This new drug-taking hippy scene was strange and new. In some ways it was frightening in the way that it had changed attitudes and upset the balance of power within my environment.

But ...perhaps for me it was a way out.

Our local Young Teams soon noticed the commercial opportunities within a growing drug and hippy culture. This was the death knell for the commercial enterprise of Jimmy the Pill at our school. It wasn't long before the local thug scene twigged that there was money to be made in selling pills and other drugs to us - and Jimmy had a problem. As far as the local 'hoods' were concerned, NK was on their turf, and as such all the spoils from drug-dealing belonged to them.

Jimmy grew concerned, but he was too slow to react.

I never saw the incident that finished his dealing career, but I heard the story. Apparently he was hanging about in the toilets with a pocket full of pills, when in marched a few of the local nutters, armed with the usual assortment of knives and blunt instruments. Without any discussion, the thugs set about Jimmy with a vengeance. They carved him up, beat him to a pulp and then dragged his sorry remains outside the school gates. They remembered, of course, to divest him of all his wares, so that they had an immediate stock to use for setting up shop themselves.

Jimmy eventually managed to limp off somewhere and was never seen around our school again.

He deserved what he got for the misery that he caused, but, of course, the misery did not stop - all we got was a change of traders.

CHAPTER XXX

Enter the Dragon

'Turn on, tune in and drop out' was the credo espoused by the legendary Timothy Leary, the man who introduced recreational LSD trips to the world. It was a credo embraced by every hippy and would-be hippy that I met during this period of my life.

Hippies had a 'duty' to spread the word and spread the drugs. Hippies could change the world, if only they could get everyone stoned, and so, like an unstoppable bacteria, the drug culture was spread through all walks of life in Glasgow. Smart kids, uneducated kids, rich kids, poor kids, gang members, even some parents; it seemed as though the whole world had just been waiting for the opportunity to 'turn on, tune in and drop out'!

What this wave of change meant for me was an easy way out of the hard man scene, and an easy way into something different.

After observing the new wave of hippies and their seeming ability to float through school with relative immunity to the aggression that had previously been the norm, I moved closer to this group. They were happy to admit me into their circle, for many reasons. The major reason that they accepted me was because they were not completely immune from the occasional thug persecution. They had suffered from it in the past and were only too glad to live under the protective umbrella of my hard-man reputation. Second, they were happy to gain as much credibility as possible for their cause, and converting me to hippydom would only add more credence to the new philosophy that they had discovered.

They saw me as a useful ally - and, for me, this group offered a much-wanted way out. It was a 'win-win' marriage of convenience.

I started to spend my free time hanging out with the freaks. I didn't change the way I dressed. I probably added 'man' as a full stop to every sentence, but, apart from that, my language didn't change significantly.

I never felt the need to buy music that sounded like discordant nastiness just so that I could be seen on the streets sporting the album covers. Although I had already read much of the literature of this new age, I read some more, and I liked what I was discovering.

I remember that most of the conversations among this group were just schoolboy gibberish. Badly twisted recognition of spirituality; misguided interpretations of the new age philosophy; declarations of deeper understanding without any foundation; and, of course, as was inevitable from the environment that had nurtured these boys for so long, a gradual move towards more sinister studies, such as the works of Alistair Crowley. Hardly 'love and peace, man', but it was an alternative and so I stuck around.

Drugs were the main topic of our conversations.

'Have ye tried that 'Ti-stick' yet, man? It's brilliant, man.'

'Naw, but I got some oil frae a guy the other day and it was a cosmic smoke, man.'

'Oil's aw right, man, but ah goat a pound deal o' that Pakistani Black and I couldnae even smoke it aw, man. It was a killer, man.'

On and on and round and round the conversation would go, discussions on types of cannabis or marijuana, by boys who had probably never tried any of it, but who had heard the terms from older siblings, hippy magazines or news broadcasts on TV.

Drugs were a bit like burgeoning schoolboy sexuality at the beginning. Everyone wanted to brag about having done it, but very few had the courage to try it, or the maturity to have a chance of scoring. There were a few who could talk from experience, however, and the few became many very quickly, as the spread of drug dealerships increased throughout the city at an exponential rate.

Mandy was the first of our group to dip his toe into the psychedelic water. Unfortunately, he chose Jimmy the Pill as his supplier, and one of the worst of the drug options available, when he made his debut. Although a few others followed suit occasionally, nobody else that I knew was tempted to take pills as often as Mandy. Others were making contacts, though, and as time passed they had access to the whole range of products available at this trendy psychedelic party.

It was the Boke (he owed his strange nickname to a severe night on Mandies and vodka) who first projected most of our class head first into the psychedelic arena. I remember the day well. We were huddled in the playground adjoining the bottom school building, discussing some inane subject or other, when an obviously-pleased-with-himself Boke fast-walked towards us with bright eyes and bright red cheeks. He reached our group of would-be hippies and in an exuberant half whisper said: 'Boys, boys, ah've got some oan me, man!'

Stillness descended among us. We immediately knew what he meant of course, but what had he got? Every mind examined the possibilities and wondered if they would have the courage to participate in the Boke's discovery. We all knew it was going to be offered. The Boke wasn't a guy to try anything new himself; he would want all of us freaks in on it.

What did he have?

'Ah met this bloke, man, and he gave me these tabs, man. Says they're the best 'n that. Strawberry Fields, man - the best, man.'

(I'm sure you can begin to see how irritating the punctuation had become in these 'hippy' conversations.)

'Ah've got 20 trips, man. He laid the 20 on me an' said that Ah kin sell them tae ma mates fur a quid a piece, man. We kin aw trip oot, man.'

Acid!

Wow!

This was the real thing.

Affecting the proper hippy response, we all enthused about the Boke's score and praised his prowess in obtaining 'the real deal' for us freaks. The Boke was in hero mode. Carried away with the praise all around, the fake enthusiasm, the trust given to him by his dealer, and paranoia at holding all the contraband himself, he immediately started to hand out these innocuous, microscopic dots of a chemical that looked like minute blue aspirins.

'I thought Strawberry Fields were pink, man? Are ye sure this stuff is real?' This from one of the group.

'Jesus, it's smaw enough. What's this supposed tae dae, then?' I piped up.

Other comments came from within the group, confident to challenge once the first doubts had been cast. We all started to doubt that the Boke had obtained any drugs at all, as we stared at this microdot acid that had been passed off as Strawberry Fields. But our fat distributor was

149

undaunted:

'It's the real thing, man - honest! This bloke's a dealer, man; Ah know him, man. He wouldnae gie me duff gear, man.'

By this time, after actually handling the merchandise, there was hardly a believer amongst us. More freaks from our class had drifted over, asking what was happening, and in return had been given a 'tab' in exchange for a promise of paying the quid later. Nine lads and lassies stood in the playground looking at the possibility of their first psychedelic experience. But still no one believed that we were really in possession of the much celebrated hippy drug of choice.

There were about ten minutes left before we had to go into our English lesson. The Boke had a look on his face that indicated that he might have his own set of doubts about the transaction he had carried out this lunchtime. He persevered, though - he didn't want to lose face as much as anything else.

'Look, man, it's acid, man. Ah don't know if it's Strawberry Fields, but ah' know it's acid, man. Aw we huv tae dae is drap it and, if it disnae work, ah'll go an' see the guy an' tell him, man. Honest, man - aw we have tae dae is take it an' see.'

So, just like that - we did.

We all popped a microdot into our mouth, then, as the enormity of what we had done started to dawn on us, we waited about nervously in the playground, afraid to be parted from our fellow conspirators.

Nothing happened.

We were expecting a big boom. We were expecting something wild and wonderful to happen. We'd all read about believing that you were an orange, and about seeing fantastic hallucinatory images.

Nothing happened.

We waited, relaxing as the minutes ticked by, until the bell in the playground rang signalling our return to school and, for our group, two periods of English. Nervous laughter prevailed and the Boke was transformed in our eyes from hippy-hero to complete loser, with the usual (somewhat relieved) comments being flung at him.

Still smiling, we trooped into our English class.

But it was definitely acid!

The change was subtle. None of us had any experience to draw on and so it crept up on us unawares. We all settled into class and the teacher began our lesson. At first everything seemed to be going along as normal.

Then...

The first thing I noticed was laughter - semi-hysterical laughter. I heard our long-suffering English teacher demand to know, 'what is going on with this class today?'

Oh, shit!

I came out of my dream-state, not having realized that I had drifted into one, and was shocked into coherence by what I saw. The class was in chaos. There were kids laughing like maniacs. There were kids darting their heads around; some like scared animals, some like amazed two-year-olds. A couple of kids were wandering around the class poking at things with their fingers. The teacher, completely unaware of the psychedelic experience blossoming in her midst, was alternatively screaming at us and pleading for order.

Oh, shit; it was working!

This madness was only happening to the freaks, although a few of the other kids were picking up on the mayhem and were adding their own noise and teacher-taunts to the proceedings. But, apart from the freaks, nobody else was acting really crazy.

Oh, shit!

We had to get out of there, and fast! I stood up and, just before the next psychedelic wave hit me, I shouted: 'Out! Come oan, you lot. We're oot o' here. Come oan!'

And I made a swift move towards the door.

Some responded, but most didn't even seem to hear me. The 'straight' guys in our class were laughing, thinking I was pulling off some stunt with my gang of freaks. The teacher started yelling at me to sit down and for the rest of the class to get a grip on itself. I could feel the effects of the acid getting stronger. I could taste it, see it, touch it, and I knew that we were in deep, deep trouble if we were not out of that class in short order.

Perhaps it was because of my 'top-dog' status that I managed to pull it off, but somehow, with the help of some not-so-far-gone others, who had also realized what was happening, I managed to herd our group of 14-year-old freaks out of the English classroom, out of the school and down the hill towards the local park. I even managed to raise enough of a snarl to keep the straight guys, who didn't know what was happening but wanted to join in anyway, grounded in the classroom as we left.

We escaped from the madness of the classroom into the streets. A wave of paranoia hit me. We had to get into the park quickly, because if the police saw us cavorting around like maniacs we were in even deeper trouble.

Luckily, the park was a short walk from our school and I knew that it was a large enough haven for us to find a 'safe' spot to hang out in. The Midge was as focused on escape as me, and between us we managed to herd our small crowd.

By this time it was getting pretty hard to concentrate. We were all enveloped by varying hallucinations and were swimming around in private fantasies. The waves were becoming stronger, as we climbed the psychedelic ladder. None of us were coherent. None of us really knew what we were doing. But the common goal of 'the park' prevailed, and we stumbled into its sanctuary minutes (which seemed at the time like days) afterwards.

Once encased in this green sanctuary, oblivious to the strange looks of passers-by and the suspicious looks from park workers, we were all able to relax. There were hothouses to explore; there were flowers, beautiful enough to make some of us cry; there was grass, which we could spend eternities stroking, smelling or even, in some cases, eating. There was the sky to look at, which for one lad had become a huge TV screen, and he laughed uproariously at the cartoons displayed there, while lying on the feathery grass.

In hindsight it was a miracle that we were not spotted, corralled and taken to hospital. I can only guess that the fact that we weren't violent or particularly noisy (if you ignore the maniacal laughter) stopped anybody from interfering with us. In Glasgow, a bunch of nine teenagers from our school, who were not causing some kind of trouble, was always a bonus to the general public. This was also before the big government programmes on 'awareness about the effects of drugs', so I imagine that few citizens would have guessed at our psychedelic state. The public probably took one look and assumed that we were drunk.

Somehow we managed to stay together, remembering to look out for each other whenever the highest peaks had subsided. We were a 'freak' brother-and-sisterhood, sharing liberated minds and chemically

152

induced dreams. Within our psychedelic world there were the straight guys - and there was us. We bonded within our multi-coloured mind-cocoon and we concentrated on looking out for ourselves.

We tripped for hours in the park.

As night and darkness approached, we had all started to pass the peak of our acid experience, and some of us were gaining back a little bit of control. The Midge said to me: 'We need somewhere tae go, Les, man. What aboot the Mole's place? His maw's always oot working at night, anyway.'

Seemed that I was still the boss. I agreed, although I don't really remember seeing the problem that night-tripping would pose. I had always trusted the Midge and his cunning, though, and that trust stuck, even through this wild, cosmic roller coaster I was on.

Between us we managed to round up all of our fellow freaks, with the exception of one girl who, it turned out, had had a psychedelic sexual experience with one of the lads in the bushes. She had freaked out part of the way through and had taken off towards home, leaving a smiling lad in the bushes, with his trousers round his ankles, wondering in amazement what had happened. We at least found him before he was arrested for public indecency.

The 'tripped-out' girl was lucky. When she got home, her big sister saw her before her parents had returned from work, and, even through the hysterical bad-trip sobbing, managed to work out what was happening to her younger sibling. She was a drug-taker herself and had the presence of mind to take her sister to Jimmy the Pill's place and obtain a couple of sleeping pills from him. She got her traumatized wee sister back home (not without Jimmy trying to do a deal on her, I hear), administered the sleeping pills and put her sister to bed. That night she told her parents that our girl had been drinking too much and had passed out. Our lady got shit from her parents about the evils of drink the next day, but it could have been much, much worse if the real truth had been discovered!

The rest of us made it to the Mole's place, to trip and play until eventually we came down enough to go home.

Coming down was a bear. Most of us were sweaty, depressed, confused wrecks by the time we had recovered enough of our faculties to brave the journey. By this time it was midnight and we all had a lot of explaining to do at home, but nobody, even the confused minds of those whose trips had not been as pleasant as others, told their parents the truth.

We had got away with it.

That was our class of freaks' first psychedelic experience. The next day we were the main men and women. We had done it! Other would-be hippies said 'cool' a lot and wanted to be on our team. We all told how great it was, nobody admitting that they had ever been frightened or insecure, although everyone had been through periods of that. We even managed to get away with some minor punishment from our English teacher, when I 'owned up' to us all having had a bit of a prank at her expense.

'It wis jist actin', Miss. Ye're always saying we should transform ourselves when we act out a part, so we did!'

Miss wasn't amused or convinced by my lame excuse, and it meant extra homework for all of us and six of the belt for me, but we had got away with it!

It wasn't our last acid trip together. With the wild abandon of youth, 'tripping' became a weekly occurrence during school time, but now we had some knowledge and experience and we handled successive trips differently. The numbers of willing trippers dwindled from within our class, many of the kids finding excuses not to participate. There were plenty of other kids willing to join in, however, and over time, having graduated into 'psychedelia', we also made inroads into the hippy scene outside school and tripped with older guys and chicks.

Future trips were fairly well planned affairs, starting early in the morning and with a couple of guys always staying straight. On advice from the older freaks that we now knew, the selected two would just smoke some dope and make sure that none of the group did anything too stupid when they were tripping. The minders would administer joints of dope to the hysterical and try to talk down the bad trips. In a dire emergency we now knew of pads, the homes of older freaks, where we could take a casualty to give him or her time to recover. We all became pretty good trip counsellors.

We were real hippies now.

The Botanical Gardens, Kelvingrove Park, or the homes of those kids with two working parents were our usual venues, but as our hippy circle grew we were also able to take more and more 'trips' at the houses of our friends.

Some of these friends were less than stable, though.

CHAPTER XXXI

Hallelujah

One of the worst new friends that we met was a supposed 'Jesus freak' called McMilne. We met McMilne through some kids about a year older than us. This bunch came from different schools and also used the Botanical Gardens as one of their places to trip out on acid. Inevitably, we crossed paths during one of our 'school trips', bonded in typical hippy fashion - sharing a few joints - and became fast friends.

I thought that this was great. These were kids from completely different backgrounds from my current social circle. They mostly lived in and around the 'arty' West End of Glasgow and came from pretty good homes. They spoke differently from us and had a kind of confidence that until then I had not experienced. It was a confidence born of being secure in their homes and general environment.

These kids introduced some of us to new and older freaks, much more experienced in the ways of hippydom and the drug culture it embraced. As time passed, my circle of freaks just kept growing.

We met: 'left-wing activist freaks'; religious freaks; acid-burned freaks; paranoid freaks; Hell's Angel freaks; and many 'true believers' of the hippy philosophy. We avoided the needle-indulging junkies as if they carried the Black Death. These were the outcasts of the main 'freak' social strata at the time. Nobody trusted the junkies.

McMilne was a so-called 'religious freak'. He lived in a bedsit off the Great Western Road with his girlfriend, where he held court to younger freaks, attempting to 'show them the way, man'.

When I first met McMilne, I was less than impressed by his strange twists on a drug-fuelled route to heaven.

'Jesus would have turned on if he was here now, man. We can enter his embrace by turning on and meditating. I've seen him, man. You can see him too.'

By now I'd seen Charlie Chaplin chasing Tom and Jerry through a field of multi-coloured jelly babies; I'd seen cars take off from the streets, headlight eyes blinking and radiator grill mouths grinning; I'd seen buildings melt and animal-headed people perform ballets in the streets. He'd seen Jesus while he was tripping - so what?

McMilne talked softly, while his girlfriend rolled up the smokes (pilgrims with donations of hash or grass were always warmly welcomed). I just took a 'toke' in turn and tried to tune out his drone - easy enough when the shit kicked in. Many of the guys I knew had become pilgrims, however, and they'd sit cross-legged, smoking and worshipping at the feet of their new prophet.

They were engrossed, but McMilne was a fake.

I knew he was a fake from the outset. My new friends were wide open to any new philosophy and many of them had been taken right in. Probably a gift of my harsher background was that I was always suspicious of glib talk, having grown up around a legion of con artists and liars.

McMilne didn't work, but, from a combination of the labour of his acolyte girlfriend and the donations from his young admirers, he managed to have a pretty easy existence. I remember the amount of money that some of the guys coughed up for him when he decided that he had to take a pilgrimage to the Glastonbury pop festival to 'spread the word of Jesus'. He was given cash, some new kit, 'dope' to use and sell, a tent, a sleeping bag, and a lift down and back in a van from a dedicated follower's big brother.

It wasn't the con that made me quickly desert McMilne's as a place to hang out; after all, to me it was just another 'freak' pad where I could get high. No, it was the signs of his mania that I saw displayed all too regularly on the visible parts of his girlfriend's body.

The poor woman was apparently accident-prone. She kept banging into things, falling down the stairs of the flat, even 'banging her face on the sink tap' once while she was washing her face. This mishap left her with a very ugly and swollen eye. She said nothing, was always quiet and subservient during our visits to 'the master'. The guys saw this as adoration. I didn't; I knew that the bastard McMilne was obviously beating her up.

When I mentioned this to the dedicated, they scorned my comments, saying, 'How could a guy so spiritual do anything like that, man?' One of them brought my comments up at a 'session', and McMilne told them to pray for me.

His girlfriend stayed quiet.

I stopped going to see McMilne after that, and was not surprised to hear, much later, that the slimy weasel had been arrested for beating his girlfriend so badly that she had been admitted to hospital and put on life-support. Apparently she had almost died, because McMilne, too scared of being found out, had tried to avoid calling an ambulance for her. It was only when a bunch of acolytes dropped round, and saw McMilne covered in the blood of his poor victim, that an ambulance - as well as the police - were called by these now disillusioned kids.

Yep, although I was meeting a new range of people through my involvement in the hippy scene, it quickly became apparent that I had to be very careful about whom I chose to spend time with. The 'scene' was riddled with as many crazies as there were within my housing estate. These were, for the most part, a different type of crazy. Instead of violence, they were twisted in different ways, mostly living inside some sort of weird mental fantasy, but some of them were no less dangerous than the thugs I was used to.

It wasn't all like that, though, and in many ways I was gaining an education by meeting new and interesting people and by being exposed to new and sometimes radically different philosophies.

People talked differently, too. This new group had its own adjectives, proverbs and punctuation, but they had little or no brogue. I learned to speak without such a heavy emphasis on Glasgow slang. Both teachers and parents were pleased, although my parents, especially my mum, thought I might be developing 'airs and graces'.

The times, they were a-changing.

From the day I took my first acid trip, till the day I left NK, my life changed dramatically.

I had found the escape I had craved. Now I had to institutionalize the change in myself, and at the same time stay safe within my environment. Not everyone was a hippy. There were still the usual legions of thugs, gangs and general miscreants, looking to dole out abuse or make a name for themselves.

The freaks had a barrier of weirdness between them and the world of violence and intimidation. I had joined them and so I was also beginning to cloak myself with this thin veil. I had a history, however. I was Leslie Ronald Smith, hard man and merciless avenger. There were plenty of old enemies waiting for their chance of revenge. This wasn't going to be easy.

Somehow I managed to pull it off. I kept my outward 'bad attitude' at school and on the streets of my estate, as protection against thug persecution. At the same time I told myself that the only way I could really effect this change was never to fight again, and so I took great pains to avoid all challenges and conflicts. Sometimes it was touch-and-go, with only my reputation saving me from a bloody battle.

I managed it, though.

In the meantime, I lived a double life. I started to develop more and more acquaintances from the 'freak' scene. Within this scene I was 'Les the hippy' and I had no need to wear my old armour. I'd hang out in my spare time at freaks' houses and at freaks' gathering places, learning the rules and social protocols.

It was a pretty schizophrenic existence, but I adapted.

I had found a way out and I wasn't about to let it go.

This dual life continued right up until the first Glastonbury Free Music Festival that some of my fellow freaks and I dodged school to attend.

This festival marked the end of my school days in Glasgow, my first trip to a full-blooded hippy festival, and my final rite of passage - from thug to hippy.

Hallelujah!

CHAPTER XXXII

Camping out

For me, Glastonbury was both a trial and a pleasure, overflowing with amazing new insights.

I was 15 years old, and just about finished with school, when the word went around the freak scene about this great festival in Somerset. There was talk of all the great bands being there: Pink Floyd was going to make an appearance; George Harrison was going to play; Quintessence was going to be there; and Frank Zappa was flying over especially. As I became more knowledgeable over the years, I learned to take such unfounded rumours with a pinch of salt, but this was my first exposure to the excitement generated by a big free festival and I wanted to be there.

We all wanted to be there. The NK freaks and the mates we had made in the general hippy world were buzzing with excitement. This would be three days of ecstasy. Three days where we would live free, smoke dope, take acid, enjoy 'free love' with hippy chicks, and hear amazing sets from the coolest bands around. It was going to be our British Woodstock!

We had to get there.

Unfortunately, Glastonbury fell across some of our O level exams, but we NK freaks didn't care. We could pretend to be studying at each other's houses, providing the perfect cover for us to get down to the festival. We began planning and saving our meagre amounts of pocket money, illicitly acquired cash, and paper-round earnings.

Eventually, only six of us from our class made the decision to go. The adventurers would be: Mandy, the Midge, Cooper, Parsons, me and the now fairly depressive Mole - whom Parsons thought, 'Needs to get away, man.' He actually needed strong psychiatric help, but Parsons

160

and Mandy agreed to hitch-hike down with the Mole, and so the 'away team' was settled without protest.

We had all planned to make our way down south individually, as it would probably be easier to get lifts that way, with the exception of the Mole and his guardians. This master plan was formed by 15-year-old boys, none of whom had ever been any further south than Blackpool on holiday with their parents.

We would leave a day early and we would easily hitch-hike to Glastonbury in time for the festival - a journey as far south as we could even imagine. The prospect kept us high for weeks. School was only a place to discuss the upcoming festival, and evenings were spent getting stoned, listening to music and daydreaming of three days of unfettered ecstasy!

The day of our departure eventually arrived.

None of us had any decent camping kit. We had no sleeping bags or tents. Some of us had rucksacks, into which we slipped any food we'd purloined from home, and we also used them to stash our school uniforms in when we changed into our cooler 'flared' jeans and T-shirts for the trip ahead. We had very little money, and - apart from 'due south' - had very little idea as to how we would actually get to the place. The Midge had stolen a map for each of us from a newsagent shop and had carefully ringed Shepton Mallet in blue ink on each map. On the day before our departure we met up, and he gave us this set of directions; we split a bit of hash for the journey, and we were all ready to rock!

This was going to be great!

I remember setting off from Glasgow, small rucksack on my back, with my thumb out, waiting for a lift in the rain. When I arrived at the motorway, I saw the Midge at the far end of the queue of hitch-hikers, standing with his older sister. Lucky bastard - girls always got you lifts. He waved, but, before I could go and join him, a lorry pulled up and - with a smile in my direction - the Midge and his sister were off to the festival.

His quick departure gave me a boost of confidence. The Midge was off already. It couldn't be too long before I was also on my way.

After about 30 long minutes, I was at the top of the queue.

The journey wasn't too eventful at the beginning. I had shared a 'J' at the beginning of my journey with a couple of hippies I met who were just starting out for Glastonbury themselves. I was nicely fogged in cotton wool and dreams for my first lift, which was going all the way to Birmingham. I think the lorry driver tried to make conversation, but after a few 'sure, man - yeah' type answers he gave up on me and let me goof off while he drove. I hadn't learned the hitch-hikers 'decent conversation' code at this time. Pity, as he was a good bloke and even paid for a decent breakfast for us both on the way.

'Thanks, mate.'

After Birmingham, things got slower. I remember waiting around for about two hours for my next lift, and it turned out to be a weirdo!

I was just beginning to think that I was stuck in Birmingham, and would never get to the festival, when a blue estate car pulled over. A lady with her head covered in the strangest colour of red hair wound down her window and leaned across to say: 'Where are you goin', luv? I can take you as far as Bournemouth if you like?'

I was freshly mind-fogged, having just had another joint while I was waiting, and paid no attention to anything other than the fact that this was a lift. I had no idea where Bournemouth was geographically - but at least it wasn't Birmingham. I opened the car door and jumped in.

I turned to thank my deliverer and, when I looked at her, I thought I must be having an acid flashback. Her hair was SO red! I then noticed that she was dressed in a skin-tight leather catsuit and was wearing pointy high-heeled boots. She was no spring chicken and had enough make-up on to re-plaster the Houses of Parliament. The car also had a pungent too-sweet smell of cheap perfume, mixed with old cigarette smoke.

'Jesus!'

Well, at least she was a smoker. I could probably get a couple of fags out of her on the journey if I was lucky.

'Er...thanks for stoppin', man. I was waitin' there for ages.'

'No problem, luv. What's a young lad like you doing on the road anyway - eh?'

No chance of a 'kip' here, then. I filled her in on the details, waxing lyrical about the big free festival and the wild times my mates and I were going to have down there.

'Ooh. Sounds wild all right, luv. You must be a bit of a wild boy, then. Are you, then? Wild, like?'

Gulp!

'No' really, man. It's just a big festival. It's just a bit wild, I suppose.'

I hadn't liked the way she seemed to be sweating, or the predatory glint in her eye when she emphasized the word 'wild'. Thank the lord it was only just a smelly old girl I had to deal with, and not some gay pervert of the type I had heard discussed among my older and hitch-hiking-experienced mates. I was pretty uncomfortable all the same as she continued to talk.

'I'm in show business, you know.'

Here we go, I thought.

'You won't have heard of me, you being so young,' she chuckled. 'See that stuff in the back there?'

'Yeah, man, I see it,' I said, as I twisted myself round to look at the masses of suitcases and boxes in the back of her estate car.

'Well, I'm what's called an 'exotic entertainer'. My stage name's Kinky Katrina; what do you think of that - eh? Lucky pick-up for you - eh, luv?' (Many more chuckles.)

Oh NO!

My hash-induced fog cleared immediately. Just my bloody luck to get picked up by an ageing porn star, who to my adolescent mind was obviously gagging for it.

Why me? Why bloody well me? This should have happened to Mandy. He'd have shagged a donkey if he thought he could get away with it.

Why ME?

I figured I had to think quickly. She was giving me a lecherous kind of smile that left no room for doubt as to the kind of response she was expecting. If I had been older, wiser and living in a more enlightened age, I might have told her that I was gay or something. I didn't want to lose either the lift or my earlier breakfast, so I had to come up with something that would keep me in the car till Bournemouth (wherever that was), and keep her paws out of my flairs.

Kinky Katrina was not my idea of free love with hippy chicks!

'That's cool, man. I've never seen an exotic entertainer before, man. How did you get into that, then, man?'

I had to keep her talking; maybe then she would cool off.

No chance.

'It's the money, luv. I make a lot of money doing this type of work and I've always had a bit of a thing for the stage, ye know. Would you like to see my act sometime, then?'

Fuck!

I felt cornered. If I said 'no', then she would probably get pissed off with me and drop me at the next exit. If I said 'yes', then I imagined she would be looking for the nearest lay-by and would be expecting payment for the lift in kind - the thought was too nauseating to contemplate.

I clutched at straws.

'Fancy a 'J', man?'

'A what, luv?'

'You know, man. A joint; some grass. I've got a ready-rolled yin here, man.'

'Ooooh, very exotic. I've never tried that, luv. What's it like, then?'

'Here', I said, producing a joint from the stash in my jacket pocket, 'try it and see. It makes you very sensitive and relaxed, man.'

'Ooooh, well, we'll have to try that, then, won't we? Go on, then, luv - light up.'

Thank the lord. I'd found an escape route from Kinky Katrina's horrible clutches that kept me in the car. After a few tokes on this Ti-stick, she'd be easy to control. I lit up, being careful to ingest only a minuscule amount of the potent brew. I wound down my window as well; I was going to get stoned enough from the secondary smoke, and I also didn't want old 'Kinky' crashing the car.

Sure enough, a few tokes later and Kinky Katrina was putty in my hands. She alternated between wow, laughter and - unfortunately - drowsiness. For ten more miles, I managed to keep her focused on driving - just. After that it was just becoming a bit too dangerous.

I had to part company with my exotic dancer before she killed us both.

'Er, Katrina, why don't you pull over at this next service station, man.'

'Ooooh yes, luv, I'm starving - are you?'

The 'munchies' had kicked in.

'Yeah, man; let's get something to eat.'

The 'kinky' one got us relatively safely to the next service station and we parked up. I got her, laughing like a teenager, into the restaurant past the shaking heads and stares of the citizens who were milling about. A

15-year-old boy, half carrying a leather-clad, bewigged, ancient exotic dancer, does draw a few stares. I got us some food, courtesy of funds from the generous old 'Kinky', and we sat and satisfied our munchies.

That was the only thing I was prepared to satisfy, though. I had to make a quick exit at this point.

'Want another Coke, Katrina?'

'Yeah, luv. Here's a fiver - get us some cakes as well. These cakes here are the sweetest cakes I've ever had. Must have them specially made by the cake man - eh, luv?' she laughed wildly.

'Yeah, man; they must.'

A quick body-swerve was in order. I took my rucksack with me 'to carry back the cakes', which the old dear thought was pretty clever of me, and instead of joining the food line I marched straight outside. I almost ran to the exit point and began hitch-hiking again.

Please, God, get me a lift before the 'kinky' one realises I'm gone.

Thankfully, within 15 minutes a lorry pulled up and I was on the road again. Five pounds richer (sorry Katrina) I had purloined a lift that was going as far as Bristol. Bristol was near Glastonbury - what a score!

The lorry driver was a decent, normal guy, and we enjoyed a good chat on the journey. He gave me a few warnings about hitch-hiking so young, as they usually did. He told me that there were plenty of weir-does around and that I should be careful.

'For example, son, you should have seen the state of the redhead I just saw sleeping at one of the tables in the restaurant. Talk about weird. You wouldn't want a lift from that one, I can tell you.'

No, believe me - I wouldn't, mate!

Thanks for that short lift anyway, Katrina. I'm glad you got to sleep off the worst of the effects of the hash.

I owe you a fiver.

++++++++

From Bristol (I remember having to walk the length of that city to get to the motorway again) it was a short trip to Shepton Mallet and the festival.

It was raining and, as I had no decent waterproof clothing, I was drenched to the skin. I was hunched up at the side of the road, school jacket over my 'cool' denim jacket, and was waiting with my frozen thumb out for a lift. I'd finished the last of my stash, but even this did nothing to cheer me up. I was cold, wet, getting hungry again and felt pretty fed up with my adventure.

I got lucky. A van pulled over.

'Hey, man; want a lift, man?'

Hippies! I was saved.

'Great, man; I'm goin' to the festival, man.'

'Cool, so are we. Hop into the back, man, and we'll take you down, man.'

All the way to the festival - could life get any better?

It certainly got stranger.

It turned out that the two lads who had picked me up were going to the festival to deal acid. They had a huge stash of the stuff with them and were planning to live in the back of their van, properly kitted out with mattress and blankets. They planned to deal dope, meet chicks and listen to the music. This was the real stuff of hippydom. I was going to the big festival and dealers were taking me there. I couldn't wait to tell my mates. The other NK-ites would know just how cool this was.

'Want to score some for the festival, man?' asked the non-driving guy, through the small window that separated me in the back of the van from the dealers at the front.

'Sorry, man - no bread,' I lied.

'That's cool, man. Here - take one of these anyway, man; we've got plenty,' he said as he handed me a tab of acid.

'Thanks, man; how long till we get there, then?'

'About an hour, man.'

'Cool, man.'

I was an hour away from the festival. If I took the acid now, I wouldn't be too wasted to find the rest of the guys, but I'd be well up and ready to party. I dropped the acid onto my tongue and relaxed on the cosy mattress.

I didn't realise how tired I was. Before the acid had even started to work I fell asleep in the back of the van, on a soft mattress, listening to Bob Dylan crooning from the van's eight-track.

I awoke into weirdness.

'Hey, man, we're here. Joe - he's right out of it, man.'

'He'll be OK. Come on, man; let's get him out and check out the music.'

I 'came around', high as a kite, strong hallucinations dominating my vision, beside strangers who were walking me through crowds of hippies towards a stage. It was the beginning of the wildest three days of my life.

The rest of those days passed in a mad psychedelic haze.

I remember hanging around with 'the dealers' for a while. I remember listening to music. I remember coming down, scoring some more acid and a little bit of dope, and then going straight back up again.

I remember sitting at strangers' tents sharing food with them. I lost the plot about finding my mates from NK, but I saw Mandy, who had been spray-painted by hippy kids while he slept, staggering through the crowd, laughing like a maniac. I sat and watched as a couple of hippies who had decided to make love in their tent with candles burning, while obviously stoned out of their heads, were dragged out by other hippies, still on their sleeping bag and still 'at it' while their tent burned around them.

I remember the feeling of colours, music, community, macrobiotic nourishment, people coming and going, and the maniac speed freaks who seemed to bang out the same monotonous rhythm on their bongo drums for the whole festival.

It rained and then it was sunny. We were all caked in mud and filth. We were all high as the moon and completely carefree.

It was an amazing time.

I was out of it. I had no idea what I was doing for most of the festival. I was just a young hippy, enjoying a feeling of being completely unfettered for the first time. The first stage of actual comprehension came to me when I woke up and found out that I was in a field close to the festival lying in a tent. I was still filthy and my naked body was pressed up against a hippy chick who, it turned out, was called Jackie.

'You OK, man?' a sleepy, red-haired Jackie said to me.

'Er, yeah, man - I'm cool.'

'That was brilliant - eh, man?'

'Yeah, man, that was really something - er, where are we, man?'

She was a slightly plump girl with long red hair, partially dressed in hippy clothes equally as smelly as mine. She gave me a warm and welcoming smile.

'You were really out of it, man. I thought we'd better camp here for the night when everything started breaking up. We're not far away. There's a lot of people round the tor, man.'

It turned out that we were in a field at the bottom of Glastonbury Tor, the site of pagan rituals for the many Druidic folk who came to watch the sun set and then rise at the times of the solstice. Jackie, who apparently had also been my festival girlfriend, had packed up her tent and taken us here when the festival was over and the hippies were asked to move along. Her girlfriend was with somebody else and Jackie thought that they were probably heading home to Bath as we spoke. She had figured out that I was too stoned to travel far (pretty easy to figure), and so we were hanging out at 'the tor' till I got my head together.

Wow! That really had been some festival. I had only a vague inkling of what she was talking about. Although I remembered being with someone, my use of psychedelics had manufactured so many different images that I hardly recognized her face.

'I'd better get home, Jackie, man.' I remembered her name! 'My folks'll be goin' crazy.'

'Yeah, so will mine. They think I'm staying at Suzy's. I don't care, though; it was a great festival, man - really amazing.'

It was that, but calculation was creeping back into my head now and I knew that the party was over and somehow I had to make my way back home to Glasgow. I told this to Jackie.

'We could hitch together, man - OK?'

'Sure, Jackie; that would be cool.'

After a short embrace, we dressed, packed up Jackie's tent and prepared to leave. Remarkably, Jackie had managed to get me to bring my rucksack. Apparently I had been of the opinion that there was 'no need for possessions, man', but a slightly less stoned Jackie had persuaded me to hold on to my pack. What a girl! I performed a quick inventory and found that I still had my school uniform and that I had even managed to hold on to the fiver purloined from Kinky Katrina. How on earth had I survived? How had I managed to get so stoned? How had I eaten and drunk for the last three days without spending any money? That was just one of the many post-festival mysteries I retained, and so I just shook my head and thanked the lords of chance.

Jackie and I set off home, and I soon discovered how quickly you could travel using your thumb if a pretty hippy chick accompanied you - even smelling as we did. We had the odd comment on our condition from both car and lorry drivers, but we were too mellow to care, and so we just got comfortable and hugged the journey away.

Inevitably we parted company, Jackie and I. With much affection and promises to keep in touch, Jackie went back to her parents and her school in Bath and I went back to my life in Glasgow.

I continued to hitch the remainder of the journey alone, and without any significant incidents I made it home the next day.

I had some fast-talking to do at home when I arrived back. I was filthy, smelly and my head was not quite back together from all the drugs I had consumed. My folks didn't care too much about where I had been, though, as long as I had not got into any trouble. They even swallowed my story about camping with the boys that weekend. I endured lectures on 'letting people know where you are' and on 'washing my own smelly clothes'; then I took a bath and retired gratefully to bed for the rest of that day and night. A couple of days later I was back to normal, eager to share my stories with the other freaks at school.

We met in the playground as usual, all of the travellers feeling ten feet tall after our wild adventure to the festival. The guys had loved the festival, but it hadn't all been roses.

Mandy and Parsons practically had to drag the depressive Mole into a car at the end, to get him to the festival. Once there, he had refused to leave the tent of some friendly freaks who took them in. After a day of this, Parsons reluctantly went home with the Mole, using their combined money to take a part of the long journey by bus.

Mandy had got completely wasted, had been spray-painted like a mannequin, and had lost his shoes, his rucksack and all his money, but had eventually managed to borrow an old pair of ill-fitting trainers to use to get home. He said that he had a brilliant time anyway, and he made it back to Glasgow without mishap on the day after me.

The Midge, with his usual aplomb, fared well. Unbeknown to us, he had taken 50 tabs of acid with him to the festival. He and his sister stuck together and found a tent to sleep in for all three days, the space bartered with acid. He had sold the tabs and eaten well on the proceeds of his sales. He had enjoyed the music and had even managed to buy a change of clothes and a night in a motorway motel, complete with bath and TV, for him and his sister on the way home. He'd had a great time. The Midge always worked things out. I wouldn't be surprised to hear one day that he had become the new chairman of IBM!

Cooper, like me, ended up with a hippy chick. He got stoned, he tripped out and he thoroughly enjoyed the festival. Apparently we had spent some time together during the festival with our chicks, but I don't remember any of that! He got home the latest, having made a detour to London, where he spent an extra day saying farewell to his temporary love before getting the train home - on money she had lent him.

Everyone agreed that Glastonbury had been amazing, and we all planned (with the exception of the Mole) to 'do' another festival as soon as we could.

Glastonbury marked the end of an era at school for my class of NK freaks, and the start of a new and unconventional existence for me.

We had all changed.

For me, the final traces of any youthful innocence were lost and I'd made the transition from my 'old' life, into a new life of hippydom. It was the end of term in more ways than one, and my schooldays were truly gone. The beginnings of a new life awaited me.

But how would it eventually develop for the NK freaks?

Longer term, the psychedelic experience affected our wee group in varying ways.

The Mole, who was already a depressive, became a manic-depressive and ended his own life shortly after our time at school together, by taking a massive overdose of pills while he was in a mental institution.

Some of the guys graduated from hash and acid to harder and more addictive substances, such as heroin. As far as I know, most of them died before the age of 25.

One group pursued their Alistair Crowley teachings with drug-induced fervour. I read about one of them in the newspapers years later. He was a part of the Highgate cemetery graveyard-defiling group that had been caught and arrested by the police. This was a group who performed satanic rituals in graveyards, drugged out of their heads. My poor old school mate was well past the accepted bounds of sanity at a very early age.

Parsons stayed on at school, eventually forgoing the ways of the hippy. The last I heard, he was a junior dealer in the London stock exchange.

Some went on to explore the wider world of being a hippy. I was one of these.

It was my rebirth and I'd found an alternative way to live, far from the life of the Glasgow hard man. I could cast off the 'old me' and start to be free.

At least, I imagined that I was free at the time, but the worst trials of my transition were - unfortunately - yet to come.

CHAPTER XXXIII

Subjugating another Demon

'Snick, click, bang!' had been subdued.

Leslie Ronald Smith had moved from a world of violence into the world of 'peace, love, turn on, tune in and drop out'.

But he still lived in the same home and on the same street. He was also just about to discover another side to life inside the Glasgow freak scene.

++++++++

I thought that I had really killed my demon of violence when it was put to a rough test one sunny day at the Botanical Gardens, in Glasgow's west end.

We were hanging out. A bunch of ex-NK-ites just getting stoned with a few of our hippy friends. It was a sunny summer day, and we were enjoying the brief time we had between being school kids and finding a source of income so that we could become responsible for our own physical survival.

A couple of days beforehand, the Boke had scored us some supposed acid, which turned out to be constipation pills. Rip-offs were becoming more and more popular on the drug scene and it had been our turn to fall. We had tried to make the Boke go and get us our money back, but he was scared. The guy he had scored from came with a close friend who had a very violent reputation. The Boke had been to see his dealer, had said that the acid didn't work, and was greeted with: 'Are you callin' me a rip-off merchant, man? Just fuck off, man! The stuff was OK - see?'

The Boke had said that one of his mates (me) was really pissed off and was demanding his money back. The rip-off dealer had told him that he and his hard mate would take care of it. The Boke left and neglected to tell me about this minor turn of events.

So, as I was lying on the grass with these freaks, in the sun, stoned, drifting and minding my own business, I was surprised when the dealer appeared in front of me. He had been crossing through the park with his minder, looking for some more soft touches to sell constipation tablets to, when he spotted the Boke. As he came over to talk to him, he saw me, remembered my complaints, and pounced!

I was lying, looking at the sky, when I felt a kick in my leg.

'Hey, you, ya wee bastard; are you the cunt that's been saying my gear's bad, man?'

Snick, click!

I levered myself into a sitting position and calmly looked into my aggressor's face. I recognized the guy and remembered the bad gear that he had sold us. I worked out that somebody must have told him about my complaints.

In my stoned stupor, I saw this as an opportunity to test the new me.

I wasn't going to fight. No matter what happened here, I was certain that I could handle the situation without fighting.

'I'm talkin' to you, man. Did you hear me?'

I mentally banished my weapons, relaxed myself and said: 'Yeah, man, your stuff didn't work. I think you gave us constipation tablets by mistake.'

'Mistake?' he shrieked, as he leaned down and grabbed the front of my shirt with his left hand and punched me in the face with his right.

Snick, click! I fought hard to suppress my demon. I turned my head away from his fist, trying to locate the glasses that he had knocked from my face.

'Listen, man, that gear was good - see? If I ever hear you sayin' that I sell duff gear again, I'll do you. Just watch what you're sayin' about me, man.'

With that he stood up, nodded to the Boke and a few of the other hippies, and swaggered confidently away with his minder, blissfully unaware of how close he had been to my well-honed demon and a potentially long stay in hospital. He wasn't big or particularly tough and the minder that the Boke had been so scared of would not have lasted ten minutes on my estate. I didn't have to take a punch from that guy

- but it had worked!

OK, so I had got a punch in the face, but - so what? I had killed the demon, I had stayed in control. I was incredibly pleased with myself, and I put my glasses back on with a smile. My fellow freaks were looking at me in amazement.

I heard, 'What was that about, Les?' from one of my fellow NK-ites. 'I thought you'd kill that bastard, man. You could easily kill that scrawny fucker, man.'

I stood up, smiled at the gathered freaks and left behind their incredulous looks to start my walk home. I had no comment to make about what had happened. None of them would have understood it anyway, having never been in my position in the first place.

They thought that I had turned into a coward, but I didn't care. I had passed my own special test and my demon of violence was dead. I had moved into a state of mind where I didn't need the armour and weapons I had so carefully developed over the years.

...Or so I thought then. It didn't take me long to discover just how wrong I was

I was still living in the same violent world and, unfortunately, I would still need the armour of my demon to survive.

Fortunately, my demon of violence was only sleeping.

SONG 9 - CATCHING FISH WITH MY MIND

Where am I now? Where am I anyway? Where am I now?
Catching fish with my mind

Where have they gone? Swimming away from me.
What have I done?
I'm just here catching fish with my mind

Seems I'm under water all the time
Blowing bubbles, I can't get out
Water flowing past my ears
I'm here catching fish with my mind

There goes a coloured one
There goes a fish with no ears
There goes a walking, talking fish
Bright scales glitter
Eyes clear

Where am I now? Where am I going to?
What am I doing here at all? Catching fish with my mind

I'm just here catching fish with my mind

PART THREE -

Innocence to Adolescence, Insecurity breeds - Demons

CHAPTER XXXIV

Closing Doors

I had closed the doors on a part of myself that I was no longer comfortable with. I had taken off my armour and hung up my weapons, and was living in a foggy new reality.

It was a very dangerous time.

One door that I had not yet closed was the door to my home. I had wanted to escape from this part of my existence for so long that I could almost taste the feeling. I was now almost 16 years old and was beginning to feel that I could strike out on my own.

By this time, things at home were intolerable for us all. I was a hippy with an attitude. I was embracing the 'turn on, tune in, drop out' culture I had discovered, using it as a vehicle to change my character and develop a new persona. My mother and father had no clue as to what was happening to me. They could no longer bully me - I was too big for that - and in our environment physical strength was law.

My parents used to lecture me on 'using the house as a hotel', or 'the types of friends that I hung about with', or even the amount of phone calls that I would get. They were unhappy with my clothes, my Afro-style curly hair and the smell of patchouli oil I carried around with me. The only person in my circle of drop-outs that they liked was the well-dressed Peter. They would have been horrified about that choice, of course, if they had known that Peter was gay. They understood nothing about me or about the changing times that we lived in, so they labelled me a waster and I labelled them straight, dictatorial and fascist.

Such a relationship had nowhere constructive to go. I held my parents in less and less esteem as time passed, and finally, one night, after receiving numerous lectures and putting up with hours of browbeating, I decided that my parents needed to turn on.

We were watching television in our badly decorated living room. I was sitting on worn out furniture and was tired of breathing my dad's smelly second-hand pipe smoke. The living room was a pit and the decor looked as if it had been thrown together from the leftovers of a pig's party. Sure, we were poor, but that was OK. I'd never had a problem with poverty, but my parents had never been the house-proud types, and our place always verged on the downright unsanitary.

One of my favourite programmes, The Prisoner, was about to start on TV. I figured that it would be a trial to watch this episode, with the amount of nagging going on, and decided that I would make myself a surreptitious cup of hash coffee, to get me through another boring night in the house. I went into the kitchen and boiled the kettle. I washed a mug that had already been put away as washed, but that I wouldn't have let the cat (if we'd had one) drink from. I could hear my parents continuing to run me down in the living room as I worked away.

I found the jar of instant coffee, put a spoonful into my cup, and dug my hash-stash out of my pocket. I had a big bit of crumbly Afghan Red left. It was easier to make a quiet hash coffee with the crumbly stuff: you had none of that cooking in tin foil business that you had to consider with a decent bit of Pakistani Black. You could just crumble the Afghan into some well-boiled water, and stir - instant harmony in a cup! This stuff didn't even smell too strong and I figured that a big dollop of instant would mask any discordant odour from the noses of my folks. After living for years with heavy pipe smoke, their sense of smell was probably shot anyway!

As I started to crumble a decent piece into my cup, I suddenly had a thought. 'Mum, dad - do you want some coffee, man?' Even my parents had attained the adage of 'man' by now.

They paused long enough in their character assassination to yell back:

177

'Aye, we'll have some. Ye may as well do somethin' useful aroond here.'

Miserable old bastards, I thought; let's see how miserable you are with some of this brew inside you!

I had decided that I would spike my parent's coffee with some Afghan Red, and maybe I would get peace to watch my TV programme without their persistent niggling. Besides, my juvenile but idealistic mind thought that they might become better people if they 'turned on'.

Spiking was not something that I either adhered to or approved of normally. It had become a favoured pastime of the partially insane, who hung about hippy joints such as the State Bar or the Byre. I had been through a horrible experience of getting on the bus to go home when my head started to explode and my surroundings began to melt and distort into a psychedelic puddle, because some crazy bastard had put a tab of acid into my pint without me knowing about it. What had followed was a night in my bedroom, tripped out of my skull, trying to stay quiet enough so that my state of mind would go unnoticed by my parents. Not a good trip. Spiking was not very cool at all.

But, with the flawed reasoning of youth, I figured that these guys deserved it; and - I told myself -it was only hash, after all.

I split my stash of Afghan between the three cups of coffee, careful to make sure that the water was well boiled and that the hash was well absorbed into the coffee, before adding my parents' milk and sugar - lots of sugar!

'Are you burning that bloody incense stuff in there, you? Dae ye smell that, Pat; it's that evil bloody incense again. He knows ah'll no' have that stuff in this hoose!'

'It's not incense, man - it's just my patchouli oil. Ah put it on ages ago an' the smell'll fade soon, man.'

'You'll fade ya bloody wee toe-rag if yer lightin' any o' that incense!'

Although I could have argued that incense would have improved the smell of our house 500%, I was too pleased with my ploy and too nervous about this wee experiment to care. I figured that now, even if they smelled the hash in the coffee, they would think that it was coming from my fragrant oil. Cool!

I brought our potions into the living room and gave a cup each to my mum and dad. The Prisoner was about to start in ten minutes - just enough time for the hash to start to kick in. My parents sipped, complaining about the strength, warmth and sweetness of the coffee, blissfully unaware as to what they were imbibing. I gulped my cup down and relaxed.

The ten minutes passed slowly and then The Prisoner started.

I was starting to feel pretty stoned; the Afghan had a nice mellow feel, and so I never paid much attention to my parent-spiking plot to begin with. In fact, I'd almost forgotten that I'd spiked them until the show started and the big balloon, which was used in the series to chase down escapees, burst dramatically out of the water and into the air.

'Wow! Did ye see that, Agnes? That balloon - did ye see that? This is good stuff - eh, son?'

Shit, they were getting pretty out of it. Maybe I should have put a bit less hash into their coffee. I started to panic a bit, hoping that they wouldn't twig exactly what stuff was actually so good.

Long pause.

'That's great that is, Pat. Ah've never noticed that before. It's a big yin - eh?'

Totally out of it.

'Fancy a wee nip, Pat?'

Absolutely and completely out of it. My mother was actually offering strong drink to my dad? It was a mind-blowing concept, completely unheard of in our house. My mother was fully aware of the horrible consequences we had to suffer when my dad used to get drunk and act like a psychopath. I looked on in amazement as my dad nodded in agreement, eyes completely glued to the TV, and my mum put down her knitting, went to the sideboard, and poured my dad a large-ish nip of whisky and herself a glass of sherry.

Shit! They were going to be completely wasted soon. But at least they were having a drink. Maybe they would put any hash-like effects they noticed down to the alcohol. They had no education at all on drugs, so I might get away with it. Silently I prayed.

Eyes still riveted to the TV show, my parents quickly scoffed their respective drinks.

'That wis great, Agnes; hud a real burn tae it. Ah' wouldnae mind another wee nip, hen.'

'Right enough, Pat,' she giggled. 'I feel a wee bit tipsy, though.' Both of them collapsed in laughter at that wee gem.

Round two of the booze.

I was becoming a bit unglued myself. Here were my severe and miserable parents, sitting in our living room, knocking back booze and laughing out loud! This was a sight to behold, and almost far too much for this hippy pilgrim to digest in one sitting. In my mindlessness, I had only expected them to keep quiet and crash early. This was amazing!

Round two of the booze was also quickly imbibed, and my parents, as if they were true blue hippy freaks, were laughing till tears cascaded down their faces.

'Oh, that wis great, Agnes. Fancy' ha, ha, ha! 'an early night, hen?'

He, he he! 'Right, Pat. He, he, he! 'I'm a bit tired tae...' Ho, ho! 'Must be the sherry!'

At which point, they both almost fell off of their seats with laughter.

I, sitting hunched up in horror at the end of the couch, as my parents went into orbit, was completely ignored. I was thankfully not even close to their sphere of distorted consciousness. I watched, incredulous, as Pat and Agnes stumbled through to their bedroom together, giggling like five-year-olds.

Wow!

I sat on the couch and rolled up a spliff, certain that these two were not going to make another appearance that night. I had to turn up the TV to shouting pitch, so that I could ignore the tortured creaking of bedsprings, which probably hadn't seen such a horrible turn of events in a decade. I was so turned off that I eventually went round to a friend's house to share yet another joint and wait out their rediscovered passion. Luckily, by the time I returned home that night, the only sounds to greet me were the loud snores of my now comatose parents.

Spiking my parents - that had been some trip. But, I tell you, it was an experience I was never going to repeat!

The next day, when the alarm clock bellowed to get them out of bed, Pat and Agnes were their usual miserable selves. I took the brunt of their nagging as, with cloudy heads, they tried to get themselves together for work and almost-housekeeping respectively.

Mum was also giving out about drinking, how Pat should have stopped her from having that much sherry, and that the bottle 'must huv been aff, or somethin'.' Pat just grumbled a lot, obviously the worse for wear, after his hash/alcohol mega-mix. I listened to their complaining, taking the brunt as usual. Ah, well; back to reality. These old sods would never change.

I really had to get out of this place.

I went about my own business with a sanctimonious feeling that I had done everything I could to change my parents for the better. I'd even shared my good blow with them and they were still idiots. What could I do? I was lumbered with parents who didn't understand me and who were determined to nag me to death, having failed to beat me to death when I was smaller.

I could probably have grown up, looked at what I had done and been ashamed of it. I could probably have realized that I had committed a severe crime against their personal freedom and that I had no excuse at all for what I had done. I could probably have even extrapolated the circumstances that might have developed, if they had done something mad like go outside, instead of just having a drink and going to bed.

I could have thought a lot of things.

Instead, wrapped up in my surreal world of 'turn on, tune in and drop out', I wrote them off and went about my hippy business. I widened the chasm between us that morning, to a point where it could never be crossed.

But this time, it was definitely my fault.

++++++++

The door to any sort of relationship with my parents closed firmly, in my mind, the day after the 'spiking' incident. As you will have gathered from previous chapters, this incident was not the root cause of the gulf; the disrespect and the hatred had much earlier and more consistent beginnings. It was a field of hatred that had been sown long ago and had been nurtured throughout my childhood.

At least in the past, my parents and I had lived within the same world. The spiking incident now highlighted the fact that we were not even living in the same reality any more. I had grown into something very alien to my parents and had lost any hope of bridging the gap between us. I was wrong to have spiked their drinks, but this was an indication of how little consideration there was between us and how dangerously unlikely it was that I would sit passively and take their constant nagging abuse.

It was only a matter of time before our conflict reached its inevitable conclusion, and the inevitable happened only a week later.

I came home late as usual one Friday night. I had been out most of the night with some freak friends, listening to music and getting stoned at a club that specially catered for our hippy tastes. I had let myself into the house and had gone to bed that night planning a lie-in the next morning to recover, followed by a day with my friends in the botanical gardens.

Morning came and I was rudely awakened with: 'Where dae ye think you were last night - eh?! Me and yer mother are sick of you usin' this place like a bloody hotel. Ye're just a waster. Get out of that pit! If ye think ye can use this hoose like a bloody doss hoose, ye can go and live wi' that hippy scum ye hang aboot wi'!'

...And the bedclothes were unceremoniously yanked off me and thrown on to the floor of my bedroom.

This was not an uncommon ritual in my house: attack on my lifestyle, personality and friends, backed up with some kind of physical presence and finished off with emotional blackmail. Just the norm for my parents' ideas on living with a teenager.

Undisturbed, I awaited the finale so that I could go back to sleep.

'Ye're just like yer sister! Nae interest in anybody but yersel'. Ye're no' interested in me, are ye? It's ma' hoose and ye can just get oot. He's just nothin', Pat. Ye're right - he's just a bloody waster.'

This was hurled from the sidelines by my mother.

By this time, my sister was long gone. Two years earlier she had met and married a bloke from the south side of Glasgow. She had received the same level of anti unchristian support that we always got: disparagement of her choice, threats, a big dollop of emotional blackmail, and - in the end - her parents didn't even attend her wedding. She had emigrated to New Zealand with her new husband shortly after the marriage, so since the age of 13 I had had very little contact with her. I often missed my sister and held to the firm belief that my parents were largely responsible for the disappearance of my only childhood ally.

Normally I would have ignored the vocal turmoil, given up on any chance of sleep, got washed and dressed and then left the house to pursue my real life outside these walls. Today, however, I was tired, frustrated and didn't want to deal with the abuse.

'Oh, shut up for fuck's sake! I'm getting' up. Just leave it!'

Of course, this was the catalyst for even more abuse. As I staggered out of bed, grabbed my clothes and made my way to the bathroom to wash and dress, I was subjected to a constant and ever more virulent stream of verbal abuse, some finger-poking from my dad, and lots of hysterical interludes from my mum.

I finished my ablutions and, now that I was dressed, I wandered down the hall to the living room, to tell my parents that I was going out. In my absence, some church friends of my parents had turned up and were in the living room with them. As I entered the room, I could hear my mum sobbing about what a terrible son I was and about what they had to put up with. I could also hear my dad's determined voice going on and on about how he would sort me out one day.

I walked into this scene, and was about to say goodbye to the disapproving faces arrayed in front of me when I was accosted with: 'There he is. Just look at him; he's a bloody state! What did we do tae deserve him?'

That little speech was delivered by my mother.

'Aye, ya little toe-rag! Ye can just get oot o' here. We don't want you in this hoose!'

Snick, click!

Want me? There had been many feelings in my life to date that related to my home life, but being wanted was never one of them.

My father strode towards me. 'And another thing...'

He was up for it and determined to demonstrate his mastery over me with a physical imposition. One finger of his left hand was jabbing in my face and his right fist was waving about menacingly.

Snick, click!

I snapped. Years of abuse, both mental and physical, streamed into my consciousness. I could hear the roar beginning in my head, and his abusive, angry face filled me with hatred.

Snick, click, bang!

I snap-punched him on the chin with my left, stepped back and delivered a full-on right-fisted punch into his face.

He staggered backwards.

There was complete silence for a few moments, and then my mother and her crony screamed, my father's friend went pale, and he reached out to grab my dad's shoulders.

'Jesus! The little bastard! Imagine hitting your own father. What kind of boy are you? Leave him, Pat; he's no' worth it.'

I turned on my heel, went to my room and quickly threw my meagre belongings into my rucksack. I was out of there!

Nobody followed me. My parents and their friends were in shock, although for different reasons. My parents' friends had just witnessed a vile boy attacking his parents. My parents had just witnessed the worm turning. Both parties were equally stunned.

I didn't give my room, the hall or the open door of the living room a second glance as I left. It was over. Here and now I was out of there and I was never going back. I had just turned 16, and nobody could force me to live with these people any more.

As I opened the door I heard the bravado: 'It didnae hurt, anyway. The wee bugger's lucky I didnae kill him...'

I slammed the door, not caring.

The slamming of the door marked the end of my final tie to a horrible childhood. I never lived with them again, although in later years I was to visit occasionally, especially when my mother contracted bowel cancer and I could not bury my feelings deep enough to ignore her distress. That was seven years later, though. I even spent a single night in that house with my girlfriend, as a base for visiting my mother in hospital when she was ill. That turned out to be my last willing visit to my old home, and it also marked my mother's last night on this earth.

For now, it was over, and I was truly embarking on a new life, with only my own choices to consider. I could start to bury my demon of an awful childhood, now that I had finally been able to close this door.

Closing doors was a practice I became very, very proficient at.

SONG 10 - MAKES ME STRANGE

These psychedelics in my head (makes me strange), it's just
not like old Timothy Leary said
First of all it's nothing, going up
Then it starts to change - floating away - it's all so weird,
so weird
I can feel the colours in my brain (weird sounds)
Clouds are parting, senses go insane
Then the telephone rings - but that's my shoe! (shoe?) -
what will I do? - how will I speak, to you?
Ring around the roses, here I am (where am I?)
That's all right, I'm just here, getting high
I can look down on this crazy room (it's moving)
But what if I fall (down?) - I'm not so tall! - I feel so small,
so small
But Indians eat peyote, they say (in their pipes)
I've had pie so I must be OK
Had a secret potion back in time
Time stopped! - I'm lost (here!) - where's the plot?
Lost in time with Indiana Jones (he's strange)
Looking through a treasure trove
Look at all the diamonds they cut
I'm cut! - why don't I hurt? - where, where's my blood?
Up and down I go but waves recede (eventually)
In and out of ecstasy and need.
Isn't all like Mr Leary said (he was lying)
This stuff (is strange) - messes up my head (it's strange) -
I've gotta get right down
Seems I'm back to normal now, I'm here - it's strange
It's getting very strange inside my head - why does it feel
this way? strange - so strange

CHAPTER XXXV

In the Scene, Man

It was the beginning of a very strange time for me. I was 16 years old and homeless, with no idea about where I was going. I had a few friends that I could stay with, and I got a job as a store boy in a garage. I had a fresh start, but now had to deal with the physical insecurity of having no permanent home to live in.

Emotional insecurity was 'old hat'. I had long ago built armour to deal with that particular circumstance. I had always had a room and a bed, however, and this new change of circumstance was a little daunting. I crashed at the flats of a few hippy friends, and through contacts in this scene I met some other guys who were planning to get a flat together. I was able to get myself included in their plans and so, within a few weeks, I shared my first flat in a run-down part of Glasgow, surrounded by prostitutes, drug-dealers, violence and crime.

++++++++

The next nine months that I spent in Glasgow, living as a hippy, were some of the strangest months of my life. Time passed in a haze of drugs, punctuated by paranoia, and with survival a constant struggle. I was immersed in a world of new faces and was surrounded by a rapidly changing freak culture.

In the beginning, I was ready to embrace the peace and love philosophy wholeheartedly. After all, this was my chosen way out, and the attractions of a non-violent existence had not diminished. I was naive enough to believe that my peers were equally engaged on the same path, and that - together - we were founding an alternative and more Utopian type of pattern for life.

I was not even close to the mark in my assumption.

At the heart of the scene were drugs. There were two types of freaks in Glasgow at the time: there were the hippy freaks who smoked dope and took acid, and there was the junkie scene - considered the seedy dark side and not welcomed into the hippy community. My new flatmates were just hippy freaks, out to have a good time and do as many drugs as they could in the process. The whole 'peace and love' philosophy was no more than a vehicle that they used to get laid and appear cool.

There was a positive social aspect to this scene that had a direct bearing on me. Being a half-caste was far from being a liability. Black was considered cool and, as I had the big Afro-hair, along with the half-caste features and colouring, I found myself enjoying kudos, rather than derision, for my ethnic-type looks. I finally fitted in!

The beginning of my life in the Glasgow freak scene felt great. I was permanently high, I met lots of new people, I was regularly meeting cool chicks, and I was partying all the time. My much older flatmates all seemed to be cool guys, too: just hanging out most of the time, getting stoned and making out with chicks.

At this time I did not really see the political side of the freak scene, where anybody who did not look cool, who didn't at least smoke dope and dress and talk like a hippy, or who worked at a regular job or - worse still - a career was openly ostracized. It was only as time moved on that I noticed that my cool flatmates were always sniping at somebody and eventually each other. It was only later that I noticed that the banner of

187

equality for women was used as a part of a guy's image so that he could enjoy a physical relationship with them, but was also used to put them down if they got pregnant, or wanted a stronger relationship than the occasional stoned night together. Women who wanted more were considered 'uncool psychos'.

As time moved on, my perspective of the hippy scene changed dramatically. At first I was just stoned all the time, bouncing from flat to flat and socializing, if you can call sitting around in a stupor while listening to loud music socializing. During these social days and nights, hippy philosophy was constantly spouted, and everyone thought that they were really living an alternative life. For example, some freaks truly believed that being completely immersed in loud rock music, enjoyed through their headphones, actually constituted meditation.

'What are you doin', man?'

'Meditating, man. This new Dead album's really spiritual, man.'

During this period of my life I didn't say very much. Not many of us did. It was considered cool not to talk a lot, although some people took this aspect of freak behaviour to the extreme of visiting a flat, getting stoned and leaving again without uttering a single word to anyone. Most of these people were pretty far gone and used to annoy even the most die-hard freaks on the scene; this silent aspect of hippy life suited me, however.

I used the accepted silence to observe and learn. Most of the time I was out of my mind, but I was always conscious enough to drink in what was happening around me and to digest the new scene that I found myself in.

I might have learned about hippy life in Glasgow through a drug-filled haze - but I did learn.

CHAPTER XXXVI

Paranoia Pays

'Hey, man; how's things?'

'Cool, man.'

'Fancy coming round for a smoke?'

'Sure, man; where do you stay now?'

'I'll take you round, man - but don't tell anybody where the pad is. I've heard the DS are watching me, man.'

Absolute paranoia, founded on the startling fact that, as he was dealing dope, the Drug Squad - or DS, as we referred to them - were probably trying to catch him.

Could it be he was in the wrong line of work?

Chick's attitude was typical of a large majority of the Glasgow freaks at this time. At first it had been a banner of high status to be a drug-dealing hippy freak. You were a cool dude with admirers, you had plenty of chicks, and you could sport a superior swagger in your stride.

Not now.

More and more people were becoming paranoid about getting: busted by the police; ripped off by the ever growing number of gangster-type thieves infiltrating the scene; or preyed on by 'tough' drug-taking hippies, crazy thugs or dangerous Hell's Angels, who were increasing in numbers within our community.

As much as the freak scene was influencing the Glasgow world, the Glasgow underworld was encroaching on the freak scene.

For Chick, this was a permanent trauma. He was not a freak from the hard school of the housing estates. He was a comfortably brought-up freak, with a fairly posh accent and a soft manner. There was no way that Chick could deal with the burgeoning darkness creeping into the freak scene, and he knew it.

For Chick, a big part of that darkness was the aggression with which the DS were attacking the drug culture. They had more and more informants, mostly junkies that they could lead around by the nose. They were making more and more drug busts. They were leaning heavily towards the hard tactics of smashing down doors and entering violently and in force, as the drug scene itself became more commercial, more aggressive and moved towards a more intensive use of the most addictive substances.

So Chick lived like a partial hermit and tried to keep his clientele small and elite. Piece by piece, the poor guy kept shrinking into himself. He always looked worried and furtive if you saw him on the streets.

The times they were a-changing, and, for a guy of his sensibilities and fears, Chick had definitely chosen the wrong type of work!

Chick's social circle was mainly composed of users rather than dealers, although most would turn their hands to distribution occasionally to improve their income - which was based generally on what the government handed out each week to the unemployed. These were old-school hippy freaks, not junkies, who spouted lots of hippy philosophy, listened to plenty of Hendrix music and took daily doses of the best dope. I was accepted in this circle of friends, as I'd known Chick and his mates since I was 14 years old and had been considered a cool kid when I was just entering into the hippy scene.

Throughout the couple of years that I'd known them, I just kept watching them get weirder and weirder.

By the time I was 16, this crew had had as many bad trips as good, and were in and out of mental stability like the proverbial jack-in-the-box. The strain had taken its steady toll, and each member of Chick's scene was just as paranoid as Chick was himself. They would hang out at each other's flats, addresses kept a firm secret within the group. They had been known to pack up and move to another flat quickly, if somebody they considered uncool saw them go into their building, or if some mistrusted hippy moved into a flat within spying distance. There was only one permanent girl member of this crew. This was Jane, a girlfriend of one of the worst of the acid-burned, who had been in the year below me at school. At 15, she was the only one of the group unfazed by their lifestyle.

Paranoia was even creeping into what used to be carefree, stoned-out hours in Chick's flat.

Chick had installed so many bolts on his reinforced front door that standing outside as he scrutinized you from his peephole, and then waiting while the huge multiple bolts were thrown to offer you admittance, started the visit off with a definite feeling of unease. Then it would be a case of: 'Hi, man. Come on in, you're cool. Did anybody see you coming here, man..?'

It was a ridiculous attitude, which immediately dragged visitors into his paranoid world. Then you would walk the short distance down the hall to enter a hazy, smoke-filled room, where people, fists clenched around lumps of dope, would be nervously staring at the door and would relax only as they saw who it was who was entering their space.

'It's OK, guys - it's only Les...'

It was a scene of nervousness and fear. What was I doing there? You may think that I could have chosen a more relaxed atmosphere to enjoy a smoke with friends, but it wouldn't really have mattered whose pad I'd chosen to hang out in. This scene was repeated in hippy pads across the city on a daily basis.

Paranoia ruled!

Funnily enough, Chick's eventual downfall was not actually his paranoia, but his lack of paranoia with regard to the fairer sex.

Like every warm-blooded Homo sapiens male, Chick liked to get laid occasionally. He was well known as a hippy dealer dude, which seemed to be particularly attractive to the girls in their teens and early twenties on the scene. Whenever the urge took him, Chick would find a willing girl at the Byre or the State Bar and take her back to his place to get stoned and screw the night away. (The dope and stroking his dealer status always took precedence, though; from what I heard, the sex was usually a minor event, enjoyed mainly by Chick.) For a guy as paranoid as Chick was, he was surprisingly lax on security when it came to these occasional sexual liaisons.

One night, his security slip came firmly home to roost.

There was a girl called Irene on the scene. Irene was a junkie and, as such, not a face at any of the flats where I - or, in fact, Chick - used to hang out. Irene was always on the scrounge for dope or money for junk, and she used to frequent the same bars and clubs that we did. Irene had close acquaintance with some strange crews: junkies, thugs and - as it eventually turned - out a certain officer from the Drug Squad. It was well known that being able to bed the actually quite pretty Irene only involved having some kind of a high that you were willing to share. Irene, as a part of her survival armoury, had developed the ability, with smiles and grand strokes of the male ego, to make anyone who did not know her very well, feel that they were special, and that she was quite a prize for the night.

It certainly worked on Chick.

It was a Saturday night. I remember seeing Chick enter the bar, looking pretty wasted. I was standing at the back of the pub talking to a friend, but I kept one eye on him, as I wanted to score some dope later on in the evening. It took my notice when he was accosted by a seductively smiling Irene, and I noted their adjournment to a side table for a chat. I at first suspected that Irene was hitting him up for a smoke and knew that, as she was not on the preferred friends list, she had no chance. I kept talking to my mate, waiting till Irene was dismissed with the customary shrug of Chick's shoulders and the, 'can't help you, man - sorry, man,' before I could move in to greet him and arrange my own transaction.

It didn't happen. Out of the corner of my eye, I saw Irene lean into Chick, hand on his lap, her lips engaging his in a passionate tongue-filled kiss.

'Wow! Chick must be stoned tonight,' my mate, who had also taken an interest in the proceedings, commented on the strange development between Chick and Irene. Stoned or not, on the preferred customer list or not, it looked as if Irene had scored.

I turned to my mate.

'Think I should give him the nod, Jaz? She's pretty bad news, man.'

'No, man, ye'd better stay put - look.'

I looked over to where he was surreptitiously pointing. Some of Irene's closer junkie/thug associates were sitting not far from Chick and were watching the seduction unfolding. Knowing Irene's volatile personality, I would have had to be pretty discreet with the 'word' if I was going to avoid a nasty incident, involving her getting crazed at me for interfering and her cronies possibly stabbing me in the back.

I was still debating having a word with Chick when I saw Irene shift over to these same thugs. She whispered something to them, smiled and then went back to a grinning Chick, now standing up and looking as though he was leaving.

My God, he was leaving with Irene!

With a backward glance and a wave of farewell in the thugs' general direction, Irene tucked her body close to Chick's and they left for the inevitable private party.

'Just leave it, Les,' said Jaz as he saw the look on my face. 'He's a big boy, man.'

I sighed and put the incident out of my mind. I returned to my pint, my conversation and the wait until somebody else arrived who could fix me up with a smoke. I imagined that the worst that could happen would be that Irene would slip out of his door with some of his dope in the morning. At least it would teach Chick to be more discerning when the call of the loins was upon him.

Poor Chick; if only I, or one of his other friends who had seen the incident, had been smart enough to have a chat with him and stoke up his normally dominant paranoia. But nobody did, and the end result turned out to be a double-negative whammy for the wee man.

His whammy number one came several hours after he left the bar with Irene. Chick was lying in a heavy, post-coital, post-Afghan-Red stupor and was listening to music on his bedroom stereo system. Irene, supposedly going to the toilet, got up, went down the hall and quietly slipped all of the security bolts to Chick's front door and then left it ajar. The mercenary bitch then went back to Chick's room, got dressed, saying that she had to get back to her flat soon, and asked if they could have

193

another joint before she left. Chick, magnanimous inside his velvety mind-cocoon, said: 'Sure, man; roll one an' take a bit with you if you want, man. No problem, babe.'

This was the moment that the junkies/thugs who had followed them back to Chick's flat chose to come bursting in, armed with pickaxe handles and assorted knives. They had just been waiting for the door to be opened before making their move.

It was a set-up.

Chick took a beating for no reason, as he was never going to face down these thugs; it was just a wanton act of mad-junkie brutality that made them give him such a kicking. They beat him half senseless and then, while a smiling Irene looked on, the thugs emptied his drug stash, directed by Chick's erstwhile lover.

They made off with all of his dope, most of his record collection and all the cash that they found. They carried off a few other valuables, and broke up the few things that they did not want or were unable to carry away. As she was leaving with her henchmen, Irene threw a small bit of dope at Chick and said: 'Here, man, keep that wee bit. Roll yourself a smoke. No problem, ya capitalist bastard.'

And then she left - laughing all the way.

The complete bitch!

Chick called Jason, who rounded some of us up at the pub to go over and help the wee man out. Later on, as a broken Chick related this first whammy to us, he said he was grateful that the thugs had never found his big stash of cash, or he would have been right out of business. As it was, he was able to score another lump of dope and some acid the next day, to fulfil some outstanding orders for his inner circle. He only planned to get rid of this score over a couple of days, raise a deposit and then to move to a new pad, which a friend had agreed to suss out for him. Bruised, battered and fully paranoid, Chick knew that he had no recourse to law and no ability to wreak personal vengeance. He just had to content himself with taking a couple of days to re-establish himself, and then to being much more careful where he placed his manhood in the future.

He didn't have two days.

The Drug Squad picked up Irene the very next day. She was out of her head on junk, scored on the proceeds of her betrayal, and it didn't take much pressure for the DS to convince Irene that she was better off working for them and staying free than being banged up in jail and going through a forced withdrawal from her 'H' habit.

Chick was her first offering to the Drug Squad.

Less than 24 hours after his ordeal with Irene and her bandits, the Drug Squad axed his front door, broke into his house sporting a fresh search warrant, and then arrested him for the possession of three-quarters of a pound of the best 'Black' and 240 tabs of blotting paper acid. Poor Chick; now he would be wearing short hair and taking nervous showers for a long, long time. I guess it wasn't so lucky that the thugs hadn't found Chick's major stash of cash, after all.

Poor, paranoid Chick.

A few years later, on a rare return visit to the west end of Glasgow, I bumped into an old acquaintance from those days. I enquired about Chick, and found out that prison had been too much for him. He had committed suicide in his cell with pills smuggled in by a friend, about five months after his incarceration.

If only he had been more paranoid and had included pretty women in his fears. It turned out that, paranoid as he was, Chick just hadn't been paranoid enough for the lifestyle that he lived.

Irene, who had been on a hiding to nothing with her 'H' habit, died of an overdose a scant few years after her night with Chick.

Chick was 23 years old when he committed suicide. Irene was 17 years old when she betrayed Chick to thugs and police, and she was 20 years old when she died of an overdose.

Love and peace, man!

CHAPTER XXXVII

It's cool, Man

I met so many different people during the Glasgow hippy phase of my life that I could fill a book with stories just about these colourful characters and these nine short months.

As I observed the scene, I was a part of it, but I always felt like an observer watching from behind a misty veil. I saw people change. I watched transitions from child to ageing youth; I saw the descent from ecstasy into fear; I watched confidence dissolve into anxiety, and anxiety transform into mania. Only occasionally would I see someone blossom. A hippy freak who would develop an artistic talent, or discover a hitherto hidden spark within themselves, going on to develop into a stronger, better, brighter human being. Such beauty was rare, and, when it occurred, it usually heralded that individual's exit from the scene, moving on to something new and untainted by the psychedelic chaos happening daily around us.

I observed the scene and I learned, by watching the antics of the sup- posedly cool freaks within it. There were just so many strange and dif- ferent characters.

++++++++

Wee Col was the guy that took acid every day for a fortnight. At first everybody thought that he was real cool. I met him at the Windsor pop festival a few months after his psychedelic binge, and he was still com- pletely out of it. He was so badly acid-burned that I doubt if there was a route back to sanity open to his young head. He was absolutely filthy, with lank, smelly hair, a stained and faded lace-up shirt and tattered and soiled trousers. Even the vast amounts of patchouli oil that scented his kaftan coat failed to disguise the odour. His bare feet were black and scabbed, and he wandered around the park mumbling incoherently.

Nobody saw that as being cool. I remember my girlfriend Muni, a beautiful Asian girl I was with at the time, asking, 'Who is that?' I just nodded my head as Col mumbled some incoherent nonsense at us and stumbled on. I didn't have an answer for Muni. Whoever he was, he was no longer the same 18-year-old hippy freak that I had occasionally spent time with in the past. He had become just another acid-burned lost soul.

++++++++

Fifi was a girl who had embraced the free-love philosophy wholeheart- edly, from within a well-drugged bubble. Fifi had long natural-blonde hair, blue eyes and a full figure. She was never the brightest coin in the till, and, as time and tripping went on, she seemed to lose the ability to make any sensible survival decision on her own. She was considered cool by the legions of male hippies and the few girl hippies who slept with her. That wouldn't have been so bad, as it was free-love time and there was supposed to be no stigma attached to sharing physical union, no matter how widely. Unfortunately, this was an urban myth. Although plenty of lip service was paid to the philosophy, the reality was very different. Women were cool when a guy was horny. Once enough horny guys had taken advantage of this 'hippy glasnost', the said woman began to be regarded more as a commodity than a human being - and she was generally treated accordingly.

During my nine hippy months in Glasgow, I saw Fifi change from an attractive and bubbly 16-year-old girl into a disturbed, used and abused shadow of her former self.

I remember the day that I heard someone in The Byre recount how he had just come back from the oil rigs with one of his mates and, as his mate was blind drunk and feeling horny, he had taken him to Fifi's place, propped him up against the door, rung the bell and gone home. Apparently Fifi had answered the door, and the drunken rigger, who mumbled, 'Pat brought me round,' promptly collapsed. Fifi took the rigger into her one-bedroomed apartment, put him to bed and later - according to Pat - fucked his brains out. The rigger left in the morning, declaring how cool that chick had been.

Knowing Fifi, I can imagine that she saw a guy in a state of collapse outside her door and, being a Good Samaritan, took him in to sober him up. I have no doubt that, in her innocence, she would share her bed with him, and I have no doubts that sex took place. Fifi would never have denied him that warm comfort. In Fifi's mind, however, the scene would not have been as sordid as Pat was making out. In her mind, she would have been simply living as a warm hippy chick, giving love and expecting nothing in return.

The poor kid took an incredible amount of insidious baiting for that night.

'Hey, Fifi, I've got a mate with a hard-on - can I drop him round?'

'Fifi, man; how about coming round to our flat tonight - eh? You don't know the boys, but at least they're all sober!'

The story did the rounds for months.

I saw laughter and snide comments gnaw away at her self-respect. I saw her propositioned by guys in any state of mind. I saw the expectancy in the eyes of anyone who wanted her and derision in the eyes of others, particularly the chicks on the scene. Oh, the chicks were the most brutal. To them, Fifi was the type of chick that gave them all a bad name. She was soft and pretty, she was loving and giving, but she was not particularly intelligent; - they treated her like a plague - even though they themselves had probably experienced as many lovers as poor, chastened Fifi.

I tried to talk to Fifi about her circumstance one night in The Byre, ignoring the knowing winks and looks I was getting from some of the guys. I tried to convince her to either go back home or at least move on from this scene. Poor Fifi didn't really understand. She was pretty stoned as usual and she thought I wanted to take her home for sex. When I tried to convince her that I was only trying to help her and didn't want to bed her, she cried and told me the story about her ex-fiance, who was killed in a motorbike accident, and that she had nowhere to go now. I hugged her until she calmed down and then left her after buying her a drink and telling her that she was OK. Later on that night, someone else took her home.

The poor chick could never understand the cruelty she received in those days, just for being what everyone told her was a cool type of person to be. The wee 16-year-old lass did not have the experience and was never given the guidance to rise above the testosterone-charged demands of her male peers. She was even prey to the less scrupulous lesbian and bisexual females on the scene.

With my inner isolation and drug-induced confusion, I had nothing to offer the poor lassie. I wish that I had - she deserved a white knight who would take her loving nature and nurture it with warmth and kindness in return. She was a nice girl, who deserved a whole lot better than she ever received within the 'peace and love' scene where she lived.

A couple of years later, when I heard that an unscrupulous bastard called Geo had put Fifi on the game in Edinburgh, I felt sick to my stomach.

Poor Fifi.

You were OK, babe.

It was the scene that wasn't so cool.

++++++++

Aquarian Rich was also considered cool. He always had some dope and some patter. He lived the hippy lifestyle and subsidized his lifestyle by occasional dealing and regular shoplifting. When I first met his wife, I thought that she was Chinese. This was because she never said anything, sat passively in the room rolling joints, and had a yellow skin tone.

It turned out that her skin tone was due to jaundice, contracted through a dirty needle. Her passivity was because of the beatings that she received from the Aquarian. The poor girl lived in terror of this

respected hippy.
Not so cool.

++++++++

Most of the cool guys were cheating on their girlfriends or wives. Most of the cheating was with the wives or girlfriends of people that they were friends with or were acquaintances of. A lot of the cool girls also hopped from guy to guy, depending on what they had to offer. It could have been a better flat, a regular supply of dope, status within the scene, many things - but the changes went round and round. The 'no ownership, man' philosophy kept everybody feeling righteous and free from judgement by their peers.

Lyn was a prime example of the no-ownership philosophy. She had a young baby when I met her. She was a beautiful child, who was regularly neglected, so that Lyn could pursue the drugs, mystic philosophy and men that defined her quiet personality. The poor kid didn't learn to talk till she was four years old, as her mother hardly ever spoke to her. I can still remember my horror when I heard that Lyn went out regularly, leaving the baby alone in the flat, and giving word to a neighbour to try and listen out for the kid crying. The wee soul must have spent many a long hour peering out of her cot in darkened silence, with sodden nappies, wondering when someone would come to give her a cuddle.

Lyn was a slim and reasonably good-looking hippy chick. She would spend hours reading futures, performing pseudo-mystic rites and doing tarot cards, ably supported by regular doses of amphetamine sulphate.

Lyn was always on the lookout for a 'better guy'. It never mattered who the guy was with at the time. If the guy had a steady relationship already, had a family, or was settled, it mattered not. What was important to Lyn was that the guy had a nice place, a car, a steady income or savings, a good drug supply and could fit into her mystic bubble.

Lyn broke up many relationships. Like a Mountie, she always seemed to have the knack of getting her man. She was hated by most of the other chicks on the scene, but she never cared as long as she got what she wanted.

With few exceptions, the men she chose did nothing to improve the lot of her poor baby. I heard years later that she had at one time found a good guy, who looked after both her and her baby and proved to be the first real parent that the poor kid ever had. He spent time with the kid, giving her the love and attention that she had been deprived of for so long, and he even managed to teach the child to speak. He got caught in Germany, smuggling hash from India, and, although he was acquitted and released a few months later, by that time Lyn had entered into a relationship with someone who abandoned his wife and three children to be with her.

It was another conquest for Lyn at the expense of someone else's family, and did not help to provide stability for her own wee baby.

Definitely not cool.

++++++++

Grassing to the police became more and more prevalent. A one-time massive crime against the community, it was starting to become almost routine that a freak who was arrested for possession by the DS would buy his freedom at the expense of some other hippy. I was occasionally stunned to find out that certain formerly cool individuals had grassed someone up.

Big Wain was an ex-junkie who lived in the west end of Glasgow. He was not very bright and survived through the odd painting and decorating job. He lived in bottom-of-the-range flats and claimed unemployment benefit on the side. He was a big lad - hence the nickname. Although he had been a junkie in the past, he was one of the few to have kicked the habit, mainly through the support of a smart and compassionate half-Asian friend and his English girlfriend. He was considered cool, as he was a big softie who would do anything for anybody.

I heard from a reliable source that he got busted for possession and put several of his mates away in order that he could stay on the outside. He had become a grass, and was from that time on always in the pockets of the Drug Squad.

He started hanging out with a flame-haired hippy called Wee Bill. Wee Bill eventually grassed on Big Wain's compassionate friends to escape a drugs charge. This couple were just hash-smokers and not dealers, but the resulting fines and publicity cost them their jobs and for a while destabilized their relationship.

++++++++

201

Theft from friends also grew larger in Glasgow. By this time, the police had so many informants that they need only wait and the freak scene would collapse of its own volition. Paranoia spread from getting busted by the police and into getting turned over by someone on the scene. The 'hippy integrity' had dissolved in most quarters. It was becoming a dog-eat-dog alternative society, and one that I had quickly become disenchanted with.

Wee Bill had been a pupil at NK in the year below me. At one time I had thought he was a friend. He hung around our scene, smoking dope, tripping and meditating to loud rock music - just the general run-of-the-mill freak activities.

Wee Bill wasn't cool, either. Another little guy who reneged on taking responsibility for his own actions, he got busted by the police and immediately grassed up some dealers to get off. I heard about this, as I knew the dealers, and Wee Bill had used my name to get in with them. They are probably still hunting him.

Wee Bill's biggest crime against his chosen community was much worse. He lived in a flat in Kelvinside, next door to another freak. The freak in question had a large record collection and a hi-fi system that Wee Bill always coveted.

Bill made friends with the guy next door. They often shared a joint and spaced out together, listening to music. Then, one day, the flat of this freak was burgled. A nasty couple of Hell's Angels had broken into the flat and cleared it out. The young victim was distraught. He had worked hard and saved hard for his hi-fi and record collection. In the process of thieving, the nasties had also trashed his pad and destroyed a lot of the nice bits and pieces he had collected. He had no insurance and would take a long time to replace his worldly goods.

All of a sudden, Bill's record collection grew, and he suddenly had two brand new speakers in his flat. This was the pay-off from the Angels, whom he had organized to perform the raid. The little shite kept away from his neighbour for a few weeks and then moved flats.

He was never caught, but had boasted to Big Wain about his score, and Big Wain had passed on the story until I got to hear about it. Bill and Wain ended up sharing a flat together, and I hear that they became a gay couple over the years - well matched as two very nasty pieces of work.

I also heard, much later, that Bill had died of AIDS and that Wain was in a bad way on junk again.

I guess what goes around...

++++++++

There were some genuinely cool guys on the scene. Some were into politics and sincerely wanted to change the world for the better. They would campaign for miners' rights, women's rights, gay rights - in fact any minority platform where they could make a positive contribution. I started to meet some of the people from this scene - usually older freaks - and I learned a lot about having a social conscience from them.

There were also some spiritual people within our community, who had taken integrity to a high level and followed a code of good that I learned to admire.

There were ordinary guys, who spent their time getting into music and trying to form bands together. These guys had no side to them and had nothing in common with the losers I have described in other parts of this story. They were in the scene, but had a sub-scene that they kept well apart from the darker side of the Glasgow freaks.

There were other nice people from varied walks of life, whom I was privileged to meet. They all added something to my life and my learning. Many of them advised me to quit the scene. I was only 16, they said, and spaced out too much, and should get out before I was sucked down by the crazies.

As I watched and learned from this cool scene, I knew that they were right.

CHAPTER XXXVIII

Fatal Friendships

I think that the following incident was the major turning point of my hippy existence.

My friends and acquaintances among the Glasgow scene were wide and diverse. There was the ex-NK bunch; there was a group of politically active individuals; I was friendly with a group who were into spirituality; there were the freaks and dealers, and musicians and actors; but one group I knew particularly well were a bunch of guys from a similar set of circumstances as me - and I spent quite a bit of time with them.

It was like calling to like, I guess.

This was a group of lads, mainly, who used to be a gang until they had collectively decided to turn on, tune in and drop out. They still addressed themselves by the gang pseudonym of 'the Wolves' and they had stayed together as a loyal pack of hippy friends.

From our first meeting, the Wolves and I recognized each other. Without discussion, it was understood that we had shared the same background and, but for the grace of God, we would all have been mired in the violent gangland scene of our roots. We had escaped and we were all on the same new path. I was always accepted; I felt relaxed within this bunch, and enjoyed a lot of quality time with them.

The problem was drugs, though. The same changes I had observed elsewhere had been infiltrating the space of the Wolves. The drug scene was becoming more and more commercial, as the vast profits to be made drew in unsavoury opportunists from the darker side of the city. Scoring dope became a major operation, with back-up in case of rip-offs - which were becoming more and more common.

Dealers had minders.

Minders were starting to carry guns.

A few of the Wolves decided to venture into the dealing business themselves. At first it was only to supply the rest of the pack at a reasonable price, with a wee bit of profit - enough for a smoke - on the side. As their contacts, risks and profits grew, however, a couple of brothers decided to get more heavily into dealing and to distribute through the Wolves on a wider scale. Of course, they were unafraid. They were all ex-hard-men and had the warmth of the pack for security. But this was a new league, with new rules and a different type of player.

The Wolves were about to find this out the hard way.

The two brothers, John and Tony, who started the pack dealing, also had a younger brother called Moe. Moe always hung around his older siblings and, as a result, he got to know many of the dealing contacts that they developed. Moe looked up to his two big brothers. They were his heroes and role models, so it was inevitable that the young lad would start to get into drugs as well. When he was 15, he had his first acid trip with the Wolves - and he loved it. The Wolves treated Moe like a mascot and he was carefully looked after to ensure that he suffered no ill effects. He raved about his psychedelic experience for days, and took every opportunity that presented itself to get another smoke or to petition for more acid.

Having John and Tony as big brothers meant that there was lots of opportunity to get his young hands on drugs.

Eventually, Moe started to branch out and make his own friends. He turned 16 and moved into a flat with some male peers and his girlfriend from his old school. He entered into drug experimentation seriously and was the kingpin of his peer group, because of his brothers' contacts and access to a ready supply of drugs. Tony and John had by this time started to get into 'the big league', and some of their contacts were far from safe suppliers. Moe, with the perceived immortality of a 16-year-old youth, ignored the dangers and stepped onto more and more dangerous ground.

First it was amphetamines. His brothers gave him hell when they found out, and threatened to cut off his supply and have him ostracized from within the scene. They were afraid for their young brother, but, in reality, this was a business these days and they were powerless to stop him from following his own course.

Next it was morphine. Moe was given a freebee by one of the most unsavoury dealers on the scene. This was a guy who sold morphine and heroin to children and who was always willing to give the first couple of hits for free, complete with all the works necessary to complete the fix. This guy was always armed and had a vicious crew of minders, notorious for torturing or killing people who owed the crew money.

Moe got sucked in. Within a couple of months he was a heroin addict.

Tony and John were mortified. They tried to threaten his supplier into laying off, backed up by the full Wolves pack. They were laughed at and told to mind their own patch if they didn't want it to be taken over. They took Moe in and tried to wean him off junk and back onto a casual smoke. It never worked for more than a couple of days, before Moe would disappear off to score again and end up in a state.

Tony knew that it was useless to approach the dealers again. He knew that they would not back off, and that Moe would just find another supplier if this one stopped delivering the goods. John did, too, but he couldn't stop himself from issuing threats any time his path crossed theirs. A strong hatred developed between the two sets of dealers.

It all came to a head one weekend.

Moe went out to score as usual on a Friday night. The bad squad, fed up with John's perpetual berating, decided to give Moe a special fix, cut with a cleaning product. Moe scored the hit, took it home, fixed it up and was dead within the hour.

It was a tragic waste of a 16-year-old life, and nothing less than pure premeditated murder by the dealers.

As Tony was away in London, scoring some hash for resale at the time, along with a couple of the pack, John was the one who was informed of his brother's death by the police.

He went nuts. I got a frantic call to my flat at 03:00.

'Les, Les, man - it's Moe! The bastards have killed him, man!'

John was sobbing and screaming, clearly hysterical.

'John. What's happened, man? Moe dead. Fuck!'

'I'm goin' to get them, man. I'm taking some of the boys round. Jake's got hold of a couple of shotguns, man. They're dead, man. You comin', man?'

Shit! This was getting really crazy. This crew were total nutters, and if John didn't calm down there would be an unholy bloodbath. Poor Moe - he didn't deserve that - but the way he was going...

'Look, John. You need to calm down, man, and wait for Tony to get back. Don't do anything now, man; just wait and see what Tony says.'

Tony was always the pragmatic one, and, if I could prevent blood-shed now, maybe Tony could calm the whole thing down.

Maybe.

'Sure, man. It's OK. Tony knows the score, man,' said John...and he hung up.

I didn't know what to do. I called John back immediately - no answer. I called round a few of the pack. Some of them were out and only one of the others had heard about Moe, through a similar phone call to mine. He said: 'It's cool, Les. I said the same as you, to wait for Tony. He said, 'OK, man'. I think he's going over to his ma's place. These bastards deserve tae get it, though.' I agreed and hung up, hoping John would stay at his mother's place and not do anything stupid that night.

Unfortunately, that night John and four of the Wolves broke down the murdering dealer's front door and blasted three of his henchmen to bits with their shotguns. They made a swift getaway before the police arrived and they hung out at Jake's place. The dealer had been out on his rounds with the guy who had sold the bad fix to Moe, and so they had missed striking at the head of this small operation.

A girl, who had been in the flat during the raid, described the faces of the guys who had taken out the dealer's henchmen to him on his return, although, to the police, she said that she had been in the bedroom and had seen nothing. The police were in the dark, but the dealer knew who had turned him over from the descriptions he received.

It was war.

John, Jake and the others stayed ensconced at Jake's house for a time; Tony, meanwhile, returned from London with his score.

Tony had been out of communication, so he got the full story of what happened from one of the pack only when he returned. He was completely destroyed. His wee brother was dead and John had disappeared after making an assault on the crazy bastards who had done Moe. He was inconsolable, and stayed in the flat he usually shared with John, just getting stoned and crying his eyes out.

Two of the junk-dealer's henchmen had been watching the flat for John's return. When they saw Tony come back, they informed their boss. It took him 24 hours to get tooled up and put the necessary alibis in place.

The next day, Tony was dead. Shot in the head at point-blank range, trussed up like an animal carcass. He hadn't had a chance when the junk crew broke in, stabbed him, tied him up and then shot him.

This time I never got a call from John. Nobody did. When word got to him about his brother's murder, he grabbed a pump-action shotgun, jumped into his car and raced round to the flat of the junkie dealers. They were expecting him. He kicked in the door and was met by a hail of bullets. He died instantly.

The police were quickly on the scene and the dealer and his crew were busted. They got long custodial sentences for possession of firearms, manslaughter, possession of class 'A' drugs, and drug distribution. It didn't bring back the boys, though. A whole family had been needlessly wiped out.

I was shaken to the core of my being. It was definitely time to move on from this crazy scene.

My mind woke up as if from a long dream. This alternative lifestyle was not a viable alternative for me. I just had to look around me. People were being killed, people were killing themselves; people were going crazy here. The few groups of people I knew who were doing OK were older and were well out of the centre of this mad scene.

At the core of the problem were the drugs. What had initially started for me as a catalyst to get me out of a violent childhood had become an evil, which was in danger of destroying me as it was destroying many of those around me. The cannabis was harmless; the acid was dangerous; any of the other shit was a ticket to go completely crazy or kill yourself.

Before I got sucked in any deeper I was getting out - fast.

SONG 11 - BRAIN PUDDING

Yes, it looks very small
But if you want to make a successful brain pudding
This is what you do

You take one of these
Lie back
And wait till your brain becomes runny

Please, don't try this at home

CHAPTER XXXIX

Subjugating more Demons

Although I've talked about grassing as a crime within the hippy community - and have mentioned that the guys who were considered cool were also the ones who were into the most drugs, or were dealers, or criminals of other types - I hold to none of these beliefs. I am merely recounting the feeling prevalent in the hippy scene during that era in Glasgow.

I watched and I learned.

What I learned was this.

Although cannabis was a fairly innocuous drug, in scoring you had to deal with people who gave you access to many other types of drugs.

Drugs are dangerous. I saw many, many people become casualties of acid, speed, morphine, heroin, uppers and downers galore. Many paid the ultimate price and died before they were out of their teens. Others avoided early death but went insane. Only a few survived this scene as a rite of passage and came out whole at the other end.

Dealers are unscrupulous scumbags, who have no care about the misery that they perpetuate with their crimes. From Jimmy the Pill selling uppers and downers in my playground, to junk-dealers offering the initial fixes to hook their victims, they are people without moral scruple, who constitute a dark blot on the soul of humanity.

The freak scene in Glasgow was no different from any other small community. It had its good people and its bad people. The fact that they were following a trend in how they looked and talked, and in sharing a common recreation in using drugs, did not make this group of people any better than any others. As an alternative, though, it was a wash-out.

'Love and peace, man' - good words and a pure philosophy, but shrouded too often in false smiles and hugs - backstabbing and betrayal - and full of wrongful, anti-social behaviour patterns.

With the deaths of the three Wolves, my rose-coloured glasses shattered. I stepped outside my environment and looked back in.

It was just another demon; another seductive demon, posing as a comfortable setting, given credibility through the cushioning of drug-abuse.

A few days after the shooting, I went down to the job centre, looking for a fresh start. I was still just 16 years old, and there were plenty of opportunities around. I was lucky that day. There was a fresh job in. A company based in London but with Scottish roots was looking for young men to start office training in London at their head office. They were offering a reasonable starting salary and guaranteed training. Apparently, this company adhered to its Celtic roots and took on an intake of Scottish lads each year.

This was for me. I applied and was accepted. Four weeks later I was on the train to London, a small bunch of possessions in my rucksack, including a second-hand suit and shoes that I had purchased from a local charity shop. I was shrugging off of my Glasgow roots completely and I was moving on.

Well, perhaps I still carried a wee bit of Glasgow with me...

Maybe the Glasgow demon was still only sleeping.

SONG 12 - TIME TO CHANGE

I don't want to be here anymore
Done this crazy scene I know the score
Love and peace man, let's be free - to screw our heads with LSD
I don't want to groove with them no more

They are fond of saying that the straight guys are un-cool
These guys they play at meditating, with their music blasting
out
They're paranoid from doing drugs; they hand around false
smiles and hugs
I don't want to be like that no more

I just think it's time to change my scene (man)
I don't even want to know where I've just been
I'm going to pick myself back up, I'm going to change and get
some work
This alternative don't work for me no more

Got myself a place to stay down here
Got some friends whose concentration's clear
(when they're not drunk)
Drink's the driver that makes them wild, they care about the
chicks - and style
Wash themselves in action bathed in beer

They are fond of posing, showing muscles, breaking rules
At night each one's an anarchist, by day obey the rules
They read the prince not Steppenwolf
They wrap an image round themselves
Is this life the one I really want

Got a job and found a brand new life (here)
Do the chicks, the work and cope with strife
Live the clubs, the flats, the squats
Party hard and drink a lot
Getting old so fast - I'm sure

CHAPTER XL

Baptism

London. I arrived at Euston station on a Saturday, with my small suitcase of belongings and £3.50 in my wallet. In my pocket was the address of a youth hostel, run by the Church of Scotland for Scottish boys under 21. All I had to do was find this place, which was in the Euston area, check in - and I was set for work on Monday, with a day in hand to explore my new world.

I pushed my way through the crowded train station and, when I got outside, I asked directions to the street that held the club, where I was to be living. It took quite a few attempts. This was my first experience of both the size of my new environment and the cosmopolitan mix of its occupants. By the time I found a citizen who spoke English, who was knowledgeable on the area and who was willing to talk to me - never mind direct me - it was pretty late.

I made my way to the club - eventually. It was an imposing old building, right in the heart of the city. Day one in London and I had a WC1 address! The club was on a corner, next door to a YWCA residence, and across the road from Hillel House, headquarters of the Jewish faith in London.

Not bad. No slum area, this. Feeling that I had definitely taken a step-up, I walked up to the door and pressed the bell, to be admitted by a Scottish lad of about the same age as me.

'What dae you want, mate?'

'I've got some accommodation booked here through my company, man. Who do I see to check in?'

I was answered by a hybrid Glasgow/London accent, heavily weighted in favour of the Glasgow portion. 'Oh, OK, mate; I'll take you to the warden's office.'

This was my introduction to Teej and my first contact inside the club.

I was ushered through a grand vestibule, where other boys in and around my age were hanging about, up a set of stairs, to the apartment used by the warden of the club. Teej introduced me to the man and, after hearing my story, he took me downstairs to his office, to register me as a guest and get me a key to the room I would be sharing with two other boys.

This place looked pretty cushy!

Teej hung around, curious about the new boy, and, when the warden had sorted out my registration and handed me the key, he volunteered to show me to my room on the second floor.

'Where ye frae, mate?' asked the diminutive Teej in a strong Glasgow accent.

'Glasgow.' I didn't know the lay of the land, and so I was keeping my face impassive and myself to myself until I knew the score.

'Me tae,' he replied, as if it wasn't obvious. 'Where aboots, mate?'

The question, posed by a fellow Glaswegian, even one as obviously unthreatening as Teej, caused me to fall back on my roots. Armour immediately locked into place inside my head.

'Cawder.' I stopped and looked at him, face still impassive. 'Why? Is that a problem, pal?'

'Naw, mate, naw. Ah wis just curious. Ah'm no intae gangs or any o' that stuff, mate.'

Strange.

I started moving again and let Teej continue his babble, giving me the low-down on my two new room-mates as we went. In the back of my mind I was calculating: hostel full of Scottish lads all about my age; maybe lots of lads from Glasgow; Teej asking about where I came from and then mentioning gangs without any prompting; this could equal trouble. I'd better keep up my guard till I was sure this soft-looking place didn't hide some nasty side I'd have to defend myself against.

My room was another pleasant surprise. High ceilings, spacious, with big windows looking out on to Endsleigh Gardens; this was comfort, even with the three beds spaced around inside. The furnishings consisted of three single beds, four sideboards, three wardrobes, and shelves above and around each of the beds, which were situated at each corner of the room - except one, which contained a spare sideboard. The curtains were cotton and the carpet was comfortable, if a little used.

This was going to be OK!

One of the other beds looked as if it was being used and the other two were neatly squared away, so I selected one of them as mine and dumped my rucksack on top of it. Either I was bunking with a Borstal-trained or Army-trained companion, or there were only two of us in residence in the room at this time.

'Where's the boys, man?' I asked Teej, who was still hanging around as I unpacked my meagre possessions.

'You've only got one guy in here with you, mate,' he replied. 'The other bed's empty just noo. The guy you're sharing with's called Paul. He's a bit of a prat, but you'll never see him. Spends most of his spare time humping one of the Spanish maids down in her quarters in the basement.'

Useful. I had space, a guy I would hardly see and - maid service! Wow, this just kept getting better! My face betrayed none of my excitement.

'So, we get maids, then?'

'Yeah. There's a bunch of Spanish people, who cook and clean here. They make a good job of the place. The food's no bad, tae.'

I could hardly stop myself from clicking my heels together. The Church of Scotland certainly did well by their wee Scots boys down here. I could hardly believe the facilities, given the tiny rent we paid.

'Seems to be pretty cheap for all this, Teej?'

'Yeah, mate, it's sponsored by the Kirk. You only pay a nominal amount here. It's tae keep young Scots boys out o' trouble when they're down here. Great, eh?'

'Brilliant, man. Show me the rest of this place, then.'

A guided tour followed. Teej had been living at the club for six months already, and he knew the place inside out, as well as all of the current residents. He showed me the showers, the toilets and the games room, which sported a full-sized snooker table. He took me up to the top of the building and showed me the flat roof used for sunbathing and general partying. He explained the added bonus of being adjoined to the YWCA building. 'It's great, mate. We can sneak intae the YWCA across the roof if we get fixed up. If you get fixed up with a girl who lives in one of the top rooms, she can let you into her room through her windae. Party time - eh? You've just got tae make sure that you don't get caught by their warden. The old bird's always trying tae catch us at it. She'll get you thrown oot and she'll throw oot your girlfriend. Handy though, Les, having the girls next door - eh?'

'Pretty cool, man.'

On each of the floors down from the flat roof, which adjoined the YWCA, Teej gave me a potted history of the residents. I listened for threats. 'There's a good few boys from Glasgow, Les. A couple that say they were in the Cumbie, one that says he was in the Merryhill Fleet; ye might know him - eh?' and he rattled off a name I had never heard of. 'A couple from...'

And he continued with a litany of young boys, between the ages of 16 and 21 (the cut-off point, after which you had to leave this establishment). He knew their supposed ex-gang affiliations, which sounded to me like the boasts of kids trying to impress their peers. Teej himself was just a boy from Easterhouse, who had come down here as a trainee, on a ticket from one of the big banks.

'There's a few English boys, tae. No' many, though, as it's supposed tae be for Scottish boys, but when it's quiet they sometimes let the odd English boy in.'

He described each of the English boys. Not much threat there, either. In fact, I figured that - if there was any rough and tumble in this place - it would be better not to be an English boy, living with a host of Scottish kids, most of whom seemed to be from Glasgow.

'A couple of the boys think they're tough, mate, but you look as if ye can take care of yourself. Cawder's a bit wild - eh?'

I wasn't getting into my own history. That was a part of me that I wanted to leave behind. A few bullies to watch out for here; fresh Glasgow chip on my shoulder - I figured that I'd best root it out early.

'Who are these tough guys, then, Teej?'

'Joe's the worst one, Les. He's a big bastard. Rugby-player. He's Scottish, but he sounds English, since he went tae some public school. Thinks he's the kingpin here.'

'Thanks for the warning, Teej.'

'Nae bother, Les. Do you want tae get some grub? It's about dinner time.'

I was ravenous by this time, so I followed Teej as he took me downstairs, nodding to the lads he passed, and we went through the entrance hall into the dining room.

The dining area was a huge room, decked out with long tables, covered in white tablecloths and furnished with reasonably comfortable wooden seats. It looked like a dining room straight out of the Victorian era, where the family would sit around a large dinner table, with the mother and father at opposite ends and servants milling about to wait on their masters.

The room looked freshly painted, with high ceilings and fancy covings around the edges. There was a big bay window, which looked out onto the road, which was partially visible through lace curtains. The room was light, airy and comfortable.

A line had formed up just inside the door by the time we arrived. Teej explained that we had to get into the line, pick up cutlery as we passed it, and get our food from a hatch on our right that led into the kitchen area, where the Spanish cooks prepared everything. The food smelt mouth-wateringly good at this point, and I stood in line while Teej chatted to the boys around us and occasionally introduced me to some of them. Teej seemed pleased about having someone new to talk about and was enjoying the attention and curiosity that I was bringing.

I was eyeing each of the new boys that I saw or talked to with suspicion. I wasn't aggressive, but I projected little warmth. Teej's little introduction and his description of guys who thought that they were hard was in the back of my mind, and my armour was full on - just in case.

I moved along in line and picked up my cutlery as I passed it.

'So, you're a new boy, then. I imagine you'll want to let me take your place in the line?'

Shit. I wanted to root out the bullies, but I'd only been in the place for five minutes! It was obvious that the voice, coming from my left-hand side, was talking to me - the only new boy in the place.

How to handle this? I'd just spent a year throwing off the shackles of my old hard-man image. I wasn't going there again. I knew that saying 'peace and love, man' was probably not going to have a significant effect. Thing was, I didn't know this scene yet, and the psychology of the players was still a mystery. Lost for a response that would not drag me into a defining situation, I chose to ignore the guy and didn't even turn to look at him, but just kept my place in the queue. Unfortunately, judging by the eerie silence that had descended around me, I got the impression this wasn't going to go away easily.

'Ha, ha, ha! Another wee Scottish boy, scared stiff at being in the big city. Look at him, boys - I bet you're pissing your pants, son.'

'Leave him alone, Joe. He's just arrived frae Glasgow and he doesn't want any trouble - do ye, Les?'

I spared Teej a look and a nod, silently thanking him for his intervention. Maybe this bully would just walk away. I still refused to look at him and kept my eye on the front of the dinner queue.

'Glasgow, eh? You must be another one of these Glasgow hard men. Ha, ha, ha! Well, hard man, I told you to move over and give me your place in the line,'...and with that he punched me in the shoulder.

Snick, click, bang!

I turned, grabbed this bullying piece of trash by the throat with my left hand, dragged him forward and plunged the cutlery, grasped in my right hand, towards his face.

But some little voice inside me yelled, 'Stop!'

What was I doing? In the split second before I started to turn the face of this bullying public-school fool into meat paste, something inside me screamed, 'NO!'

This wasn't the way I wanted to go. I had escaped all that. I was starting a new life now.

I stopped myself just before I went all the way and, with my face still contorted like a madman, I looked into the face of my would-be oppressor.

Joe's eyes were wide open, as was his mouth, which looked as if it was locked in a silent scream. He had his two hands locked around my left wrist, as my fingers dug into his throat. His face was a pasty white colour and he was staring at the sharp edges of my cutlery, hovering threateningly a quarter of an inch from his face.

Looking into that picture of abject fear, I managed to control the volcano that was erupting inside me, and grunt, 'You really want to do this thing, man?'

'No! Please! I was only kidding, mate. I wasn't looking for a fight. Really.'

I could smell something bad and looked down. Joe had peed his pants and had a nasty stain developing across the front of his trousers.

Against all the rules of self-preservation that I had developed over a chequered childhood, I let the bully go, composed myself and turned away from him to stand back in the queue. I made no retort, issued no threat; I was just waiting for my meal with the rest of the guys.

It wasn't a misguided decision. Joe had had enough. Although I never looked at him again, he mumbled, 'Sorry,' in a small shaky voice, and made his exit from the dining room.

'Wow, Les; nobody's going tae mess with you here, mate,' said Teej, as he gave me an excited smile and a tentative congratulatory pat on the back.

I wasn't smiling, though, as Teej kept on gloating over the defeat of the erstwhile 'kingpin' and I heard the odd 'Cawder' creep into his description of me as he talked to some guys behind us in the queue.

Shit! This was exactly what I didn't want: having myself defined by an ability to react violently to threats. Now I would have to work fucking hard at removing this taint. Day one in the club and - if I wasn't very, very clever - it could turn into the same scenario as day one at NK.

No matter. I'd show the lads who I was over time. At least I knew that I had nothing to worry about in terms of more physical challenges here. If Joe had been the main man (and he could continue to be so, for all I cared), then nobody else was going to try it on after that little exhibition. Maybe it was for the best, then. I'd be safe from threats and I could take my time and establish myself here when the memory of tonight dimmed a bit.

I collected some soup - the first part of a three-course meal that I could look forward to each evening - found a place at one of the tables and was joined by Teej and a few others. We chatted through dinner and I pointedly avoided any discussions about my roots, what had happened with Joe, or anything remotely connected with violence. The guys didn't push me and I managed to get them talking about themselves, London life and the possibilities down here.

I gradually relaxed over dinner and, when it was over, told the lads I was tired and went up to my bedroom. As I lay on my bed and contemplated my new environment, I made a solemn pledge to make a go of my life here. I'd drop the hippy talk, avoid any drug culture, suppress the automatic survival responses and develop a new life.

I was determined.

Optimistic, 16 and a bit naive - even with the best will in the world, life was never going to be that simple.

CHAPTER XLI

Apprenticeship

I started work at the headquarters of the national building company that had sponsored me. I was a trainee buyer. It wasn't a high-profile, high-paying job, but it was a start; my only other experience of full-time employment was as a store boy at a car parts department in Glasgow. I remember donning my second-hand suit on that first Monday morning, eating breakfast with a couple of the boys, and feeling mounting excitement as I took the short walk from the club to my new place of work.

I was on my way in a new and very different world from the one I had left behind. I had a place to live, luxury by previous standards in my life, and I had an apprenticeship that promised an education and a path to a bright future.

Today I was optimistic.

I spent the first day being inducted. A young personnel assistant showed me around the building. She told me the rules, pointed out the toilets and the canteen, and eventually took me to the buying department to introduce me to my new boss. I hardly said anything during my induction. I soaked up all of the information I was given, trying to commit every little detail to memory. I wanted to do well. I wanted to impress.

I can still remember my new boss, who was a middle-aged middle manager, with ambition far above his ability to achieve his desire of eventually becoming a director in the company.

I remember my co-workers vividly as well. I sat behind two fast-talking Londoners, one of whom was the departmental comedian. Jake was his name, and he had seniority within the department. Beside him sat Sam. Sam was also a bit of a comedian. He was as camp as they come and used to upset the site foremen on the phone by calling them 'precious' or 'sugarplum' during his conversations with them.

David sat at the desk to my right. He was not much older than me. An English boy from the West Country, Dave tried his best to make me feel comfortable, while Jake and Sam either ignored me or made some occasional amusing comment or other at my expense. At first my hackles rose at their comments, but it didn't take me long to realize that this was their way of communicating about or to anyone in the company - that is, anyone who didn't have the power to promote or fire them. It was also my first lesson in office politics.

My daily routine as a trainee buyer was to file and retrieve endless pieces of paper.

At first I tried to understand each of the pieces of paper I was filing. The system was a simple one. There were files for invoices, purchase orders and purchase requisitions pertaining to each of the building projects we had. Each file was sectioned by months. All I had to do each day was collect all the paperwork, file it, and make the files or pertinent documents available to other members of the team for use in their jobs.

After a couple of days I was bored rigid.

I wasn't the only filing clerk. This was a job in the dark days before computerized records and sophisticated information-retrieval systems, so a company such as mine had a veritable army of paper-shufflers around. Filing clerks were high-turnover staff. Nobody really wanted to do the job, and so each of the filing clerks was constantly vying for any other open position. To gain the attention of the people who could make that happen, filing clerks stooped to bad-mouthing each other within the earshot of senior staff, taking credit for other people's work, and even occasionally messing up a rival's set of files, so that the victim would be chastised by their supervisor.

I wasn't bothered with the competition. For a start, Dave was my supervisor, and he was a good guy. Also, as had been explained to me at my induction, I was only temporarily in this department as I was on the 'round robin' training scheme, and I would be moved through all the departments in order to learn the overall business. Then I would be given a career job, based on both my aptitude and on the area that I found most interesting.

Not bad, and I could put up with this tedium for a while.

There was also a social life connected to the office. Lunchtime at the pub, or evening darts competitions and drinking sessions, were the accepted form of inter-office socializing, and yet another avenue for personal recognition and political manipulation by the wannabes.

I barely participated in any of this.

For a start, I was paid a very meagre salary and needed my money for everything. Clothes, shoes, rent, even basics such as toiletries, took the majority of my salary. The rest of my salary was swallowed up by the social life at the club, with precious little left over each month to save. I also hated the petty politics going on around me. It all seemed so trivial and meaningless. Being from a working-class environment, I guess I still believed in the 'work hard and do well' ethic. I ignored the office politics, but was very quickly re-educated on that particular working-class theory.

It soon dawned on me that I was going nowhere. The movement from department to department was only a movement from filing cabinet to filing cabinet. I was a stopgap. I was a resource to be used to catch up with filing in any department that had a backlog. As I had been quick to learn and efficient in my efforts, this meant only that I was valued as a filing clerk and was always in demand for such work. As I was fairly quiet and unresisting at the office and had never got into the usual sucking-up that went on at my level, this meant that I was never given an opportunity to try any other type of work.

Each day I hated filing more and more. Each day I was becoming more and more temperamental and miserable with my lot. After four months of this work, I was verging on insanity, and dreaded the short walk to the office each morning to face yet another mundane day.

I finally knew that it was time to take some action when I came across Roger, who - I discovered - had already crossed the invisible line.

It was just another Friday afternoon at the office. I was as bored as it was possible to feel and was looking forward to the weekend, when the only paper I would handle would be the pound notes I handed over at the bar in exchange for strong drink. I had been at the pub this lunchtime, for no other reason than to escape my office prison, but I'd had a few pints and was in and out of the loo all afternoon.

Now, once more, the call had to be answered and I entered the loo adjacent to our office.

An aggressive sounding, 'Fucking crap! Fucking useless rubbish!' drifted to my ears from a cubicle at the end of the line, punctuated by the sound of flushing. Curious, I strolled down to that cubicle.

'Fucking, fucking, fucking! You know what you can fucking do with it, mate!' Flush!

It was Roger. He had a huge bundle of what looked like purchase requisitions, and he was flushing them down the toilet pan while swearing at them as they disappeared around the S-bend. It looked as if Roger's marbles had disappeared around the selfsame S-bend some time earlier.

'What are you doing, Roger?' I asked.

Roger turned quickly. He obviously hadn't heard me approach and he looked a bit like a rabbit caught in strong headlights. Then he saw that it was me, a fellow filing clerk.

'Ha! I'm filing, Les. Let's see the bastards retrieve this stuff, then. They said I'd lost the March requisitions, mate. Fucking lost them! They'll be struggling to find April to September now, mate! Ha, ha, ha, ha, ha!'

...And he continued with his filing.

I couldn't help but smile. Poor Roger; he'd taken that one paper trail too many. For a few minutes I stood and watched Roger as he lived out a fantasy that I bet many of us have contemplated in the past, but have not been quite far enough over the edge to carry out. As I watched, I could see Roger's state of mental health as being somehow inevitable in this line of work. It seemed to be the natural effect of being a long-term filing clerk, and I wondered how long it would be before I was either doing the same or torching the filing cabinets with a maniacal grin on my face.

It was time for me to institute some changes around here.

'You should shut the door, Roger mate, so that nobody can see what you're doing.'

I don't think he even heard my parting words of advice, as I did what I had come for and made my way from the scene of the crime.

Instead of going back to my desk, I made my way towards the personnel office. I had done enough filing; it was time for them to give me something different. Either I got a change of job and really started to learn something, or I was off. I wasn't going to follow in my fellow filing victim's footsteps.

I squared my shoulders and marched down the corridor.

I was sure that today was going to see a turnaround in my circumstances. If I had learned anything so far, it was that the meek would only ever inherit the filing cabinet, until the day came for them to be led out of the building in a straitjacket. I refused to let that happen to me.

I approached the personnel office with a strong resolve!

As for Roger - the inevitable happened and he got caught. Apparently, the slight to his character over losing those requisitions had happened a couple of weeks earlier. Since then he had been flushing paperwork at every opportunity. He got found out when one of the managers went to the loo and discovered Roger drowning the whole of the current year's invoice file for a major project. Being a benevolent company, they didn't fire Roger. They gave him three months' paid leave of absence to 'get himself calmed down', and then took him back on, in - of all places - the accounts department.

They sponsored night school classes for him and gave him an opportunity to become an accountant within the firm.

It never seemed the sanest of choices to me.

I hope Roger didn't mind counting up endless rows of figures each day...

CHAPTER XLII

On the Piss again!

As my non-career dragged on, I had fallen into a routine within the club. By this time my best friends at the club were: a young Norwegian boy called Thomas; an English boy called Ralph with a taste for Captain Beefheart albums; a boy called Shane, who was educated in England but whose father lived in Spain; a Scottish guy called Crazy Pete, who had eventually moved into my shared room; and a Scottish boy called Bill, who talked about being an ex-hard man from Glasgow, but who was as soft as putty for all of his bulky six foot two inches. I had other acquaintances and not so close friends, such as Teej, Tony and Cheater, but for the most part I hung around with the five I mentioned at the beginning.

Our social routine revolved around a local pub called the Eliza Dolittle, which was situated within the Euston area and was adjacent to the local theatre. This was the drinking hole for the club members, most of whom were a couple of years shy of the legal age to consume alcohol. It was a short walk to the 'Liza' from Endsleigh Gardens, where we lived. A short, rowdy, boisterous walk on the way there and a wild, noisy, detour-via-the-Indian-restaurant walk on the way home again.

We had many club anthems to sing, mostly based around Scottish patriotism, but the chant that must have been best renowned in the area went like this:

The Cally boys are on the piss again!
On the piss again!
On the piss again!
The Cally boys are on the piss again!

Look out, London town!

I imagine the local residents hated us.

After work, lads who had spent the day dressed in suits and minding their Ps and Qs in respectable establishments such as banks, major offices and accountancy firms would don their casual clothes and step into their street personae, to swagger out to the pub and get themselves completely plastered. There were up to 70 young lads living at the club at any one time, and so the local London lads avoided us, and the publican at the 'Liza' put up with our antics because of the money we were spending.

We were ably supported and encouraged by the girls from the YWCA next door, who would join us on our excursions into alcoholic stupor. Some of the lads would be dating girls from this hormonal paradise, but the majority of the girls were just mates, as large-scale drink consumption and teenage shyness generally created a potent barrier between our lads' desire and the young girls' most private parts.

The Caledonian boys - Cally boys - were a tight-knit team. As all of us were alone in London, we bonded in much the same way as the kids did in The Lord Of The Flies. Our standard was a foaming mug of beer over a blue and white Scottish flag, worshipped even by the few English boys and foreigners in our clan. Our aims were to have as wild a time as possible, making noise, getting drunk, getting laid and - whenever appropriate - defending our name and each other with our fists and overwhelming numbers. Apart from the noticeable lack of violence - after all, who picks on this number of drunken lads? - our wee clan bore a disturbing similarity to the gang structure I had despised at home.

I went along because of two things.

This was London, and, compared to the Glasgow I knew, it was a soft place to be, with almost no threat of violence to our Cally boys clan. Even in the 'riskier' places of the West End - Brixton, parts of north London, etc. - life was very non-threatening, where people duelled more with their mouths than with their fists or weapons. I knew that heavy violence, intimidation and exploitation went on, but London was a huge place and such angry depths didn't often cross into my sphere of influence; when they did, they were minor and very simple to destroy. So, being in our Caledonian clan did not mean that I was stepping into a world of violence like the one I had just left behind.

Also, for the first time in my life, I was experiencing joining something. As a guy who had always avoided becoming a central part of any gang, group or club, it felt good to be a central figure within the Cally boys club. As the boy who had humiliated Joe, I had become a minor celebrity within our residence, and - as such - was always a welcome participant in any of our adolescent jamborees. I added to the security of the team because I was seen as someone else with fighting prowess. Not all of the young lads felt as secure as I did, living so far away from home. These lads looked to the womb of the Cally boys clan for security as well as comradeship, and I was one of the few lads who, to them, embodied that feeling of security.

This was OK, as, in all the time I lived at the club, I was never called on to use my fighting prowess to any great extent. In fact, the only big 'ruck' that I can remember was at a student union disco, where some drunken students threw beer over the lads at our table and we had to make a swift exit after we had bloodied a few noses in revenge. It was all pretty tame stuff.

Night after night, with drunken dances at the weekends, our routine continued, following a club tradition instilled from its inception. This probably seems mindless and useless from the outside. I guess to most people it would be, but for me it was an opportunity to learn and develop new social skills.

I watched how some of the lads handled the group dynamic through humour and I developed a bit of that skill myself. Although at the beginning my humour was fairly deadpan and guarded, by the time I had left this group I was able to amuse with the rest.

I noticed how disagreements, especially between the better-heeled or better-educated elements within our group, were fought out through verbal duels - the victory going to the sharpest and quickest of mind. This skill was not one that I learned quickly. At first I was just a wee lad from Glasgow with a big chip on his shoulder. So, whenever I was accosted verbally, the result was usually physical retaliation, which ranged from a bloody nose when I was sober to a hefty beating when I was drunk. But the reaction from the lads told me that this was the least socially acceptable form of rebuke, and over time I was able to condition my response into a verbal riposte.

Again, at the beginning, I was a pretty weak duellist and would often resort to my former method of antagonist control when it looked as though I was being beaten or about to be humiliated. This certainly made folk less relaxed in my company, and so I worked harder at being better with words and on reducing the chip on my shoulder to a mere splinter

Instead of snick, click, bang! I developed a sort of snick, click, slap! with the slap being delivered verbally, though with no less precision, and bringing an equally satisfying result. Being a part of the club taught me social skills that allowed me to shelve my double-headed axe and bring a rapier into play in its stead.

Mixing with a bunch of lads from such a diversity of backgrounds, both domestic and foreign, also improved my diction and increased my vocabulary. When I had first arrived in London, I still talked like a half-educated, housing-estate hippy. Hardly anyone could understand my accent, let alone keep up with the speed of my verbal delivery. I was now mixing with a range of foreigners, people from other parts of the UK and public-school boys, as well as lads from a similar background to mine. I quickly got fed up with, 'What was that, mate?' every time I spoke. I learned to speak much more slowly and much more concisely. I picked up a kind of Scottish hybrid accent, much easier to comprehend than the accent of my native Glasgow, and I unconsciously added to my active vocabulary on a daily basis through conversations with lads from within the club.

I was learning to communicate.

I learned the value of close friends and of having a support network. I had always been the perennial loner. Although I had had friends and acquaintances throughout my previous social lives, I had never really bonded deeply with anyone or any group. Now, here I was, entrenched within the club, and I had joined the Cally boys and bonded closely with a few guys in the team.

It felt good.

We lent each other money, mostly for drink. We bought each other pints and curries. We played together, sang together and we looked out for each other's backs. We pulled girls together within my small sub-group and we explored the wider reaches of London, savouring all that it had to offer six 16- to 18-year-old boys.

Although some of the lads very quickly became institutionalized within the club, it never affected me that way. I never felt that I could not survive outside the club environs, and I certainly never felt that I would stay in this place forever. No, the club for me was just a vehicle to learn the value of being a part of a team.

I was also developing the ability to become a team player.

The Cally boys are on the piss again.

I'll never forget our anthem, or the routine within the club. It was a new and different experience for me, and one that preceded a big social change. Although, in the main, the scene was about teenage drunkenness, it was also for me about social development. At the time I was as mercurial as I have ever been in my life, but I learned lessons, most of which were valuable and all of which were to stick with me, adding to my armour and giving that armour a socially acceptable polish.

I can't say that every boy had the same end experiences or realizations as me, though.

Look out, London town.

In some cases it should have been:

Look out, Cally boys!

CHAPTER XLIII

Using my Head

Meanwhile, at work, I had challenged my position as a filing clerk and had been well received in the personnel office. I was told that the company was pleased with my progress and that they also felt that I should be moving on. I wondered how forthcoming that information and action would have been if I'd just kept my mouth shut and continued with the drab daily filing I had been given.

Education was at the top of my agenda. I had realized that the highest-placed in our organization were people who had some sort of academic qualification. I knew that my NK O levels would hardly cut it, and so I had petitioned the personnel officer for some support in gaining more impressive qualifications.

They agreed, and we decided on a course in business studies, on a day-release basis. I was on my way.

Meanwhile, I had been persuaded that, in order to get to know the business better, I should spend some time out on site. I would rotate across some of the projects in London as a timekeeper.

That was a laugh.

If I had any major fault, it was definitely timekeeping. My idea of being on time for work was to arrive only five minutes late. Most of the time, I was on my last cup of tea over breakfast at nine o'clock, with a ten-minute walk ahead of me. My boss once said to me: 'Mr Smith, if you could only get into the office at five minutes to nine, your day would be perfect.'

I replied: 'Boss, if I ever get into the office at five minutes to nine, send me back home, because you'll know that my day has been totally destroyed!'

He never brought up the subject again, as he was smart enough to realise that the only options he had were either to accept my timekeeping - or to fire me. They were always reluctant to fire the wee Scots boys that had been especially imported from their founder's home nation.

Me - a timekeeper? Ah, well; I might as well give it a try; after all, it was the education I was interested in. I couldn't care less how I earned my living in the meantime.

CHAPTER XLIV

Muck away

Life on a building site was something completely different for me. To date, I had always worked in offices during my two-job career. As a store boy in the parts department in Glasgow, I had interacted with the mechanics coming up for their parts and the ancillary workers and salesmen. I had been mainly responsible for paperwork, fetching and carrying. As a filing clerk in a huge headquarters building, I had never met any of the manual workers in the business, and so my experience was only of dealing with white-collar workers. In these environments I understood the wit, the politics, the backstabbing and the processes used.

Now, I was to go out on site, and this would be something completely new. I was looking forward to it.

I was given an allowance to buy some appropriate site clothing. Harder-wearing black trousers, a blue shirt and a tie were the order of the day. I duly complied over the weekend, and on Monday morning at 08:15 I arrived at Brent Cross and reported to the site foreman's hut to be tutored in my new regime.

'You're late, son. Not much good in a timekeeper, that - eh?' were the first words spoken to me on that chilly Monday morning. I had been due on site at 08:00.

'Never mind, son; let's go and get some breakfast and I'll fill you in on the job,' the foreman continued, and we marched across the site towards perk number one - the on-site food van.

It was an unwritten fact in those days that building-site workers could not perform without warm, greasy food inside them. The food van would always be available on site for breakfast (08:00 - 08:30); morning break time (10:30 - 11:00); lunchtime (1:00 - 1:30 p.m.); and afternoon break time (2:30 - 3:00 p.m.).

A typical breakfast was sausage, bacon, eggs, fried bread and a huge mug of tea. All of the fry-up would be swimming in fat and the tea would be ingested with a mountain of sugar. There were lighter options, such as a bacon, sausage and egg roll, for those stalwarts who were watching their waistline. Every other break offered similarly greased-up fare and, at lunchtime, there were also sandwiches and soup on offer.

When I saw the menu available at this van, I fully understood the phenomenon of builder's bum, and why it was that most manual workers had guts like a pregnant hippopotamus. I wondered if the entire world of darts champions started out as building-site workers! I learned later, as the pattern of my new co-workers' lives unfolded, that normal behaviour after work was for the guys to go home for a quick wash, so that they could get down the pub for half a dozen pints to give themselves an appetite for a full dinner.

It still makes me shudder to think about it. There are much easier ways to die.

I can only surmise that the reason half the labourers on the building site did not keel over dead after the first six months of this regime was that the work that they carried out (at least, the amount that they could fit in between eating and cigarette breaks) was heavy enough to burn up a few calories on the way.

I ate my own fry-up and waddled back to the hut with the site foreman.

'Well, Les; so you're from head office - learning the business, eh? Must have you marked out for great things, then, son.' Perhaps they were planning to make me into bars of soap, I thought. They'd get a few bars out of my arterial walls at least, this way.

'Well, son - the job's pretty simple. Do you see these lorries driving around the site? These are the muck away lorries. They fill up with the earth we are dredging out of the site and we pay them by the lorry-load to dump the earth at an approved unloading site. It's all sub-contractor work, son, and these guys are as sharp as knives - so keep a good eye on them and be sure to count each load. We issue them with a ticket for every trip they make and they get paid by the number of tickets they have at the end of the week. Watch for them driving out of one gate and driving back in through the back gate with the same load. They'll try any trick to get paid twice for the same load.

'Anything else you want to know for now, son?'

I couldn't think of anything.

'Right, then; Jimmy will be working with you. He's a good lad and has been doing this job for years, so he'll keep you on the right track. Off you go to the timekeeper's hut over at the gate and let him get away for some breakfast, son - good luck.' And he turned away to get on with whatever problems he had to sort out that morning.

Jesus! I was the paper-shuffler of the building site and the site fore-man thought I was getting a break. If they needed to bring someone in from head office to put ticks in a column and then count them up at the end of the day, then my co-workers were going to be a real bundle of laughs.

Depressed but feeling arrogant, I made my way across the site to the timekeeper's hut at the gate and to meet Mr Experience.

'Jimmy? I'm Les, the new timekeeper from head office.'

Jimmy was a skinny and dour-looking bloke with NHS spectacles and thinning mousy-brown hair. He wore the timekeeper uniform and a pair of stout builder's boots, which were laced up over the bottom of his trousers. Jimmy looked to be about 40 and had the 'gave up on life years ago' look that too much time spent in a mundane, lowly-paid job will give to a man. His wife probably hated sex too, but I never found that out for sure.

'Humph! Don't suppose you'll be here long,' he said as he thrust a clipboard and a wad of 'muck away' tickets in my direction, along with a fat HB pencil. 'I'm off for a cup of tea. The foreman tell you what to do? Good; just make sure you mark them all going past and watch out for their tricks - they're a crafty lot, son.' And with that he left me, clipboard and tickets in hand, to go and get himself greased up inside.

I duly stood outside the hut and ticked off the lorries as they went by.

The building site covered a vast area of land. I can't even remember what we were supposed to be building, as I never lasted past the 'muck away' stage of the job and I never cared enough to ask. The site was covered with diggers, dredgers, lorries, miscellaneous equipment, Portakabins, huts and an army of worker-ant-like people, bustling about or just standing about as if waiting for the second coming.

A veritable hive environment.

There were mounds of muck all over the site, and it was to these mounds that the lorries coming in through the bottom gate would head, to be loaded up and truck their way to my hut, where I would issue them a ticket and mark them off on the sheet attached to my clipboard.

Mind-numbing work.

Over time, I got to know the drivers. As the foreman had stated, they were as sharp as knives and would regularly come up with another scam to get paid for the same load, or to get an extra ticket because they had somehow either forgotten to get one last time or had lost one along the way. Although I never really cared too much about the building work economics, I diligently made my ticks, ignored the scams and handed out the appropriate number of tickets.

I did this for several months.

It was only the day-release that kept me going. I was getting plenty of time in the hut to study and, although the course was pretty easy, I wanted to get a good pass mark and start to build up some decent qualifications. So I stuck out the job. But I was becoming slacker and slacker through lack of interest.

One of the timekeeper tasks relating to the 'muck away' was to occasionally wander around the piles of muck and ensure that the lorries were being properly filled up. Jimmy performed this task with gusto and took great pleasure in bossing the drivers and the guys with the diggers into squeezing every last spoonful of dirt into a lorry. Jimmy couldn't have been having sex, because he used to get such a hard-on every time he had an excuse to send back a lorry to get topped up, or to refuse a driver a ticket for what he called a partial load. His eyes would glitter and he'd say, 'See, Les; these bastards know they cant fuck me around.

You'll get there, son.' And he'd light up and have his after-orgasm cigarette, while he contemplated his enormous power.

The drivers and probably every worker on the site hated the smug
git. I thought he was a complete tosser, myself.

Another job we had to perform was to wander around the perimeter
of the site and make sure that there were no gaps where the lorries could
sneak into the site unnoticed. Apparently, Jimmy had previously caught
a bunch of drivers who had removed some of the fencing and were getting tickets for the same load. This had happened before I arrived, and
Jimmy still crowed about his masterful sleuthing and the praise heaped
upon him by the site foreman for discovering the scam.

Whatever gets you off, Jimmy!

I took my turn at these tasks, but, as I got to know the drivers and as
I got more and more wearied by the mundane nature of my job, I used
to hitch a lift around the site in a lorry and spare no more than a cursory glance at the actual perimeter fencing. This was to be my downfall.

Jimmy got sick. He had an awful flu and was forced to spend three
days in bed. It must have been pretty bad, or my Mr Jobsworth would
never have taken any time away from his power base. I can imagine that
his wife must have been going nuts at home, being sent back to the
kitchen to fill up his mug of tea to the appropriate height or lose her TV
privileges. Poor woman; it was bad enough working with Mr Diligent -
I couldn't even imagine the horror of having to live with him.

Word spread quickly across the site that Jimmy was off on sick leave
and, unbeknown to me, the drivers were dancing with glee as they plot-
ted three days of increasing their personal fortunes. It was well known
on the site that the wee Scottish boy from headquarters didn't give two
figs for the job and was only biding his time till he got his qualifications.
I had told many of the drivers my story, on my frowned-upon-by-Jimmy
excursions around the site by lorry. He had warned me: 'You're getting
too thick with these bastards, son. They'll take the pish, I'm telling you.'

He was right, of course, but what did I care? A few more months
and, if I wasn't back in headquarters, I was leaving with my business
studies qualifications tucked under my arm. When we worked together Jimmy diligently watched my back - not to protect me, you understand, but it gave him a feeling of superiority to catch the tricks that I
missed through a complete lack of concern. Jimmy was away, though,

and nobody was watching my back now.

The foreman gave me a wee speech.

'It's all down to you for a few days, Les. I'm sure you can handle it, though. You've been working with Jimmy long enough. Just remember - if you have any problems, just to come to my office. The door's always open, son.'

Jesus! He didn't think I'd be able to put ticks on a sheet and write out tickets without a big brother around to hold my hand. Just another insult from this insult of a job! I walked away even more demotivated than I normally was, but I really should have shelved my arrogance and paid more attention.

It started on the first day. I spotted Dick, a guy who I had developed a good banter with, coming around for the third time with a load of muck, in a remarkably short time.

'What's this, Dick? There's no way you could have dumped these loads that quickly. Are you taking the pish, mate?'

'It's a new dump up the road, Les. The governor's got the contract for some landfill. Want to see it?'

I knew I shouldn't leave my post, but I was bored out of my skull and I could always tell the foreman that I was checking out a new dump to legitimize my absence. I put my stuff in the hut, padlocked the door and jumped into the lorry for a quick drive to the new site. Sure enough, Dick took me to an open piece of ground up the road, tipped his load and brought me back to the site.

'See, Les - I told you, mate. We wouldn't take the pish with you, son - we like you; it's that bastard Jimmy we hate.'

Complete bollocks, of course. These guys would take the pish out of their grandmothers to get a few extra tickets. I didn't care, though; I'd seen the dump site and I could legitimately hand out his 'muck away' tickets.

I handed out a lot of tickets that day.

By the end of the three days I had handed out more 'muck away' tickets than I had done in the previous two weeks. I guess at the back of my mind I knew I was being scammed, but I couldn't raise the enthusiasm to do anything about it. The drivers were especially friendly over these three days, proclaiming Jimmy's absence as the reason for their good humour. I was bought a breakfast, included in a lunchtime card game where I won a few bob, and chauffeured around the building site like a king. This was more fun than I had had in months.

Jimmy returned on the Thursday. The first thing he did was to review the tick list, recount my totals, and tally it up with the holy-ticket-book stubs.

'What the fuck's been going on here, Les? You've handed out a book and a half of chits, son. That's impossible. Nobody could have taken away so much muck!'

'It's a new dump site, Jimmy. I went and saw it myself with Dick. It's a landfill just up the road. I'll get one of the guys to take you up there if you like?'

'Landfill? The bastards are taking the pish, son. I've just walked down from the tube station and I didn't see any new landfill project. Anyway, the site foreman always tells us if there is a new contract for muck. You've let these clever bastards screw you!'

And with that he grabbed the sheets and ticket books to go and report this situation to the foreman.

Fuck! I'd screwed up royally. I should have checked the site on my way home the first night, or I should have checked it out with the site foreman. I was in trouble now and Jimmy would never let me hear the end of it.

Of course, a quick investigation proved that I had been good and scammed. There was no new landfill site. Dick had just dumped his first load on a piece of waste ground to kid me. I had duly been suckered and as a result I had issued three times more tickets than I should have on each day that I had been in charge. In fact, it was more like four times the number on the third day, as the lads, knowing Jimmy would be back soon, went for broke.

Jimmy found the piece of broken fence at the back of the site that the drivers had been using as their entrance for still-undumped loads. Apparently, the digger-drivers had been only partially filling the trucks as well, for a small financial consideration.

Everyone but the site foreman was happy. Jimmy was happy to have got one up on the useless headquarters boy and to have shown how indispensable he was to the project. The drivers were happy to have made an enormous amount of money over these days, as the company had no choice but to pay on receipt of the signed chits, when I couldn't remember who had started the scam. Even the digger-operators were happy, as they had got a nice wee kickback from the drivers over the three days.

The foreman was livid. 'What did you think you were doing here, you stupid little prat? Do you realize how much over-budget we're going to be for 'muck away' on this job now? Well, you can explain it to headquarters. I'm contacting personnel and having you taken out of here as soon as possible, you useless little bastard!'

He stomped away to do his worst. Jimmy, leaning against the time-keeper's desk, with a barely disguised grin on his face, just shook his head and tut-tutted.

Bollocks!

I didn't really care. The 'muck away' budget meant nothing to me. My career in this company meant nothing to me. As long as I got to finish my course, who cared if I was on site or off? I was only depressed about the thought of having to put up with Jimmy's smirks and comments till I was moved off site.

I was duly recalled to head office that week. I was to finish off my site experience on Friday and then report to personnel on the following Monday morning for a new assignment. Back to filing, I supposed.

I was pleasantly surprised during my last Friday on site. The drivers, feeling a wee bit guilty about causing my on-site demise, had clubbed together and handed me an envelope stuffed with money, as my send-off present from them. I was bought my lunch and - excluding Jimmy - we all went to the far side of the site and downed a few beers together. I guess they could afford it, having made a bonus of about a couple of weeks' money over three days. It was a nice thought, though, and I knew that it was something they would have never done for Jimmy. Even though they had well and truly scammed me, they liked me. For me, on my lowly pay, the money represented about a month's salary. I was a lot less fed up by the end of that day.

I decided that I wasn't cut out for a career in muck!

CHAPTER XLV

Laugh - we certainly did!

My mates at the club - Ralph, Shane, Thomas, Crazy Pete and Bill - were a fun bunch of guys to hang out with. Thrown together in this artificial environment, our diverse backgrounds and characters only added some colour to our friendship.

And we were indeed a diverse bunch of lads.

++++++++

Thomas, the Norwegian boy, was 18 years old when I met him. He was taking a European break with another friend called Terry from his home town before returning to face his turn at national service. Thomas was a soft-featured, tall and skinny lad, with a fresh honesty and a contagious smile.

Like most Scandinavian youths, Thomas liked to drink and party after work. He and I hit it off almost immediately and became firm friends. Thomas is the only person from this era that I am still in touch with and who has remained a friend after all this time.

In those days he and I would head off into London, carousing and drinking and having good teenage fun. He tempered my tendency towards volcanic mood eruptions with his easygoing attitude to life. Thomas was a gem whom I was proud to meet and I am proud to know, even though it is now from a distance. He taught me many things about just living to enjoy life, and especially valued were the lessons I learned from watching him interact with members of the opposite sex. Thomas

241

was handsome and popular with the girls. He never seemed to allow this fact to change anything about his demeanour when we were lucky enough to find ourselves in the company of such damsels. He was always laid-back with women, always respectful, and - even though he was as hot-blooded and desirous as the rest of us - he was never pushy, demanding, aggressive or demeaning.

During this period of my life I was more interested in finding out about and developing who I was than in forming close relationships with girls. I had a multitude of 'flings', but I rarely talked about them and never followed up on any of them. I learned from Thomas, though, and through his lessons I have come to enjoy and be relaxed about being in the company of women.

Thomas's friend Terry was also a fresh-faced youth. He was a much more serious boy than Thomas or I, and from the beginning he formed a relationship with a girl from the YWCA and spent most of his time with her. Terry rarely joined us on our excursions, and it is probably just as well, considering the trouble that exploded on the one night he joined us in the West End.

++++++++

Aggressive homosexuality had never been a feature of either my youth or the Scandinavian guys' youth. Open homosexuality in Glasgow was tantamount to painting a target on your back and handing out machine-guns to a bunch of thick-headed skinheads. Since arriving in London, Thomas and I had occasionally come across this new-to-us phenomenon during our drinking binges across the West End. Thinking back, two teenage boys, one of whom had the fresh-faced look of a 14-year-old, must have presented a tempting picture to the more aggressive members of the gay culture that existed around many of the pubs of London.

Thomas and I had learned to deal with it by scowling, ignoring, or just plain threatening. At such times, my Glasgow accent came back full strength and the body language I had learned in the streets of my home town acted as a fairly persuasive barrier to molestation. Having spent most of his London time with his girl, though, Terry hadn't had to learn to deal with it.

One Friday night Terry decided to join us on the town.

His girlfriend was out with her pals and Terry wanted to taste some of the action that we were always raving about. So, off we went to the West End, visiting our usual haunts and consuming masses of alcohol. We were having the best of times, until we hit one particular bar in Windmill Street.

Thomas and I were talking at the bar, well under the weather by this time, and Terry had gone to the loo to divest himself of the first of many half gallons. I glanced over and nodded at Terry as he returned, looking a bit fed-up and serious, with a grinning, middle-aged and stocky-looking well-dressed Londoner trailing in his wake. Terry took his seat at the bar and started to down the rest of his pint.

'What's up, mate?' I asked.

'Nothing, Les; nothing.'

But Terry didn't look as if it was nothing.

Thomas looked at the two of us, with a half-sober grin still plastered on his face, and shrugged his shoulders at Terry as if to say, 'He's always so serious, Les; forget it,' and continued to drink up. As Thomas ordered another round, I looked across at the grinning gent, who was now talking to two similarly clad middle-aged friends of his, with the occasional smile and thumb directed in Terry's direction. They seemed to be having a good laugh.

'Sure you're OK, Terry?'

'Of course, Les,' said Terry - all serious Scandinavian stalwart as usual. 'Let's get some more beers!'

I shrugged my shoulders and prepared my liver for the next onslaught of alcohol.

About halfway through the next beer, with the three of us laughing and having a good time, the gent, ghosted by his two friends, sidled up to the part of the bar beside Terry.

'Thought about my offer, son?' he said, with a sleazy grin on his face.

Terry turned his back away from the guy and looked towards us with a face that could have melted iron. Terry was a controlled guy. Unlike mercurial me, Terry could take a fair few verbal hits without feeling the need to retaliate. Don't get me wrong - both of the Scandinavian boys were big strong lads, well capable of taking care of themselves in any physical contest. It was just that these lads were fairly civilized by any street standards and never courted trouble.

Mr Middle-aged obviously mistook this attitude for timidity and pressed his luck. With an over-the-shoulder grin to his mates, he sneaked his arm around Terry's shoulder, pulled him towards his face and whispered something obscene in his ear.

Snick, click, bang!

All I can remember is Terry leaping away from the guy as if his buttocks had caught fire, Thomas snapping out of his drunken stupor with wide eyes, hearing myself roar, and then...

Blood.

As Niagara Falls subsided behind my ears, I came back to myself as I was being dragged out of the pub by Thomas and Terry, snarling like a wild animal and with my clothes drenched in blood. I could barely remember what had happened, but the scene in front of me was one of utter devastation. Chairs were broken; glasses were broken and crunched into the floor; most of the punters had receded to the sides of the bar; and in the middle of this mess were the moaning bodies of three middle-aged gents, plus a couple of others, one of whom looked to be the barman who had been serving us.

Thomas later explained to me that, when the gay antagonist had made his move on Terry, I had launched myself from my bar stool with a growl, head first into the face of the pushy gay guy, bowling both him and Terry out of the way. I had then started to pound this guy into a bloody mess with my fists, while Terry and Thomas had had to box with his two mates as they tried to intervene. Our barman, apparently sympathetic to our cause having witnessed the whole incident, had tried to prise me off the guy, fearing that I was about to kill him. I had not recognized him, being fully immersed in my berserk rage, and, as he pulled me away, I had grabbed a handy chair and started to break it into pieces against his body. When he fell, I started launching glasses off the bar at another bystander, who was also trying to calm things down. He tripped in his retreat, and I had started to kick him viciously in the ribs.

Thomas and Terry had finally beaten down the other guys, seen both the state I was in and the damage I was doing, and had grabbed my arms and managed to wrestle me towards the door, kicking and screaming.

Then I had come round.

The police had been called and Thomas said that we had to run.

That incident gave me a bit of a fright. Although I had been involved in fights before in London, I had never before lost control of my faculties. My late-schooldays anger had resurfaced once again and I was pretty shaken to realize what had happened. It was then that I realized that I had to cut down on the amount of alcohol that I was consuming. The alcohol was obviously destroying any control I had on my temper, and if I happened to be under threat and react when I was drunk...

It didn't bear thinking about.

From that night onwards, I was a much more cautious drinker. It seemed that beer was my problem. I did not have much body weight and, as a result, I got drunk very quickly when I drowned my liver in beer. I didn't stop drinking, but I switched to shorts. First tequila, then Pernod (which I had to quit when I found that I was still drunk when I went to work the next day) and finally whisky. That old Celtic favourite finally became my alcoholic beverage of choice, and I never got as out of control with this refreshment as I had been that night on beer.

Thomas, being the understanding and extremely homophobic guy that he was, quickly forgot the incident as we continued our regular debauchery together.

Terry never joined our drinking excursions again after that night, however.

CHAPTER XLVI

Ralph the Mouth

Ralph was pretty different from me. He came from a fairly civilized part of the world called Boscombe, near Bournemouth, in Dorset. Ralph fancied that he was well able to take care of himself, although he avoided physical conflicts both inside and outside the club. He was about five foot ten, of fairly normal build, with a pigeon-chest and lanky black hair. He talked a lot of the time in phrases borrowed from albums by Captain Beefheart and Frank Zappa.

Ralph was a colourful character, with a great imagination. We had a lot of fun one summer when Thomas and Terry had gone home for a brief visit to Norway, and we stayed fast friends from then on. I think it was our similar tastes in alternative music that brought us together, but it was the laughs and adventures that we shared which kept our friendship going.

I remember the time that summer when we thought it would be fun to get a tape recorder, dress up like maniacs and interview people in the street, asking them such questions as: 'Can you please quote Einstein's theory of relativity?' or 'What is your opinion of the fat people in our society?' or 'Do you think goldfish deserve a vote in the next election?'

Mundane stuff which could be funny if addressed to the right people.

The responses ranged from the clever guy who knew Einstein's theory, through some other pretty funny responses, to the fat guy who tried to chase us down Euston Road while we cackled like witches. We were probably a complete pain, but it was always a lot of fun.

I also remember the frisbee summer. Meltingly hot days, when Ralph and I played frisbee in the street outside the club, trying out new tricks and then retiring to the flat roof for music and beer.

The flat roof of the club was a real boon. From this vantage point you had a clear view across the Euston area and could sunbathe, party, or flirt with the girls from the YWCA all day long. A few of the guys brought up massive speakers, which were attached through the skylight to an 'amped-up' record player in the room below. We had great parties up there - until the night that the police were called.

A normal club party was under way at about eight o'clock one Friday evening. The YWCA girls were there and the drink was flowing. The warden from our place was turning a blind eye to our fun and the beady orbs of the YWCA warden had not clocked our behaviour. Everyone was having fun and the laughs abounded, until Crazy Pete, desperate for a pee and too lazy to go down to the toilets, relieved himself over the edge of the roof. We might have got away with it, if he had not scored a direct hit on some returning theatregoers, who just happened to be in the wrong place at the wrong time.

The furious and pee-soaked passers-by started screaming about calling the police, so we had to quickly dismantle the party and put away the sound gear. The police duly arrived and found nothing more than a few empty beer cans on the roof, but, from then on, the warden stopped turning a blind eye and full-scale roof parties stopped being possible.

I remember Ralph and I had a go at Crazy Pete, who looked sheepish, but really didn't have the intelligence to see what the problem was.

Roof parties were over for that year, but Ralph and I found plenty of other open-air concerts to amuse us during that hot summer of fun.

After Thomas, he was probably my closest buddy in our gang of six.

CHAPTER XLVII

Shane the Repressed

When I met Ralph, his best friend in the club was Shane.

Shane was a strange and complex boy. He was five foot nine, running to fat, with sallow, acne-marked features and unkempt hair. He had the mannerism of always flicking his hair away from his face, which seemed to suit him better than getting the unruly mop cut. He was a chain-smoker, who I doubt could have lasted into his forties if he continued with his habit to the extremes that he used to practice when I knew him. Shane used to amaze me by not only smoking between courses, but by pausing to light up during some courses in a meal.

Shane was in London studying to be an architect, having spent his preceding youth in London as a resident at a posh public school. Although he came from a family with money he didn't have that many friends in his higher-class circle, so had chosen the club for its opportunity to meet some new people. He introduced me to some fascinating rich guys during our acquaintance. They were people who lived in mansion houses in London, talked with a pound of plums in their mouths, and could speak on any subject without having anything concrete to say about any of them. Shane treated such people with disdain, even as he continued to count them as friends.

Shane was an intellectual and I enjoyed talking to him about politics and social issues. I learned most of what I knew about international issues from him at this time.

Shane's father was a retired English gentleman, living in Spain in a luxury house, complete with butler and servants. Although he had lived for many years at this location, while he fought an international court case over the seizure of his string of hotels somewhere, he never even learned to speak Spanish. Shane used to deride his father for this, and also his sister, who apparently was incensed by their Spanish servants' seeming inability to master the English language.

Shane educated me in Spanish politics, although we never agreed on the value of Franco's dictatorship versus an independent and democratic Spain.

I met Shane when I met Ralph, and, although he was never as diligent in his pursuit of fun as we were, he was always a part of our small crowd.

Shane was never really comfortable in the big club crowd. He would tag along, drinking with the rest of the gang, but he was much more subdued than when he was in a small group or in a one-to-one situation. It was a pity, as Shane had a remarkable wit. He could caricature any situation and painted humorous and vivid pictures with his dialogue. Most often his wit was in the nature of black humour, but I loved to hear him talk.

One of the closest one-to-ones I remember with him was the night that he and I picked up a couple of girls from the YWCA. We took them back to my shared room and, as was the custom at the time, I left a note on the door for my room-mates, to the effect that they would have to seek an alternative bed for the night. After the musical preliminaries, the lights were doused and we settled in for a night of hanky-panky in beds at each end of the room. I was having some fun with my girl, when I heard, 'Don't worry, Shane,' as Shane fairly flew out of the bed he was sharing with his one-night love and headed towards the door.

'What's up, Shane? Shane? Shane!'

Shane never answered my query, as the door slammed behind him. Leaving my disgruntled love, I got out of bed, pulled on some jocks and headed out to see what was wrong. I found Shane in the toilets closest to my room, hands on the sink, head bowed, and leaning against the mirror on the wall.

'What's up, mate?' I asked.

Shane looked up with a face full of misery. His eyes were red as if he had been crying and his face was a pasty white colour.

'I couldn't do it, Les.'

'What's wrong, Shane? Do what?'

I was 17 years old. Being able to have sex was only a matter of having a woman to have sex with. I had never imagined or encountered the possibility that it got any more complex than that.

Shane looked at me and blurted out, 'I couldn't do it, Les! I couldn't seem to get it up, mate.'

'Maybe you don't fancy her, mate - wanna swap?'

It all seemed pretty simple to me. Shane didn't fancy his; I wasn't fussed one way or another about mine; these girls from the YWCA were unlikely to care either way - no problem.

Shane smiled back at me.

'It's OK, Les; I'll just go back and take her up to my room. Maybe I'm a bit shy.'

'No problem, mate.'

...And that was that.

It was only much later, and after I had left the club, that I heard through Ralph that Shane had turned out to be gay. Living in a testosterone-charged adolescent teenage environment, he had suppressed his feelings and tried to fit in with gang. The poor guy must have been completely miserable, lying to himself and others about his sexuality and entering into temporary (and most probably inconsequential) relationships with girls, to keep up his masculine front.

It is a pity. I have never been homophobic and wouldn't have cared about his sexuality either way. He could at least have had one friend in whom he could have confided.

Maybe even three friends. Ralph was fairly open-minded, and I doubt if Crazy Pete harboured sexuality prejudices.

But poor Shane, from our gang of six, never gave himself the chance to find that kind of emotional freedom.

I wonder if he has found his freedom even now?

CHAPTER XLVIII

Crazy Pete

Pete earned his nickname with his heart and his soul. The first time that I saw him, he was sitting in the entrance hallway of the club. He had just arrived and was debating with Garry, a Yorkshire boy, about how hard his head was. Thinking this amusing, and being reminded of Woody, I stopped to watch.

As the debate progressed, the Yorkshire boy suggested that Pete prove his theory, by sitting in a chair while being bombarded on the head by the ornamental wooden blocks that adorned the sideboard in the lounge.

Pete agreed!

I was completely bemused; as - it seemed - was Mr Yorkshire when Crazy Pete agreed to this test. The only proviso he stipulated was that he got to keep his Sherlock-Holmes-type hat on, as the side flaps would protect his ears. This could only end in tears, but I sat on a facing seat and relaxed, waiting to enjoy the show. Other boys stood or sat around also awaiting the coming comedy act. Pete, lounging in a chair, with his stupid hat on, shared a wide-mouthed grin with us all, obviously enjoying the attention.

Thwack.

The first wooden missile caught Crazy Pete square on the forehead. Pete continued to grin.

Thwack.

The second missile, launched by our Yorkshire boy, who obviously had had some passing fling with cricket, caught Pete a glancing blow to the side of the head. Pete continued to grin.

Smack.

The third block - by far the most viciously thrown missile yet - caught Pete full in the face. It was an inevitable consequence of their stupid game.

Pete leaped out of his seat, and all around the silent onlookers expected some kind of violent retribution. Pete was a lanky six foot three in his stockinged feet and his antagonist was a mere five foot ten. The latter player looked to be the more aggressive, however, and we all wondered how this would turn out.

Crazy Pete surprised us.

'Now it's yer turn, mate,' he discharged in his Aberdonian accent, sporting his biggest, gap-toothed grin.

'You must be fucking mental. I'm not letting you throw anything at me.'

'Hey, but you had your turn - I'm having mine,' said Crazy Pete, and he moved towards the stocky wee Yorkshire boy. I could see the big lanky git getting his teeth knocked out completely as Garry squared his tough little shoulders in readiness for a fight.

'Enough! You've had a laugh, Garry; just let it go.' I intervened. 'Come here, mate. Have you just arrived?' Pete looked at me and grinned a 'yes'. 'OK, I'll take you to get settled in - leave it, Garry!' - and Garry subsided. By this time I had been at the club a while and my place in the pecking order was well established.

Meek as a lamb and still sporting his stupid grin, Crazy Pete followed me up to meet the warden and carry out his registration.

With his stupid big watery eyes and his crazy grin, Pete always reminded me of a rescued puppy. From that day onwards he followed me around, always ready to fetch a stick and always grateful to be included in anything we were doing.

When we arrived in the warden's office, Crazy Pete paid his deposit and was registered. His room assignment was the spare bed in my room!

Crazy Pete was going to be my room-mate - groan.

Ah, well; at least it wouldn't be dull, and from that day onwards Pete joined our little sub-clan.

CHAPTER XLIX

The Cally Clan

Bill, the last of our six, hated Pete. Crazy Pete was the antithesis of Bill. While Bill was full of phoney bravado, made-up stories and projected testosterone, Crazy Pete's harmless, non-pretentious and jovial manner always seemed to drive Bill wild.

'Why does that prat have tae tag along with us, Les? He's a mental case.'

'I like him.'

'I know, Les, but...'

The other members of our troop also found Crazy Pete highly amusing, so Bill had to put up with it or find another sub-group to hang out in. Eventually he opted for the latter and none of us really missed him.

He wasn't so tough, either. I remember that when we had a ruck in the students' union, Bill was the last person to enter the fray and the first to run when the authorities evicted us.

I don't know why we ever let him hang out with us.

++++++++

That was my wee club sub-clan. We were very different people, but we were together as mates in a city of vast opportunities for fun and wide pitfalls full of danger.

I'm glad that I met them.

Apart from Thomas, who I know has a wife and four kids now, works for a shipping company in his home town in Norway and lives in a beautiful wooden house with a view of the fjord, I have no idea what happened to the rest.

I lost track of Crazy Pete when he got thrown out of the club because he got caught in bed with the ugliest Spanish maid we had at the time. He immediately went back home to Aberdeen.

I'd conjecture that Ralph is probably somewhere in Dorset, with a wife and two point five children, living a conventionally middle-class life. Ralph was just having his break. I can't imagine that he would ignore conformity for long.

Bill is probably a policeman. It would suit him to be able to wander around in a uniform, acting hard and having the backing of his position to use for intimidating youngsters on the streets.

Shane? Well, I can't even imagine what he would be doing. I reckon he would have passed his architectural exams. I wonder if his father ever won his international court case and bequeathed Shane his riches? With the hatred between him and his sister, he is probably fighting an international court case with her over the spoils.

Who knows?

It was a brief, secure and wonderful time I shared with that bunch.

I hope that they all have happy lives somewhere.

CHAPTER L

Changing Places

After my ticketing fiasco on the building site, I returned to headquarters.

I was given no more than a mild dressing down for my failure. Nobody really had any empathy at headquarters for the rough site-workers, and so it was more or less written off as, 'What can you expect when you deal with these types of people?'

'At least,' said the personnel officer, 'you know our business quite a bit better now.'

She had obviously never been on one of our sites. As far as the business went I wasn't sure that I knew anything more than how to take muck away. I had learned quite a lot about human nature, however, through association with the sharp wit and always-scheming work crews I'd been around. I didn't mention this at my personnel interview, though, as I was sure that this would not be greeted as good news.

'We think you would be happiest in the contracts department next, Les,' said the personnel lady. 'You can learn how we get our jobs and how carefully each one needs to be priced. Don't worry too much about the site incident. How is the day release going anyway..?'

Filing!

It was well known amongst us juniors that the contracts office had more filing per square foot than any other department in the company, and that it was the most strict about how each piece of paper was filed. The contracts office and the drawing office were one big open-plan space and, between the two of them, they must have utilized the pulp from a small forest each year.

I was back to filing again.

Now that I think of it, that was the department where Roger had worked before his filing breakdown and the incident in the loos.

Bloody filing again!

New place, same face, but I'd just have to bide my time. Not long now till my exams and I could think about moving on.

++++++++

Day release was a doddle. It turned out that I had a penchant for business administration, at least as far as I was being taught on this elementary course.

Systems, organization, a bit of finance, communications skills, etc.; they were less of a challenge than O level maths or English at school. Some of the intake seemed to struggle, though. I was in with a hotchpotch of boys and girls around my age, with the occasional more mature student thrown in. Some of this lot didn't appear to have any logical, organizational or problem-solving ability at all. Unfortunately, the pace of the course was drawn up around the weakest links and, as such, time crawled along at a snail's pace. I think that several others and I could have completed the course over four weeks, by doing a bit of extra work in our spare time. As it worked out, I had to stay the whole course and had nothing to do in my spare time, having always finished any assignments handed out during that one day a week at college.

I wanted to learn more, and so I joined a library and read up to a greater depth on the subjects that interested me. I was always pissing off one particular lecturer in economics. Having gone on a couple of levels with my extra-curricula reading, I kept asking him questions that he struggled to answer. He eventually fell back on: 'It's outside this syllabus, Les. If you want to know more, you'll just have to study it in your own time. I need to concentrate on those poor mortals who want to pass this course.'

And that was that. Not much different from school, really.

My classmates were pretty nondescript and, apart from dating a couple of the girls, I didn't pay them much attention, or form any friendships. It was one day a week and not really that sort of course. I can't remember any group activities being proffered by this lot.

Boring, boring, boring.

If this was education, then I knew that I had to take it to a higher level. Combined with my other four days of filing in the contracts department, I was sure to go insane if I didn't find something more stimulating to get my teeth into.

Thank goodness for the club and our antics!

Although, it wasn't all roses...

CHAPTER LI

Insecurity breeds...

The drinking was getting heavier, as were the social experiences of some of my Caledonian peers. There were some sad cases and some disturbing incidents unfolding, which were to mark the end of a halcyon era at the club. A couple of the worst incidents spring to mind.

++++++++

Jerry was a gambler. He was another young Scottish boy from Glasgow, recruited at 16, who worked for a bank in the city. Jerry worked in banking, but he lived for gambling. You could always find Jerry down at a bookmaker's shop each lunchtime, every evening and all day on Saturday.

This was a 17-year-old boy, rakish in appearance, with shoulder-length hair and a constantly worried expression on his thin-shaped face. Jerry always had a haunted look about him. On the few occasions that I talked to him, his eyes would dart about and he would shuffle like a cat on a hot grid. He would always have a tip for the day over breakfast, and many of the boys would give him a quid to put on for them when he was - inevitably - in the bookie's at lunchtime.

McMurty was a helper at the club. He was an ex-banker, who had retired from a high position to spend his time helping the warden at our place, and he was working with homeless youths around the city in general. I never liked McMurty. He seemed a bit too slimy for my taste, and I got a creepy feeling whenever he was about. I don't think the warden liked him very much either, and his wife definitely hated him, but McMurty was connected within the church hierarchy and so was allowed to continue living and working at our place.

Jerry didn't have the time of day for McMurty. He was just as vocal as the rest of us in his derision of the rich weirdo.

'That bastard's a slimy fucker,' was one of the less derisive comments I had heard him make. That's why I was amazed when Teej told me one morning that Jerry, who was his room-mate, had spent the night in McMurty's room, talking about his problems.

'What problems?' I asked.

'He's spent a lot of money on the horses lately, Les,' said Teej. 'I think he might have taken a bit from the bank...'

Shit! Poor Jerry was in deep trouble if that was the case. I don't know if you are classified as a Great Train Robber for stealing as an employee, but it was definitely bank robbery. I wondered how the boy was going to get out of this one.

Later on, after breakfast, I was just about to leave for work when a suited-up Jerry came fast-walking along the corridor towards the door.

'Hey - Jerry! Are you OK, mate?' I walked up to him and he had to stop. 'Teej told me about your problem - what are you gonna do?'

Jerry looked terrible: he was as white as a sheet and had obviously been crying a lot. As he looked up at me, the tears started spilling out again, and he said, 'It's sorted, Les,' in barely a whisper.

'What happened then, mate? How did it get sorted?'

'Jerry...'

The slimy voice of McMurty drifted towards our ears. I looked down the corridor, and saw him standing in dressing gown and slippers at the bottom of the stairs.

'I'm sorry, Les,' said the broken voice of wee Jerry. 'I've got to go.' And he was out of the door like a shot, sparing neither me nor the slimy McMurty a second glance.

I was getting a pretty bad smell from this and I stood and glared at McMurty, letting him know that, if my suspicions were confirmed, he was a dead man. McMurty tried a smile, failed, and sheepishly went back up the stairs.

I never got a chance to have any of my suspicions verified. That night, Jerry was nowhere to be seen. By the next night, when I returned from work, Jerry had gone. I got a bit of the story from Teej when he came down to dinner.

Apparently, Jerry had stayed away the previous night. Teej was a bit worried about him and had gone to McMurty to see if he knew what the problem was. McMurty had been less than forthcoming, but, when Teej pressed him and said that he'd have to let the warden know, the slime-ball had told him that he had used his contacts in the bank to square things away for Jerry and had paid off his debt himself. As a result, the bank was not taking the matter any further. If it had been sorted, then Teej thought he'd better let it drop.

Teej had gone to work that day and, when he returned, he had found Jerry in their room, packing up his stuff. When Teej asked him what had happened with McMurty, a shaken and shaking Jerry had confirmed that the weirdo had fixed it up with the bank, so that he would not be charged.

'Dae ye have to pay him back, Jerry?' Teej had asked.

Jerry had broken down in tears at this point and had eventually mumbled, 'I've paid the bastard back,' as he stuffed the last of his things into his suitcase. He wouldn't answer any more of his pal's questions and refused the offer of a farewell drink with the lads. With no further discussion, he grabbed his stuff, left the club and was on the next available train home to Glasgow.

When I heard this story, I felt that my worst fears were confirmed. The boys I shared this knowledge with agreed, but they also agreed that, without any solid evidence, we could do nothing about McMurty. We would all keep an eye on the bastard, though, and if he put a foot wrong...

He was too smart for that. McMurty shifted most of his time out of the club and solidly into 'helping homeless kids', and we saw less and less of him. The incident had drawn a dark shadow across life in the club, though. As word spread, nobody really felt the same innocent security that they had previously enjoyed. I wish we could have nailed that evil bastard McMurty!

If you're out there, Jerry, it's never too late to turn him in...

CHAPTER LII

End of an Era

The club was beginning to pale. The incident I have described was one of the worst, but the general attitude in the place was also changing. Some of the older lads had moved out and some of the new intake spelled trouble, in various forms.

There was the spate of thefts that we were sure was wholly attributable to one new boy at the club, though it was impossible to prove. Theft was hitherto unheard-of. We had always left our stuff lying about with impunity, and the boys' 'code' protected us against stealing from one another. These thefts stole another bit of the heart of the club.

We now housed drug-takers, thieves and would-be hard men. The number of guys on our nights out was becoming smaller and smaller. Life was becoming a bit jaded.

All of the 'old hands' were talking about getting flats of our own, and a few had already started to team up and look around. I was in the same frame of mind. Having already quit my job to take a new job as a trainee foreign exchange cashier, I was ready for even bigger changes.

It was a sad time, as I look back. The club had been my home and my cocoon as I transitioned into life in London. I had made friends, had laughs, learned a lot and buried a few demons. Although I had been away from Cawder for some time, I think that leaving the club was the first time that I actually felt as if I was leaving a home.

I teamed up with Teej, Timmy and Cheater. We found a flat in Burnt Oak and, with a few drunken farewells to the rest of the lads and promises to keep in touch, we moved into a new era of London living. We were all excited, dreaming about parties, more freedom and lots more girls.

We never thought about: losing our maid service or our cook; paying a hefty rent; paying all of our other bills; transportation to work; and, for the first time, living in close proximity with a only a few other guys - and their habits!

It wouldn't prove to be the Utopian existence our idealistic young minds had imagined.

CHAPTER LIII

Moving up a Gear

With a new job and new place to live, I was eager to experience the life of living in a London flat to the full.

My choice of housemates had been made mostly by default. My gang of six had now split up, and most were back in their native cities. Shane had recently moved into a flat of his own. Crazy Pete was back in Aberdeen. Bill was back in Glasgow. Thomas was carrying out his national service in Norway. Ralph was staying put - but Ralph always needed some security, and so I hadn't expected him to join us.

Teej had been a mate from day one and I was happy to share with him. Timmy had replaced Jerry as his room-mate at the club and the wee Welsh guy was OK as far as I was concerned. Cheater was new and, in fact, although he found the house for us, we only accepted him to make up the numbers. Cheater lived up to his name eventually, and he caused the problem that ended our temporary party.

The house in Burnt Oak marked the start of a new phase in my life. Away from the institutional life of the club, I was finally out on my own, albeit with a few friends, and was starting a new level of independence. I guess I should have had the maturity to handle such a change, even though I was only 17 years old. I had been out on my own for a long time and had gone through many different stages on my journey. I knew that I still had a lot to learn, though.

My new job was not turning out to be of much interest. I had been put through a crash course in bookkeeping and had been promised sponsorship to become an accountant. Apart from the education, the bulk of my work as a trainee foreign exchange cashier was pretty boring.

There were a few interesting points, such as the first time I took a trolley-load of cash down to the vaults and saw the wall-to-wall stacks of foreign exchange banknotes. I remember sneaking down on my own on some pretext or other and bathing in notes, as if I was the richest guy in the world. It was a fleeting thrill, as my first month's salary cheque quickly brought me back down to earth.

On the whole, it was just daily boredom. It was no fun handing out exchanged cash to lucky people who were going to go on holiday, while you were destined to battle traffic every morning, circle continuously for a parking space, and then stand all day in a suit feeling miserable.

I wrote my new career off as a failure and I began hatching plans to get myself out of this working environment as soon as possible.

I had been involved in the massive computerization project that the company had recently undertaken. No more would we have to rely on ledgers to archive our historical records - a revolution was happening and we would have all our information on decks of paper cards, which could be processed by computers. I was pretty interested in this development and, as nobody else seemed to be volunteering from our department, I put my hand up and jumped on the project bandwagon.

My plan was: to get some practical knowledge in this new field of computer science; to try and gain some computer-related qualifications; then to try and find a company to work in that specialized in this stuff. I could see computers as the future and felt, even then, that if I could just get started then I could eventually start a computer business of my own. Heady stuff, but I was ambitious.

Meanwhile, at the shared pad in Burnt Oak, things were going pretty badly. Cheater was not only stealing from us bits and pieces of change left around; Teej had discovered that the rent money we had given him last month had not been handed over to the landlord, who now wanted us out. I came home one night to find out that there had been a confrontation between Timmy, Teej and Cheater, and that Cheater had taken off to stay with a cousin who was living somewhere else in London.

It was the last straw for Teej, who planned to head back to Scotland. Timmy and I decided to get our own places. We were both fed up with sharing, even though we planned to stay in the smoke for a while longer. We all agreed that we would take care of Cheater when he returned!

Days passed and he didn't return. We knew we had only a month before the landlord evicted us, so we planned a party, inviting some of the old club crew, some of the YWCA ladies, and some girls we knew from work. It would be our farewell to Burnt Oak. The party would take place the following Friday.

Back at work, things were not going well, either. My boss was getting fairly cheesed off about the amount of time I was spending on the computerization project. I was actually spending 99% of my time on it, as it fitted right into my personal goals. I was only supposed to be spending 20% of my time on it. We had a furious argument one day, and I told him to stuff his job and walked out.

Not smart.

I was about to be homeless, and now I was jobless too.

Things had definitely been better.

This reckless decision was to mark the start of another very unstable part of my life, and was to reintroduce me to demons that I thought I had left far, far behind.

CHAPTER LIV

First Blood

Friday night, and our farewell to Burnt Oak party had come around. Still no sign of Cheater, but we had split up his record collection between us and had thrown out his clothes in revenge for the theft, so we were not feeling too bad about his disappearance any more.

I remember that I cooked some fruit pies. This was a habit of mine that I never lost. Whenever I feel as though I need to cast my troubles behind me, or whenever I feel as though I need to relax and have a treat - I bake some fruit pies. There's something about the smell of baking that allows me to transcend my everyday problems. Stupid, but it's effective in my case. Although I was looking forward to the party, I needed to banish my blossoming troubles of where to live and where to work, so I sank into pastry heaven and baked a couple of pies for our guests.

All three of us chipped in for a mountain of alcoholic beverages, some snacks and a hopeful amount of condoms. We dressed up in our best party gear, closed the curtains, lit candles and incense, and cranked up the music. Our guests started to arrive early at about 7:30 p.m.

After the usual slow start, it turned into a great party. Almost all of our mates turned up, bringing more booze, strange people that they'd bumped into, and some especially tasty young ladies. It didn't take long before the party had turned into a drunken orgy, with couples in various stages of heavy petting all over the living room, kitchen and stairs, and even in the garden, while the more advanced stages of passion were enacted in the four bedrooms upstairs. I remember having to evict three couples from my room at about 2:00 in the morning, so that I could settle in for the night with my own temporary squeeze. This was what London living was all about!

We rocked till we dropped, but the biggest laugh came the next morning.

I arose at about 09:30 to go to the toilet. I stepped over a naked couple on the floor, who must have sneaked in when we fell asleep and who were only just covered up by the bloke's ex-Army greatcoat. Pulling up my tight denim flares, I headed out to the toilet, leaving the soft snores of my temporary soulmate behind.

I stepped into the hall, to be greeted by a broadly smiling Timmy.

'Morning, Les.'

'Morning, Tim. Great party - eh?'

'Brilliant, Les - but you haven't seen the best bit yet!'

I perked up, thinking that the wrecking crew must have left us enough booze to continue the party for the rest of the week.

'Yeah? What's that, then, Timmy?'

'Just look into Teej's room, Les. He lost his virginity last night. Ha, ha, ha, ha, ha!' and Timmy headed down to the kitchen, hardly able to walk for laughing.

I had seen Teej sneaking off with a wench that I had been chatting to earlier. She was someone's friend from the bank and she was pretty nice. I hadn't followed up, as I was too busy drinking at that stage, but good old Teej had obviously scored - well done, the wee man! I hadn't even known that Teej had been a virgin until then. Male virginity was something lied about with a passion. Nobody who was in that unhealthy predicament would ever dream of facing the embarrassment of letting his mates know about it. Teej and Tim must have been pretty close for them to discuss such a state of affairs. As I made for his room, I could only imagine that the wee man must feel like a superstar this morning.

I crept across the hall to take a peek at the situation. I cracked open his door and stuck my head inside.

'Come on in, Les - she's gone to the bathroom for a shower, mate.'

Teej was lying in bed in near-darkness, pillows stacked behind his head, and he was grinning from ear to ear. He did indeed look as if he had just won a few million quid. I grinned back, and then squinted. There was something smeared all over his upper body, his arms, his visible hand and his face - but he seemed blissfully unaware.

'What's up, Les? Tim just gave me a weird look when he came in, tae. What the matter?'

'What's that stuff all over you, Teej?'

'What stuff?' and he slipped out of the bed and pulled open the curtains.

'Bloody hell!'

Literally true - Teej was literally covered in blood smears.

As the daylight brightened up the room, I could see that his bed was also covered in blood and he had smears of the stuff all over, from his face to around, and below, his groin. I laughed myself silly.

'Bloody hell, Teej! She must have had her period, mate.'

Poor Teej looked completely sick and disgusted. The poor girl must have woken up, discovered her dilemma, and beaten a hasty retreat to the bathroom to cover her embarrassment. I sobered up and straightened my face, as the poor almost-virgin boy was obviously having a hard time with the state of play.

'No problem, Teej; it happens, man.'

Just then, a very sheepish-looking girl emerged from the bathroom, holding a towel over most of her bits. I stepped aside, nodded to Teej and left them to it. I could hear the, 'I'm so sorry, Teej,' and a, 'Bloody hell!' as I made my way into the bathroom myself.

Safely ensconced in the bathroom, I was able to give full vent and release the humour that was threatening to choke me. My sides almost split as I could still see the look on Teej's face in my mind's eye, when he discovered that he had almost bathed in his girlfriend's period blood. Just his luck! First time, his girl has her period, and it's as heavy as anything I'd ever seen. I laughed myself silly.

Teej, after saying goodbye to his first love and after showering and changing the sheets, disappeared back to bed for some recovery sleep. He didn't show his face until around teatime that night, by which time we had finally rid our bomb-site of all the party guests. When he eventually came downstairs, Timmy took one look at his face and burst out laughing. I waited half a beat, not wanting to be too insensitive, but, when Teej burst out laughing as well, we were soon all rolling about, holding our sides.

'You're certainly blooded now, Teej,' quipped Timmy.

More laughter followed.

Teej didn't care. He had finally lost his virginity and that was all that counted. I bet he'd be a bit more cautious for his next liaison - though actually, knowing Teej, he probably wouldn't have.

'Ah well, boys. I suppose we'd better have a few beers and clean up this pit,' I said when the laughter had subsided to a trickle.

We started the house recovery.

Teej kept getting stick from us as we cleaned up. His only reply was a broad smile, and, 'At least I'm not a virgin any more.'

When we'd finished up and were ready to go down the pub, Timmy - who had got laid himself, but who had been doubly thrilled watching the other two couples, one of which was beside him in his king-sized bed and didn't seem to mind our Tim joining in by touching up the other girl's breasts during their coupling - summed it all up: 'Fucking great party - eh, boys?'

'Bloody marvellous,' said Teej, and we chortled our way down to the pub from the last event we were ever to share together.

CHAPTER LV

Moving on again

From Burnt Oak, I moved on.

Money was my major priority, so I found an agency that supplied me with temporary work and at a much higher pay rate than I had previously dreamed of. I was temping in offices around London as a clerk. At this time there was always a shortage of clerical workers, so getting jobs was easy. I also managed to wangle a night job at a record company, boxing albums to be dispatched to record shops. I was earning loads of money, and was coping with the strain by sleeping at the factory most of the nights that I should have been packing and by sleeping at home between finishing my office work and starting my packing work. On Sundays I slept all day.

There were so many people working at the record company that after I had clocked in I was almost invisible. I found a place to hide in the warehouse, and somehow I managed to get away with sleeping most of the night away.

I had saved a fair bit of money by this time, so I had enough cash for a deposit on a new place. With two salaries coming in I felt pretty rich, and decided that it was time for me to break into the property market. I found a wee house, in a less salubrious part of town than my rented place, and, after getting help from an old club-mate who worked at the bank, managed to get a loan and purchase my first place. I was on my way!

Or so I thought at the time. It was to be a short-lived journey.

I guess it was inevitable that I couldn't keep up such a pace - especially since I was drinking and clubbing pretty heavily on Friday and Saturday nights. The lads I knew were all partying heavily and they were starting to look like pretty old teenagers. Booze was taking its toll in the form of expanding beer guts, drawn and acned complexions, tired masks around the eyes and prematurely creased foreheads. I had only to look in the mirror to see my own face reflecting the same ravages of merriment.

The crunch came only a couple of months into my 'burning-the-candle-at-both-ends' routine.

One evening, I was slumbering in my usual spot on top of a stack of boxes of records, high up on the storage racks in the warehouse. The boss had taken to doing little patrols around the warehouse, as there had been a heavy spate of pilfering and he was trying to catch the thief. Thieves would have been a better description, though. Almost all the employees had fantastic record and tape collections from products lifted from the warehouse and smuggled out, taped to their bodies. At this particular time, however, it was coming up for Christmas and the lads must have gone a bit crazy trying to store up Christmas presents. The management were not prepared to ignore this spate and had finally sent out a memo to the night staff to tighten up security - or else!

The night my scam was discovered I was deep in slumber and was so tired that I was snoring like a banshee. The boss heard my snorts as he patrolled the warehouse and, after an easy bit of investigation, he found me and aroused me from my slumbers.

'What the fuck do you think you're doing, son? We don't pay you good money to sleep on the job. Get down out of there and go and clock out. You're no fucking good to me!'

I duly clocked out and, when I returned the next night, it was to pick up an envelope with a note in it saying that I had been fired.

Crap!

Here I was, struggling to eat and make payments on my house - and I had just lost my highest-paying job. I tried to make up the deficit by doing bar work in various pubs around the West End, but I discovered that I didn't have an aptitude for the work. This was summed up when, just before 'letting me go', my last bar manager said: 'Les, you do know that we are here to help the punters get drunk? Not to beat them up and throw them out when they are drunk! I think you'd better find another type of work, son...'

I, a heavy drinker myself, had discovered that I didn't like being sober in the company of drunks! My attitude was always one of 'behave or be evicted', and with my fairly short temper I was emptying the pub faster than it could make a profit. He was right; I needed to find some work better suited to my temperament.

Things went from bad to worse.

As I was no longer earning as much, I stopped hanging out with my drinking crew, and eventually they started to fade out of my life. Our post-Cally-club social scene was built around meeting up in town and getting drunk. As a non-participant I hardly saw anyone and started to get a bit lonely. Feeling a bit down and sorry for myself, I decided I needed a break. I hadn't been home to Scotland for a while, so, in my depressed state, Glasgow seemed a good place to be. I arranged a leave of absence through the agency employing me and headed 'up north'.

I slept the train journey away, enjoying the peaceful rhythm of the coach and the temporary freedom from my struggle to make ends meet. I arrived in Glasgow Central station, refreshed and ready to have an easy, laid-back holiday. The only people I knew in Glasgow were, of course, my old hippy friends and the thugs I grew up with on the estate. I didn't fancy hanging out with the thugs, so I looked up some old hippy mates and stayed with them. There followed a week of getting stoned, getting drunk and generally feeling good to be back home. While I was wasted, I got talking to Jamie about the state of play in my life.

'You know, Les - if I was you, I'd sell up my house and take off round Europe. It's a cool trip, man; you can crash with freaks in France and Holland an' that, man. If you need bread, ye can do some berry-pickin' or bar work. I'd do it man - it'll get yer head together.'

It all seemed perfectly reasonable to me. When stoned out of your head listening to rock music with mates, mortgages and survival are worlds away from your reality. Besides, I deserved a break. I determined that, as soon as I got back to London, I would get my shit together and take off for a while.

After two weeks of lazing around I returned to my now lonely life in London; but I wasn't alone for long. Thompson, Jamie, Mad Alex, Scott and Tommy all decided to follow me down. They wanted to get out of Glasgow, and what better than to crash with their mate Les. I didn't mind; I had stopped paying my loan and had put my place up for sale. Who cared if the guys came down and trashed the place? It would probably be repossessed anyway.

I learned to care.

After several weeks of: them eating me out of house and home; their filthy living habits; the constant fog of hash around the place; and the all-night music, which was making it impossible for me to stay awake at work, I made them find somewhere else to live.

'No problem, Les, man,' said Jamie. 'We were thinking of gettin' a squat together in north London anyway. Wee Joe's up there wi' his burd, Kirsty. He says it's a doddle; you just take over one of these big empty hooses and nobody can throw ye oot. You should try it yersel', man, when ye get rid of this place.'

Still friends, my social nightmares departed soon afterwards to live in a squat in north London. I made plans to travel while my house was being viewed by young couples who were just starting out. It didn't take long - only a matter of weeks and I'd sold up. I even got a little change in my pocket from the sale, into the bargain. Duty done, I dumped my few belongings at the lads' new squat, got myself my first ever passport, and set off to 'do' Europe.

This was going to be great!

CHAPTER LVI

Pan-European Hippydom

It was my first taste of overseas travel. Unlike today, in the early 1970s working-class kids had not been given the opportunity to experience foreign parts as an annual two-week holiday with their parents. The furthest I had ever been on holiday with my parents had been Morecambe Bay - and that had been a major expedition.

I had a few European contact names and addresses: a girl I had briefly dated in London, who had returned home to France; some Dutch guys I'd met who lived in Amsterdam; Thomas in Norway; and Shane down in Spain. I opted for France first, as this was the easiest hitch and I'd quite fancied wee Michelle.

Michelle lived in Toulouse.

I hitched to Dover, got a ferry across to Calais, and - after an uncomfortable night sleeping rough at a bus station - made it to the highway and started to thumb it down south. It was a great adventure. I had only my pretty awful school French to communicate with. I got some great lifts, though, and had some laughs with the drivers, many of whom fed me along the way. The French drivers were highly amused by my pigeon-French, but were always pleased that I tried.

Eventually I arrived in Toulouse.

This was a paradise to me. After a communications struggle, I got directions and eventually a lift out to Michelle's place. I discovered that she lived on a farm with her parents. Although these folks did not seem too pleased to meet me at first, Michelle was overjoyed to meet one of her contacts from London. I was housed in a spare room, vacated by Michelle's brother, who had grown up and was now working in Paris. I quickly settled in and tried to make myself useful around the place. I did some odd jobs around the dairy farm, and in return enjoyed many lazy days with my old girlfriend and some of the best home-cooked meals of my life.

This was a month of heaven.

I had never spent any time in the country before now and I found that I really liked the easy pace of French country life. Michelle had a social scene of sophisticated (by my prior standards) hippies, and, although she and I never renewed our romantic liaison (she had a boyfriend), I had some fun times with some of the French girls she introduced me to. I discovered that it's great being a new face in a country environment!

I had such a good time with one of her girlfriends, called Louise, that this lovely lady decided to join me on the next leg of my trek, which was to visit Shane's place down in Spain. Louise spoke fluent Spanish, as well as pretty good English and - of course - French. I was in seventh heaven. With a lovely linguist in tow, my trip to Spain would be a doddle!

While helping around the farm I had earned a few francs from Michelle's dad, who insisted that I take the money, even though he had been feeding and accommodating me. He seemed to like me a bit more after a month when I'd helped him out around the farm, and especially after the realization that I was quickly moving on! No disrespect, though - he was a nice guy.

Money in my pocket, good times under my belt and a pretty girl on my arm, I was ready to take the next stage of my first European adventure. This was turning out to be a great holiday. I had left my London troubles far behind and was feeling like a true free spirit for the first time in my life. I didn't believe that life could get any better than this.

Of course - it couldn't last.

Louise and I got on brilliantly until we arrived at Shane's place in

Spain, only to discover that Shane was still back in London. This meant that we had no place to live, and we were both pretty tired from the road. Louise didn't take well to sleeping rough all the time and, when we met some hippies who gave us a place to crash, Louise switched to a Spanish boy and I switched to an English girl called Victoria who was just hanging out down there.

It was OK living there at first, but, after a couple of weeks of getting stoned, getting tanned and not being able to communicate with anyone but Victoria, I started to get fed up. I was also rapidly running out of cash. I couldn't be bothered looking for work and so I supposed that I should head back to London and pick up the pieces of my life again. Typical of the hippy scene: when I told my love-in-Spain Victoria what I was thinking, she gave me a big kiss and went out for a walk. By that evening I was forgotten and Victoria was with Ricardo as if they had been soulmates forever.

I didn't bother to tell Louise about my plans. She and I rarely passed the time of day any more, and she had no doubt forgotten my name by that time anyway. I'd had a bit of a European adventure, and I was in a fairly relaxed frame of mind, so it was with no regrets at all that I packed up my rucksack, said goodbye to Spain and headed back to the smoke.

Unlike the easy hitch with Louise, my hitch-hike back to Calais was long and arduous. I had used up most of my money long before I reached the coast and was subsisting on handouts from generous drivers and the occasional bit of shoplifted food, but I was careful to keep enough to pay for my ferry crossing and a bit spare to be able to take the tube to the north London squat of my mates. I took a different route back and so I saw a bit more of Spain and France on the way home. That was interesting, but I was pretty glad, overall, when I finally looked out from the ferry and saw the white cliffs of Dover once again.

A short trip on mainland Europe, and I felt like a real world traveller! I might be back to the same old environment, and I knew that I'd be facing some harsh survival challenges, but for a while at least I had been out there.

CHAPTER LVII

Back to Squat

'Hey, it's Les, man! Hey, guys - it's Les.'

This was my greeting when I turned up on a late end-of-summer evening, at my friends' squat in north London. Mad Alex greeted me, joint hanging out of his mouth, looking every bit the greasy Hell's Angel that he had always been while I'd known him.

'Hey, Les,' he quipped as I entered the hallway, 'I suppose we'd better un-split your stuff, man. We thought you were away for good, man.'

Fuck! What little stuff I had was bound to be well distributed amongst this lot. I doubted if I'd even have a clean piece of clothing, never mind an unscratched record. I'd prise it all back out of them, though.

'Yeah, you'd fucking well better, Alex. I'm back for a good while, man.'

'No problem, man; no problem. I'll get the boys to put it all back together. Have a blast, man; you look like you need it.'

I looked around, gratefully sucking some refreshment into my lungs.

I'd been well impressed by the outside of their abode, which I first

278

saw when I made my way from the squat where I had left them, to go to France, over to this new place. Their old squat had been inhabited by some junkie types, but thankfully these guys had known where my crew were now living. They had cautioned me: 'Don't know if you want to go over there, man. These freaks are a bit crazy, like. We can put you onto some cooler places if you want, man.'

'No problem, mate - I'll just take the address. They're not so bad, man.'

Sounds like the crew had brought a wee bit of Glasgow down with them and were frightening the locals. Still, it was somewhere to stay, and I'd have a few familiar faces to talk to while I sorted out my life. I'd never squatted before, but my first impressions of their abode were encouraging.

The outside of the house was imposing. It was a big, detached Victorian-style house, with bay windows and a small lawn in the front, protected by a low stone-built wall. Walls, red-tiled roof and even the garden looked in good repair. All the windows had unbroken glass in them, as opposed to the boarded-up windows of the squat I had just come from. It probably wasn't too clean, but it looked pretty sound from where I was standing.

Inside, the house had eight high-ceilinged rooms, one of which was used as a living room. Five were used by the lads as bedrooms, leaving a choice of two rooms for me. All the rooms, with the exception of the unused dining room (which Mad Alex told me was the party room), had fireplaces. There was a lovely blaze going in the living-room fireplace as I entered.

'Hey - Les, man!' shouted Jamie as he sat cross-legged on the carpet by my stereo system, rolling a joint on one of my album covers. 'Good to see you, man; how was the trip?'

I ignored the hash burns on my album cover, threw down my rucksack and relaxed. I was back, I had a temporary home, and I could chill out until I got my act together. I spent the rest of the night: getting stoned; eating some soup that Jenny, Scott's wee girlfriend, had made; listening to my music; and recounting my adventures - with more than a few embellishments. It was a good night, and as we got more and more stoned the story of my adventures became more and more fantastic.

The crew were impressed.

That night, I picked one of the empty rooms to make my own, collected most of my belongings from the crew and settled in to live in the squat.

++++++++

I needed to earn a crust at this stage. I could have gone back to office temping, or, in such a climate of plenty, I could have found myself a permanent job. This was a boom time in London for work, when the available jobs far outweighed the city's manpower. Employment agencies were raking it in and people from all over the country were heading to London for work. The only catch people had was - accommodation. Accommodation was sparse in the city, and what accommodation there was could be pretty expensive.

I didn't have that worry, of course. I had a big house to live in and was not troubled by rent. It seemed that I wouldn't be troubled by electricity bills either, as Thompson, who had served about six months as an electrician in Glasgow, had managed to find the fuse that the electricity board removed when the previous owners left this place and had duly switched the power back on. We had full power, and no bills for us to ignore!

The lads had really landed on their feet.

The house was pretty amazing. It was a huge detached building, in a row of such buildings. Each of the houses had two big floors, and this one also had a fully converted attic. There were massive gardens at the back of the houses, all mature and all delivering up bounty in the form of fruit trees and berry bushes. Our garden even had a vegetable plot, the produce from which the lads had just about finished off before I arrived. It had also had a big garden shed. The lads told me that the shed had not been in very good condition, so they had used it for firewood. The remains were still littering the bottom of the garden. There were two bathrooms and a downstairs toilet, as well as a kitchen with the appliances still fitted and still fully functional.

The lads had also furnished their castle, and we had an array of assorted carpeting throughout - even in the attic!

What had happened was that a developer, who wanted to knock all the buildings down and use the massive acreage to build a modern housing estate, had purchased all the houses on this street, with the exception of two. He planned to build, then sell, these new houses for a massive profit. The two remaining tenants were fairly old and were reluctant to move, but this developer had been pressurizing them to sell up. He had been using dirty tricks, such as having some local lads make noise late at night in one of the empty houses next door to them. He had let the same lads dump rubbish against the fences adjacent to them. He also kept bothering them with visits and phone calls, trying to get them to move. He needed the whole street to complete his project.

As a result of the hatred that had grown up around the area for this developer, the last couple of residents in this street, the locals in the streets around us and even the local police were willing to approve of squatters on his property. So, when the lads moved in, the police followed the letter of the law and didn't try doing anything heavy to evict them. One of the two remaining property-owners in the street dropped by and suggested that the lads put a sign in the garden saying 'old furniture wanted'. It worked like a charm, and after a week the guys had second-hand furniture, beds, carpets, even blankets, towels and a couple of old TV sets.

They were set up.

The guys had stored all of the excess stuff in the attic. Jamie told me that they had to take the sign down after a couple of weeks, as they were getting so much stuff. Even after the sign came down, they had continued to find new offerings in front of the house for a few days. It was all stuff of pretty good quality, too. It just shows you that somebody's rubbish is another person's treasure! I foraged around the stuff left over from these generous donations and managed to set myself up in my room pretty comfortably.

All I needed now was some work.

The lads, of course, were not inclined to bother with anything as mundane as work. When they had settled in, they immediately signed on the unemployment register and were happily subsisting on government handouts, bolstered by regular petty shoplifting in town. One of their most popular scams for money was the 'returns game'. A couple of them would go out to the city and steal clothes from a big store. The next day, Jenny and Scott would put on their best and 'straightest' clothes and return the gear, saying that it was the wrong fit and requesting cash back. It worked most of the time. Sometimes the shopkeeper would not accept the goods back without a receipt and some of the time they had to make do with a credit note, which they could sell within the hippy community. Most of the time, though, this old scam harvested them sufficient cash for them to continue to party.

I wanted to work. It wasn't really a moral issue with me - it was a survival issue. I didn't want to get into the routine of just hanging about all day getting stoned, and I also wanted to build up my cash reserves again so that I had a few options in my life. The lads could live on their wits if they wanted to, but I was determined to get myself a job.

Around our location were a number of factories. I had never worked in a factory before, but I thought I'd give it a try - how difficult could it be, anyway? I went to the industrial estate nearest to us, and, at the very first factory I tried, they gave me a job. It didn't take more than a five-minute interview and the pay was pretty good for a broke and desperate teenager.

The work was mind-numbing, though.

It involved working at night, on a massive shop floor, using machines that did a variety of things to bits of metal. My particular machine bored square holes through small, round, piston-like pieces of shiny steel. There were also machines to bend pieces of metal, polish pieces of metal, or to cut different shapes out of metal with a variety of lengths and thicknesses. To this day I have no idea what the final product was. I neither saw nor cared to see the assembly portion of the factory, and no one in authority cared if I knew or understood the process anyway. It seemed that the only skill you had to have to be employed there was the skill of turning up each night. As there was no chance of anyone ever being promoted, the management team never saw any reason to induct us into the ways of the company. We were the lowest level, the cannon fodder, and all we had to do was turn up and press levers.

My co-workers were a strange bunch. Some of them were students, using this torturous experience to pay their way through school, but most were there because this was the best type of work they could get. I felt very sorry for the majority of these guys, as I could imagine them growing old and still doing this meaningless labour.

It was a multi-racial environment. As well as Brits, we had a strong cadre of Asian workers and a reasonable amount of West Indian and

African guys. Many of the Asian guys got through the night by placing a bit of cocoa leaf under their top lip and sucking it all night long. This was supposed to be a kind of slow-release cocaine. I tried it, but it seemed a waste of time. A lot of the African guys got through the night by being stoned all of the time. A group of them invited me to join them for a toke during our meal break one night, and I accepted. It was the last time. The stuff these guys smoked was so strong I had to plead sick and go home. I was completely wasted!

The hotchpotch of British guys were the sorriest of the lot. Most of them hated the coloured workers, thinking themselves above them just because they were white. We were all on a production bonus scheme, where we were paid a meagre basic wage with bonus payments depending on the weight of metal that we processed each night. Many of the white guys were far less capable than the others, particularly the hard-working Asian guys, and they didn't have much processed metal to show for their work each week. This, of course, meant that they were paid less, and in typical form they built up a strong resentment towards their darker co-workers. The biggest moan from these losers was that the work rate was set too high, because the coloured lads didn't know how to pace themselves! If it wasn't for the fact that the white guys were vastly outnumbered, there could have been some nasty trouble.

The 'white supremacy' attitude sickened me. It was obvious from the start that the all-England foreman and the white British manager made sure that their racist friends got the least mundane jobs and the machines that could generate the most income. On some machines the rate was higher than on others and the process was smoother, allowing a better opportunity for a big bonus each week. There wasn't a single coloured guy on one of these machines. Given this set of circumstances, the Brits had no excuse for falling behind on earnings, other than their lack of ability. They didn't see it like this, though, and were constantly bitching about 'these bastards taking their jobs and getting favouritism'. In fact, this would be the mildest of the insults delivered - and none of them was true.

As a half-caste who looked like a white hippy to the foreman and manager, I was given a reasonably decent machine. I found my own way around the bonus scheme, through a tip given to me by an ex-glue-sniffing white guy of about my age.

'Hi, Les; I used to work on your machine, man. Did you know that all of the widgets from the day shift are stored in a bay at the far end of this floor, mate?' and he gave me a wink.

Spot on! From that night onwards, I was casual with my work rate, reading a book mostly as I pulled the handle that punched the holes in my metal widgets. I got great bonuses each week, though, all because of me moving the widgets in the day-shift buckets over to my area before the weigh-in at the end of my shift. The best time to do this was always during our long break for a meal. The foremen would spend this time having something to eat in the manager's office, and none of the guys sitting around in my area cared what I was up to. Apparently, the guy who had put me onto this had been making his bonus up from the day-shift work for ages. He reckoned that, if you didn't get too greedy, then you could get away with it forever. As he said, even if you got caught - who cared? There were plenty of factories.

It was still boring, though. I settled into what must be the worst job I've had in my life. The only thing that kept me turning up was the fact that, with my wee scam, I was able to accumulate a fair bit of money in a short time.

It wasn't the best set of circumstances, but - bit by bit - I was coming back into solvency.

CHAPTER LVIII

Love's Young Dream

Working night shifts had no real effect on my social life, which was almost exclusively time spent with the other members of the squat. This crew were into getting stoned all night and sleeping all morning; so, when I arrived home at 6:30 a.m., the house was quiet and I was able to get some decent sleep till about two o'clock in the afternoon without being disturbed by anyone.

As time went by there were more girls around. The lads had met a number of young hippy ladies and now there were more girls than guys hanging out. Free love was in full swing and our sleeping arrangements fluctuated without disturbing any of the participants too much. I think, by the time I had been there a month, I must have slept with all six of the girls - the full contingent except for Jenny, who was pretty well bonded to Scott. Scott's bond was a lot looser, though, and he must have slept with at least half of the other girls around.

Free love, man!

Love and peace, man!

Sex, drugs and rock and roll, man!

It seemed as if I was firmly back into the hippy scene.

The turnover and availability of hippy chicks was fun for a while. At first it was nice to be able to while away many pleasant hours without commitment or guilt, but after a while these short relationships just all seemed to merge together and I began to get really bored. There was never any real companionship between me and any of the girls I spent time with, and I kind of envied Scott his relationship, albeit one-sided, with the lovely Jenny. Although sleeping with her was off-limits, I started to become closer to Jenny as a friend.

Jenny was a five-foot-six, brown-haired and brown-eyed girl, almost one year younger than me. She had long hair that was practically down to her waist, a ready smile and a highly contagious laugh. She was pretty thin, but she wore her regulation brightly coloured hippy blouse and worn flared trousers with a kind of sexy style. Unlike the other girls around, she could talk about things other than drugs or music, and she was one of the few who never thought that I was weird for wanting to have a job. Jenny had come to London with Scott. I had known her in Glasgow, although we had never been close, but I had always liked her.

As time went by, and the other hippy chicks became less and less interesting, I coveted Jenny more and more. I always harboured a small hope that Scott would chuck her and that I could step in and make her mine. As I couldn't have her immediately I settled for her friendship, and patiently waited for the inevitable to happen with the ever-unfaithful Scott. My patience was rewarded and I got her to myself when Scott left the squat for Glasgow some time later; and I lost her in a blink one night after a Pink Floyd concert.

Funny how things happen.

One day, when I came home from work, Scott had taken off. I asked Mad Alex what had happened to him, and he told me that Jenny had finally got fed up with him screwing every girl he could get his hands on and they had had a big scene over it. Scott had used a few final expletives and then taken off for Glasgow, telling Jenny that she wasn't cool and needed to get her head together. In Alex's opinion, Scott was right and Jenny was getting, 'a bit psycho.'

That sounded a bit rough on Jenny, but it also sounded like opportunity knocking on my door. I went up to her room to talk to her.

When I entered her room, the nicest and best kept in the squat, Jenny was lying on her bed, just staring at the ceiling. Her face bore the evidence of recent tears and she looked miserable.

She looked over at my entrance.

'I suppose you guys will want me to leave now that Scott's gone.'

'Don't be stupid, Jenny. Scott's a prat, man; he doesn't know what he has, man. He'll be back.'

Jenny gave me a strange look. 'I don't know, Les. He was pretty mad, man.'

Comforting hugs followed on from words of support - and eventually lovemaking followed on from the hugs.

I don't know why I should have, but I felt a bit guilty about Scott at first, though the more time I spent with Jenny, and the more I pondered her treatment, the less I cared what he would think when he returned. I'd coveted the fair wench for some time and now she was mine. I wasn't going to give her up without a fight. As Jamie, in his best back-room-philosophy style, said: 'Fuck him, Les. He's completely fucked up, man. Just enjoy it, man; you guys seem pretty happy.'

And we were.

This was my first meaningful relationship. Jenny and I became very close, very fast. We were friends as well as lovers and we hated being apart. We went everywhere together and resented anything that kept us apart. I was in heaven and Jenny seemed as happy as I was.

For the first time I was in love.

The only glitch in our relationship came when Scott returned to the squat a couple of weeks later.

Jenny was really nervous about seeing Scott. She imagined a big confrontation and some messy trouble. I wasn't so bothered, but I was anxious as to how Jenny would be with me when Scott came back. As it turned out, it was a great big nothing from Scott's point of view. He came back on a Saturday morning, having taken the overnight train from Glasgow down to Euston station. As soon as he arrived, I heard someone shout out, 'Hi, Scott, man.' I was with Jenny in our room at the time, nakedly pursuing our favourite bonding routine. Jenny looked scared. I told her to relax, pulled on a pair of jeans, and went downstairs to take care of it.

'Hi, Les, man. How are you doing? Seen Jenny, man? I need to talk to her.'

'Yeah, Scott. Jenny's in my room now, man. She's with me.'

Scott shrugged. 'Yeah? That's cool, man. We were finished anyway. Trisha's coming down from Glasgow next week, man, and I just wanted to let her know. Be careful, Les, man; Jenny can be a bit psycho - eh?' and he smiled his 'I'm cool' smile.

I smiled back and let the 'psycho' bit go. Problem solved - Jenny was mine now! I rushed back up to let her know it was all right.

It was not such a happy result for Jenny, it seemed. She had been listening at the top of the stairs and, when I came back up to our room, she was lying face down on the bed and was crying her wee heart out.

'The bastard! The fucking bastard! He doesn't give a shit about me; he was always just using me, the bastard."

'What's the problem, Jenny? I thought you wanted to be with me.'

Pause in sobbing.

'I do, Les. It's just that...'

More sobbing.

I was pissed off, not understanding at the time that Jenny had been very much in love with Scott and had always harboured a faint hope that he would reform and they could be together forever. I was a rebound and, although she liked me, she did not love me the way she loved Scott. I can see this in retrospect. At the time I was just fed up, and so I dressed, left the room and went downstairs to share a 'J' with the guys.

By that evening, Jenny was Jenny again, and our whirlwind romance continued. If anything, it continued with a much deeper passion. I guess Jenny was making sure Scott knew that she was OK. Poor girl; I don't think Scott even noticed.

Jenny wasn't as complacent with me as she had been with Scott. She had learned a harsh lesson, and so, during our many discussions, she made sure she got several pledges from me. She wanted me to have no other girls; she wasn't going back to that place again. She said that she wouldn't be ignored as a person any more. Jenny wanted us to be an equal couple if we were to stay together. She wanted some respect. Quite right, in my book; she wanted to be treated as a person within the group, not just as somebody's chick. I had no problem with any of her needs, and so we agreed that it was my job to make sure that the other guys didn't see her as just my current squeeze. Even though I had no notion that I would be able to change the perceptions of my squat-mates,

I loved Jenny and did my best to comply. Jenny seemed happy and started to become more confident and outgoing around the guys. I thought I'd done well and that a long relationship was in the offing, but I guess, when I broke one of the rules, it was just the inevitable coming home to roost sooner than I would have wished it to. I was still just a rebound.

There was a Pink Floyd concert on in town. We all had tickets and were looking forward to numbers such as Careful with that Axe, Eugene, complete with special effects, and a head full of the best dope we could get to smoke. On the night of the concert Jenny and I travelled down to the venue with the rest of the crew, but our seats were spread all over the hall. Jenny and I had expensive seats right up front, and so we said we'd try and meet the guys later. We split from them and made ourselves comfortable for the big event - we were high and happy hippies.

The concert was a production of the usual Pink Floyd magic. Loud music, brilliant special effects and colours, complete with a headless effigy of a guitar-player during Careful with that Axe. At one point they made a model aeroplane zoom from the back of the hall and explode in coloured fire onto the stage. As usual, the audience were treated to one of the best live acts around and a night of entertainment that we would be talking about for a long time.

Loads of the attendees were tripping on acid. Jenny and I laughed when a guy in front of us, who had punctuated each special effect with a 'wow, man', jumped up and ran screaming for the exit during the axe sequence. His wasn't the only mind blown that night. There was a ton of hash and grass at the concert. Joints were rolled by the dozen and were passed back and forth across the rows of seats and around the hall, as the gig went on. By the end of the performance, both Jenny and I were completely wasted. I was half deaf, high as a kite and hallucinating when it was time to leave the hall. With a great big grin plastered across my face, I just drifted out of the hall along with the crowd. I somehow made my way onto the last tube going north, and I could hear Pink Floyd numbers in my head all the way home.

What a night!

When I got back home, most of the others were already back. They had a fire blazing in the living room, Pink Floyd blasting from the stereo and joints of good grass already making the rounds. With a smile I threw off my coat and collapsed onto a couch. I was at peace with the world and totally spaced when I heard, 'Where's Jenny, man?' from Tommy the Aussie.

Oh fuck! I'd forgotten Jenny! What was worse, Jenny was broke; I had all the money. What was even worse, I had taken the last tube home. If she wasn't back yet, then she was stuck!

Fuck, fuck, fuck, fuck!

Tommy, guessing from my reaction that I had completely forgotten about her at the concert, said, 'Lost her in the crowd, man? Don't worry, man; Jenny's cool - she'll get a cab or something.'

I fretted for another hour, while I got even more stoned and worried about my wee love. There was no point going back, as I had no idea where I could find her, so I just stayed put and I worried.

Jenny got back an hour and a bit after me. Mad Alex let her in. She pushed past him, glared at me as she passed the open living-room door, and stormed up the stairs. I charged up after her to apologize. By the time I got to our room, she was sobbing face down on the bed, and refused to speak to me. I tried - and failed - to get a response, or even to get her to listen to my heartfelt apologies. I was too stoned and it was all too heavy. I gave up and went back downstairs, to discuss the concert with the rest of the lads. I spent the whole of that night in the living room, getting more and more stoned and waiting for the Jenny-storm to pass. I awoke to: 'Les, it's Jenny, man. You'd better go and see her.'

I'm not the best or brightest person in the morning. I staggered, bleary-eyed, out of the living room and literally bumped into Jenny in the hall. She was fully dressed, with a determined look on her face, a rucksack over her shoulders and a cloth shoulder bag draped across her body. It looked as if she was carrying her entire worldly goods

'What's up, Jenny?'

'I'm off, Les. I'm going back to Glasgow. Scott's lent me the money for the train and I'm heading back home. I told you I wouldn't put up with being used any more, man!'

And with that massive overreaction she walked out of my life for good.

I suppose I should have tried to talk her round, but even in my half-dazed state I think that I understood that this was not about the Floyd concert; it was just the inevitable coming home to roost.

I let her go - not that I could probably have done otherwise.

I missed Jenny. For a while there I had felt a brand new feeling. I'd been in love and it had felt great; it was better than just having a girl-friend - more, somehow. For that brief period of time I had felt fulfilled, even though it was obvious that I was the only half of the partnership to harbour such feelings. In my innocence I thought that we would be together forever.

But now Jenny was gone.

After a few mournful days, I was back on the usual hippy-girl circuit. The guys hardly noticed my wee first-love's departure - but I did. Although I never let anyone know how hard it hit me, I pined for wee Jenny for a long time after she left.

I hope she managed to find something good and I hope that she remembers our short time together with some fondness. Either way, I'll never forget her my first taste of love's young dream.

CHAPTER LIX

Massacre at the Squat

I haven't really described the hippy comrades with whom I shared space in the squat. I keep referring to them as hippies, and this may be as misleading to the reader as it was to a certain property-developer and our local London teenagers.

We were freaks more than hippies, and Glasgow freaks more than the average 'peace and love' crews.

Thompson and Mad Alex were Blue Angels, the Glasgow chapter of the notorious Hell's Angels brigade. I should say that they were ex-Blue-Angels, as they no longer hung out in Glasgow with their team and in fact no longer owned motorbikes. They still sported the pissed-on denims and their filthy leathers, though, and if you asked them about being bikers they would tell you that, once you were in the Angels, you were an Angel till you died. They both still had long greasy hair, utilized by both Angels and hippies. Thompson was blonde and Crazy Alex was dark-haired. They both affected the Glasgow swagger, and, if you were to take them seriously (which none of the rest of us did), you might have thought that they looked a wee bit menacing.

Mad Alex earned his nickname by drinking a full pint in the State bar that contained not only beer, but also sundry other rubbish, including cigarette butts and a female Angel's pee. This feat earned him some set of Blue Angel wings or other, as well as many hours of spewing his guts up. His breath was better these days, but he was still a mental bastard when crossed.

Thompson, our other Angel, was a well-built guy. He never displayed very much intelligence throughout the time I knew him and he was always far too stoned to have any kind of a personality. He was a pretty loyal guy, though, and the best of the crew to count on in an emergency.

Jamie and Scott were thieves. They had come into the hippy scene from the housing estates. Jamie was from Cawder and our relationship went way back. Scott was from a milder, but still traumatic street environment. Jamie and Scott would steal anything, at any time. They were as bold as brass and had even perfected stealing shoes, by getting the lefts from one shoe-shop display and then hunting down the rights from some other shoe shop in town. If all the shoe shops in London had made the decision to put only left-side shoes on display, I'm sure that these two wild men would have come up with a way to get a pair anyway. These were guys who knew no fear and had no qualms whatsoever about what they 'liberated'.

Tommy was a six-foot-three-inches tall Aussie. He was a couple of years older than all of us at 21. He had come across here to visit his Scottish relatives when he was 18, he'd got into the hippy scene, he'd liked it and he'd stayed. Tommy was the least hygienic hippy I think I ever met. He seemed to bathe only when his current girl refused to share a bed with him any more. He seemed to catch everything from head lice to scabies during the time I knew him. He had a ready smile, a huge appetite for drink and grass, and was always horny. Tommy would walk 20 miles to get laid if he had to and a big drought for him was going a couple of nights with only his well-used palm for company. He was really easygoing despite his lack of sanitation, though, so nobody gave him more than cursory stick about it.

The girls came and went, and there were always girls. The only one to stay for any length of time, apart from the recently departed Jenny, was a German girl called Olga. She was a leather-clad Amazon of a girl, with the prerequisite German hairy armpits and biceps like a man. She was an aggressive monster, but Tommy really took to her and so she stayed for quite a while.

I was living as an old version of myself. I was temporarily back in the hippy scene, working and saving money while I decided what to do next. I was still fairly strong, had my mental armour to call on in times of need, and sported a huge Afro-style curly mop, which the girls at the time seemed to think was cool. I thought I was cool - but I can't even look at an old picture of myself from these days without cringing.

That was our crew.

As life at the squat continued we were losing popularity in the local area. We had far too many hippy parties and weird goings-on for the remaining locals to stomach. We did too many drugs and Scott and Jamie were stealing bits and pieces from local shops, so the local police started to take notice. We were going through a lot of young local girls, and the local boys plus the girls' parents were starting to get a bit angry about our continued presence in the area. In general, we were becoming known as a 'bad lot'. In addition to us, there was a new squat a couple of doors away now. This was populated by a transient bunch of hippies, more into the hippy mode of peace, love and political activism. We occasionally partied with that lot, although we generally kept our distance on a daily basis, but - to the locals - we were a spreading epidemic.

After squat number two was established by the other hippies, the property-owner sent in a bunch of muscle-bound labourers to smash up any and all utilities in the remaining empty houses on the street. They pulled off half of the roofs; they smashed up all of the plumbing; they partially destroyed walls; and they ripped up floorboards. The property guy was making sure that the hippy epidemic stopped at two!

We didn't care, although the political lot down the road made a lot of noise about it being a, 'Waste of property, man, when there are people with no houses, man.'

When you boiled it down, they meant hippies with no houses - man. Of course, the said hippies were complete social parasites. They were fed and clothed by the state, they had no intention of ever working to support themselves if they could help it, and they broke the law every day. I don't just mean by smoking dope; the majority on the hippy scene felt that 'liberating' possessions from 'fat-cat business types' was fair game. They firmly believed that taking over someone else's property was justifiable, if it provided them with a home that they did not have to work to pay for. That was typical of the 1970s hippy set. By now these same people are probably all respectable middle-class citizens themselves, and would be the first to call in the law if they came home to find someone invading their home under the banner of 'liberation'!

We didn't care about the other houses being destroyed, and in fact saw it as an opportunity. A few of the lads managed to make quite a bit of money from 'liberating' the lead and copper from the plumbing and roofs of the houses that had been smashed up. We were a bit more enterprising than the soft hippies down the road!

The property-owner must have let the success of his house bust-up go to his head. The hippies from the other place had tried to do a bit of protesting to stop the demolition work. Of course, they had failed, as the labourer guys just brushed them aside and got on with the job in hand. Their governor must have had a report from his guys on this and had obviously felt that, if intimidation worked, he could use such methods to rid his properties of his problem hippies in the two squats.

It was a flawed calculation. These squats were two very different establishments, housing very different types of people. He might have got away with his plan if we had been the same type of softies as the other lot - but we were anything but that.

The governor decided to use our unpopularity with the local people and a wad of ready cash to orchestrate our exit by intimidation. He got one of his men to approach a local gang of skinheads and, with very little persuasion and a wad of banknotes, got them to agree to attack our homes and try to drive us out. The skinheads must have thought that Christmas had come early: getting paid to perform their favourite hobby of violence against hippies! They gathered with enthusiasm one night to go about their business.

Luckily for the other lot, they picked our house first.

I was dressed to go to work at the factory when it started. I was in the living room, where most of the clan were hanging out and were starting to get into the nightly smoking session. I remember I was drinking a cup of tea and contemplating another night of boredom when...

Bang!

'What the fuck?'

Bang! Crash! Bang!

Tommy looked out of the living-room window and, with a huge smile on his face, turned to the rest of us and said, 'Lads, there's a bunch of skinheads out there lobbing bricks at the house!'

Everyone's face lit up; including big Olga's, who obviously sensed that this was not going to be a dull night but one where she could let loose her full Germanic aggression.

Comments such as, 'Fucking 'A', man!' and, 'Wait till I get my boots on, man,' and, 'Let's go, man - it's a party!' resounded around the room.

Mad Alex, who had been upstairs when the noise started, was actually first to the door, having thrown on his boots, grabbed a poker and rushed downstairs, afraid to be left out of the fun.

It was a massacre.

The poor skinheads had expected the usual squeals of fear from their victims and had come totally unprepared for the all-out war that our clan was more than happy to wage. The only squeals in evidence from our end were loud squeals of laughter, as bald-headed bodies went flying, bloodied and beaten by a berserk crew of very happy hippy freaks.

There were plenty of genuine screams from the skinheads, though.

There must have been about 18 to 20 of them on our front lawn when we exited the house in a mad, heavy-clubbing rush. We waded into them like robots gone berserk. The majority of them tried to flee, but we were in a party mood and were determined to take out as much flesh as we could. We knocked them down, pounded and kicked them until there was nothing left to hit, except pitifully begging and badly beaten piles of flesh. We chased them when they tried to flee and smashed them up with pokers, bits of wood and knives taken in combat. A lot of them got away eventually, but we were happy and sated as we watched the few escapees bolt. We kicked a few on the way back home and patted each other on the back. When we arrived back at the house, we even had to wrest Olga off a struggling skinhead, who was a short couple of punches from being unconscious.

The other lot of hippies down the road had come out to see what the commotion was about, but, after witnessing a few scant seconds of the massacre, they had run back inside their squat and bolted their door.

After that night they were never quite so friendly towards us.

We dragged Olga back indoors and tended our minor wounds (some of the skinheads had tried to use knives, until we had taken them off them and they had learned the hard way that, if you can't use a knife, you shouldn't try to bring one into a fight). Big Olga had a handful of hair as a souvenir and her eyes were sparkling as she practically dragged Tommy upstairs to celebrate. For hours later we heard the noise of them proceeding to try to bust all the springs on their bed, and cave in the ceiling above us.

The rest of us just celebrated our victory with a couple of joints. I shared one of them and then I went off to work as usual.

We would have forgotten about it in a couple of days - all of us except Olga, who ranted on as if we were heroes out of some Greek myth. We were all pretty fed up with Olga; even Tommy had his fill of her bragging after the first day. To the rest of us it was no big event and the skinheads had faded from our minds within 48 hours. We assumed it was all over, but we had one more wee ruck to come. Three days later, we were attacked again. This time it was by about a dozen grown men. These were some of the fathers and brothers of the skinheads that we had beaten up, who had formed a little vigilante squad and had decided to come round and teach the hippies a lesson for messing up their boys.

Massacre number two.

Once again it was a night attack. This time, the beer-gutted and badly out-of-condition fathers and elder sons had brought a variety of pickaxe handles and metal bars with them. Although we took a few initial hits (I had an ugly bruise on my head for days, and Jamie had a cracked rib), it didn't take us long to become the owners of these handy weapons and to repeat the chastisement that we had bestowed on their sons. If anything, these guys were so unfit, overweight and scared of our maniacal aggression that it was an even easier rumble to win than the bash with the younger skinheads. Big Olga took a fair bit of parental flesh that night and once again she was in seventh heaven. There were fewer tears and wailing from the men - but there was enough damage done to send more than a few to hospital and to deter any such stupidity in the future.

These were the only two scenes of violence I experienced during an otherwise peaceful existence at the squat in north London. The landlord decided to get smart after that night and changed his tactics altogether. I like to think that we'd taught him and his agents that violence doesn't pay!

CHAPTER LX

Tolerance no more

It was a combination of factors that saw the end of the squat era for me.

For one, I had saved up quite a bit of money, and, although I could have continued to amass more wealth by working at the factory, I was going insane with the mindless routine. Secondly, Jamie's and Scott's thieving was getting completely out of hand. They had moved upmarket, having found a fence called Angus who would take and shift anything that they brought to him. They were into robbing factories and retail shops now. They had also brought Tommy and Mad Alex into their scams as well. I knew it was only a matter of time before they got caught, or Mad Alex bludgeoned some nightwatchman - and I wanted no part of it. I tried to talk them out of it, warning them that eventually they were bound to get caught, but their philosophy was: 'Got to survive, Les. These bastards won't miss a few bits and pieces, and - anyway - London's huge; how are they going to catch us, man?'

Scott had bought an old Bedford van to use to transport their plunder over to Angus's place. It was a bright orange job, which had been hippified with spray-paint and decorated with peace symbols and flowers. It was hardly discreet transportation for robbers. I don't think that a more obvious getaway car has ever been involved in a crime. When I pointed this fact out to the guys, they countered with: 'There's loads of Bedfords about, man. They'll just think we're a bunch of hippies.

Nobody will think we're robbin' anythin', man.'

As the Steely Dan song goes - Pretzel logic!

The law may sometimes move slowly, but when presented with such evidence as there being only two hippy houses in an area where shops and factories are being robbed wholesale, and a hippy Bedford van which had often been spotted in the vicinity of these crimes, the law gets there eventually! The lads' only concession to caution was to wear gloves so as not to leave incriminating fingerprints behind.

The inevitable happened.

I came home from work one morning to find nobody but some girls in the house, the lads having been picked up by the law during the night. Luckily, there was no plunder to find when they raided the house, and the guys had managed to either swallow, burn or flush our stash. The cops were onto these stupid losers. A few hours into my post-shift sleep that day I was rudely awakened by the CID, and was myself banged up on remand in that glorious health resort called Ashford Prison.

I was really pissed off.

These stupid bastards and their outrageous thieving had got both me, and Thompson, arrested as well. Neither of us had wanted anything to do with their amateur crime spree. I was going to miss work and probably get fired. If the guys were prosecuted, the chances were that a judge would never listen to the fact that I had nothing to do with it and would at least convict me as an accomplice. To top it all, as I languished on remand, my current cellmates consisted of a weird-looking black guy called William, who sat on the edge of his bed and grunted, and an over-enthusiastic gay bloke who called himself Martha and refused to give me his proper name!

Did it ever get any worse than this?

It got worse!

I was in a very ugly mood that first night in my cell, so, when Martha decided to make my acquaintance by trying to climb into my bed - I wasted him. The screws heard the commotion, and rushed into our cell to drag me off for a nice friendly police beating and a night in solitude nursing my resentment. The next morning I was transferred to Lachmere House prison, nursing some painful bruises on my torso. I stayed at Lachmere for three weeks, being occasionally questioned by the CID, before they eventually let me out without pressing any charges.

The other lads had been released two weeks earlier from Ashford, but, because of my fighting incident and my subsequent transfer, it took an extra two weeks for the release notice to catch up with me.

Complete bastards!

I gave the guys big shit when I got out. I was at the end of my tolerance level. The van was going - they could keep it at Angus's place. The thieving was stopping until I got out of the place. Thompson agreed with me and he began making his own exit plans. The lads were none too pleased with my attitude, but I was prepared to take it to the wire if I had to and they reluctantly complied. For some strange reason the girls were still there when I got back. I thought that they would have beaten a hasty exit when their guys got busted, but it seems that some teenage girls find pathetic amateur criminals interesting or something - try working that one out!

As I had predicted, I lost my job at the factory. The police had kindly phoned the factory to tell my boss that I was in prison, suspected of robbing factories. The boss had taken this as an indication that I might not have been as trustworthy as he would have liked, and had dismissed me in my absence. I got a month's pay and my marching orders.

I was completely pissed off, as I could have done with more money to get out on my own. I'd had enough of squatting and London flat deposits were not small. On top of that, it was hard to get a decent flat if you could not give your prospective landlord a reference from your employer. I was screwed - but salvation came from an unexpected source.

The property-owner had finally managed to buy out the two old dears who were the last residents to leave the street. I talked to one of the old ladies one day, and with a smile she told me that the 'crook' (as she called him) had paid her a substantial amount over the value of her property, so she had taken the money and was off to live with her daughter in Dorset. Good luck to the old lady - she deserved a big reward for her fortitude.

That just left the two squats on the street.

The property-developer was getting desperate. He had owned most of the street for some time without being able to start his plans. He now owned the whole street, but still couldn't go ahead as he had sitting tenants - i.e. hippy squatters - and the law was not helping him to resolve the issue. He'd tried unsuccessfully to muscle us out; he'd tried the courts, but that took more time than he obviously had; he'd tried almost everything; and he had failed.

He resorted to bribery.

I was hanging around the house, a couple of days after my release from prison, when there was a knock on the front door. I looked out of the window, nervous about more police hassle, and saw a middle-aged guy in a suit, shadowed by a tall muscle-man.

Could be trouble, I thought.

'Boys!' I shouted as I answered the door.

I opened the front door halfway and asked the suit what he wanted.

'Hello, son. You don't know me, but I'm the man who owns this house you're living in.'

Surprise, surprise. My face must have reflected my feelings.

'Before you get defensive, son, I've come to talk to you guys and see if we can come to some kind of agreement. Benny here is just along to make sure I don't get mugged.'

I looked at Benny and he certainly gave the impression that he could do that.

'Can I come in?'

I turned around. The guys were arrayed behind me, and they were giving me negative nods. I was still very pissed off with the lot of them, so I turned back to the suit and said, 'Sure, man. Why not?'

I brought the suit into the living room and invited him to take a seat. He wrinkled up his nose but sat on one of our ageing couches. Benny remained standing.

The gist of the matter was that Mr Suit wanted us out of the squat as soon as possible. He had sussed out by now that we were going to be the hardest to move and that, after we had gone, he would have no problem with the idealists down the road. To get us out, Mr Suit was prepared to pay us a reasonably large sum of money. All we had to do to get the money was to leave within a week. The money would be handed over if we agreed to the deal and, if we accepted his terms, he said that he would trust us to move on quietly.

From the looks I was getting from Benny, as he measured me up for a coffin, I had no doubts that this was a good offer. If there were any more Bennies around, the boys and I would be suicidal if we decided to continue to cross this increasingly frustrated and desperate gent. Judging by his fat wad, I suspected that he could hire many a Benny if he needed to. Of course, not all the lads were that quick to work things out. Mad Alex said something about nobody chucking him out if he didn't want to go, and Scott tried for a larger sum of money. To give the gent his due, he was completely non-threatening - a fact that I found a bit sinister - and he upped the ante a wee bit to placate a now grinning Scott.

Over Mad Alex's protests, I agreed to his terms on behalf of the clan. He pushed his luck a bit and offered us a wee bit more to persuade the other hippies to leave. I knew that he meant us to beat these guys up or intimidate them for our extra money, so, before Alex could accept, I refused - purely on principle.

That was OK. We shook hands and the gent and his gorilla departed. He said that he would send Benny round that same night with the wad. I was well pleased. Thompson said that he knew of another squat we could move to if we wanted. I had had enough of squats and, in particular, sharing with this lot. I was off on my own. I had an Asian girlfriend at the time, Muni, and I was sure that she would put me up for a few days, even though she shared her place with two sisters and a brother. That would tide me over until I got a place of my own, which I could now afford with my unexpected nest egg.

I went up to my room to pack - a task that was completed in less than 15 minutes. I came back down to the living room with my rucksack and suitcase, and started to gather up my record collection and dismantle my stereo system.

'Wow, Les - you're moving fast, man,' said Jamie. 'We might hang about for a bit first, man, and we'll have no sounds here, man.'

'Tough! You stupid bastards cost me three weeks in jail and my fucking job - you can fuck off. When we get the money, we're splitting it up and you can do what you like - I'm off!'

And that was that.

The lads were none too pleased with my attitude, except for Thompson, who was just as fed up as I was with his undeserved spell in jail. The boys were still feeling a bit guilty and so they let it lie. I think they thought that I'd cool down eventually and we'd all be pals again.

I never saw them again after that night.

Benny and another gorilla came around that evening and handed over a thick envelope of money. This time there was a definite air of menace and no attempt at appearing to be polite. I was right - these guys were thugs out of our league and we had better comply with our part of the bargain. Benny warned us none too gently to keep our side of the deal, and then he left. Even Alex kept his mouth shut. When they'd gone, I immediately split the stash of cash between us. We all got a tidy wad, except for the girls, who we judged to be visitors and therefore not entitled to a cut. Olga wasn't happy. I went to Muni's place after the split and stayed there till I found a flat to rent.

The guys didn't take the chance of offending Benny and moved out of the squat a couple of days later. They stayed together, with the exception of Thompson, who moved into the city somewhere. I heard through the grapevine that Scott, Jamie and Mad Alex got caught doing a big factory robbery some time later. I also heard that they were given a seriously long sentence that time. I never heard anything about Thompson. He was a half-sensible guy, and I hope he settled down somewhere far from petty crime madness.

Tommy went back to Australia that year.

I was happy to find my new rented flat, and I very quickly found some more temporary work. No more squats for me.

By this time I was nearing the end of my interest in living in London. Every day it was becoming more and more apparent that I should move on.

It took one more incident to convince me completely.

CHAPTER LXI

Windsor and bust

My last birthday in London was my 18th. It had been an eventful year to date, and most of it had not really been pleasant. Festival time had rolled round again, however, and I was having fun on this hot summer, lying about in fields with Muni, listening to music, drinking beer, getting stoned and making love.

Life wasn't too bad.

Then came the Windsor Park free festival.

Muni and I had been to a few festivals this year and so we were pretty well kitted out for Windsor. We had a decent tent, a good-quality double sleeping bag, a small gas stove and even a gas lamp. By hippy standards we had a five-star hotel.

The Windsor festival was 'unofficial' and, although it was pretty well organized, the organizers had not been given police permission for the event. I think something was said about facilities that were missing, but I'm sure that the crux of the problem was complaints from the local residents. Unofficial festivals were not unusual, so this one went ahead anyway, and there were some big acts scheduled to play.

The Reading festival overlapped the end of the Windsor Park outing by a couple of days. This meant that the bikers, who had been at Windsor from day one, would be moving on by the Saturday, along with many of the other participants who preferred heavy metal or wanted to see the Stones. Muni and I had no plans to move on, as we were having a good time at Windsor and had hooked up with quite a few friends and acquaintances. By Saturday night there were slightly fewer people, but we were still part of a huge crowd and there was a great atmosphere. I can remember falling asleep, with Muni in my arms, listening to Magma perform on the main stage. We were having a blast and the 'vibe' was fantastic - at least, it was that night!

The 'peace and love' didn't last.

The next morning we were awoken by the sound of whistles blowing and the crunch of running feet. It must have been about 07:00 - a time when all good hippies are still deep in slumber. Muni and I woke together and, while I was pulling on my boots, she stuck her head out of the tent to see what was going on...

And dived head first to the ground in front of me, blood pouring from the top of her skull!

I roared!

What the fuck was going on?

I leapt towards Muni, who was lying face down with the top half of her body sticking out of the tent. Muni was only about five foot tall. She was a cute and gentle little Asian girl - who could have done this to her? Muni was groaning and trying to turn around as I reached her head to inspect the damage.

'What the fuck happened, Muni?' I asked, and, as I looked up, I saw chaos unfolding across the field.

There were policemen with batons and ordinary guys with armbands and pickaxe handles just running through the site, knocking over tent poles and driving people towards the gates like cattle. To my left was a policeman with a baton. I assumed that he must have been the bastard who had inadvertently clubbed Muni! Seeing red, I leaped on to the back of this policeman, managed to topple him to the ground, and started laying into him with everything I had.

The next thing I remember was waking up in the back of a police van seeing stars. I was also sporting a huge bump on the back of my head.

Muni told me later that, as she came round, she saw me pummelling a policeman who was lying on the ground - she then saw two others go for me. One of them whacked me over the head with his baton while the other one dragged me off the felled policeman and also started to whack me, till I subsided and his comrade got him to stop. They then dragged me off somewhere and she was helpless to do anything about it. Her story explained my inability to breathe properly and the world-class bruises that I noticed on my face and all over my body, when I eventually got to see myself in a mirror as I stripped for the ignominy of a full body search at the remand centre.

Back to Ashford on remand!

If I had thought that Ashford was overcrowded on my previous and very recent visit, it had been a desert compared to this time. The police had arrested hundreds of us and every jail in London was full to overflowing. There were four to five people to a cell now, and some very unhappy guards handed out the threat of additional pull-up beds being added to the non-existent floor space.

'Don't get too comfortable, son; we may have to put another bed in here.'

My luck had reached rock bottom. I was banged up in jail and was probably facing some serious police assault charges. I had no idea as to the state of health of my injured girlfriend and I had absolutely no way of finding out. I knew that I could be kept here for any length of time in conditions unfit for an animal, as - apart from Muni - no one would be looking for me.

I decided there and then that, if I got out of this one, I was leaving London and heading back to Scotland. I'd had enough of this place; I wanted the familiarity of my roots. I'd take Muni with me if she wanted to go, but, if she didn't, then I was going back on my own.

As it turned out, my stay in Ashford was a brief one.

The police had made a grave error of judgement on that fateful day at Windsor Park. Their plan had seemed to be to wait until all the bikers had left, so that they would have less physical resistance to contend with, and then move in and clear what they alleged to be an illegal campsite. They had recruited some local 'stewards' to help out, who appeared to be just over-exuberant thugs with armbands. The authorities saw Windsor as a hippy festival and so made the leap that all of the attendees were therefore drug-taking hippies - you know, those people without any human rights, with little recourse to the law and therefore easy pickings if they needed to be arrested.

Big mistake.

They forgot to factor in the trend that was sweeping the world, where hippy thinking had become cool amongst the yuppie set and where going to a pop festival had become as much a middle-class preserve as it was a hippy staple. The police had arrested lawyers, doctors, solicitors and young businessmen in their haul. Along with the hippies that they set out to net, they had scooped up some very influential and very angry citizens.

There was a massive public outcry.

Civil suits were lodged and serious protests were made; the establishment couldn't get us out of prison quickly enough. I escaped with the rest, my police assault charges ignored.

I had been lucky once again.

When I got back to my place, the first thing I did was look up Muni. She was OK, except for a bit of shock and a bump on the head. No permanent damage had been done, thankfully. I told Muni of my prison-time decision to leave. She was upset as we had bonded pretty deeply, but she couldn't conceive of leaving behind her tight-knit family and her place in the Asian community. She told me that her father had already started to pressure her to drop 'the half-caste boy' and to find a good Brahmin husband.

My decision was made, though, and I wasn't about to change my mind. I understood Muni's reluctance to go against the wishes of her family and didn't press the point. Instead, I told her that, if she changed her mind, I would gladly take her with me, and I made my own preparations to leave the city. Muni didn't change her mind and, with some regret, we parted company.

I finished up a week more of the temporary work I had been doing, bought a train ticket, packed up my belongings and headed back to Scotland.

No more London - Windsor was the last straw for me and I was going back home!

SONG 13 - LOOKING INSIDE THE FAST LANE

I sit here and wonder how people can be so strange
I see the shell of these people, but they're locked inside
themselves
Travel away, as they go on life's journey they should be glad
But all they can see are reflections of goals they must meet -
they're sad

Look inside your soul 'cos it's always been open
Look inside yourself, then look at the world around you

Look inside your soul - Looking inside the fast lane
Live outside yourself - Looking inside the fast lane

But on occasion I see someone who lives outside them self
They always accept what goes down and around them if
good or bad
I wanna be one of these people I know I can live like that
I'm changing the way that I am with all of my heart

Look inside your soul - Looking inside the fast lane
Live outside yourself - Looking inside the fast lane

CHAPTER LXII

Are there any Demons out there?

I was finally on my way back home, although by this time I was not sure where home really was. I had arrived in London as a 16-year-old, fresh faced - if streetwise - hippy youth. I was leaving London as an 18-year-old jaded youth, who had had a wider variety of experiences than most people ten years older were likely to garner.

I'd learned a lot, though.

During this chapter of my life, violence, criminality, drugs and excess had drifted back, but I had at least learned something new in the art of dealing with such dangers.

I had learned self-control.

This stuff was around. It was always going to be around and, try as I might, various levels of pathologically anti-social behaviour were bound to encroach on my space. It didn't matter. I was equipped to deal with it now. I knew that I could dip into and out of any of these scenes at will and I wouldn't feel an outsider, or have any need to fully embrace their anti-social living patterns.

I'd been mixing with rich guys, poor guys, educated people and uneducated people. I'd mixed with just about every level in every caste over the last two and a half years. I didn't feel intimidated by any of them and I had learned to survive as myself, regardless of the quirks of my peers. I loved the possibilities of the comforts that my richer friends had around them, but such things didn't seduce me to the point where I was willing to give up my blossoming individuality to acquire them. From my background and experiences, having a solid roof over my head, enough to eat, no worries about bills and a wee bit over for pleasure was luxury enough for now. I hated the poverty of my poorest friends, who were always struggling just to feed themselves or buy a pair of jeans. I wasn't intimidated by it, though. I knew that, if I ever found myself in such circumstances, I could both survive and work my way out. Work and determination were the keys to escaping such poverty and I knew that these selfsame poor friends had only themselves to blame for their continuing predicament.

I had definitely buried the working-class chip on my shoulder and, with it, the demon of social discrimination. Sure, some of my earlier demons were still around, but they were mere shadows of the demons that they had once been. Although I discovered that I had not completely banished these demons, I felt stronger in their midst and was free from any danger of entrapment.

I'd gained a few other things during my time in London.

Apart from leaving the smoke with a much healthier bank balance than I had had when I went down there, I had some qualifications tucked under my belt. I also had some work experience, which would give me a boost in starting a new career and would be a strong link in the armour that I was to develop later as protection in the wild world of business.

Lifestyle examples were the best thing that I carried away with me, however - although that was not the lesson I pondered most deeply on my return journey to Scotland. I spent much more time contemplating my mistakes and determining not to repeat them. Although my path had been somewhat chequered, I had observed enough to know that there were better lifestyles out there for me, and I knew that - one day - I would find myself a comfortable one.

I had also met a variety of people that I would never have met had I stayed in Glasgow during these years. Among all the crazies, I had met some good people. I had been introduced to some thoughtful people, successful in living their lives. These good folk carried an air of certainty around them and were very happy about where they were in their lives and what they were doing with their time. I had lots of examples.

At the club, there had been some young lads who were a part of the group when they wanted to be but who pursued their own path, without making any big fuss about it, and were certain to arrive at their chosen destination. These lads enjoyed almost every yard of their journey through life.

At work, there had been the guys who were never sucked into politics or reasons to prove themselves, other than a healthy striving to do the best that they could for themselves and their families. These were guys with principles, who would not sacrifice their morality to backstab a colleague on their way through their careers. These were often guys who would never make the top levels of their professions, but they always had the (often grudging) respect of their peers and carried a sense of contentment to and from work each day that was to be admired, if not envied.

Throughout my range of social intercourse, I had come across people, from different cultural backgrounds, who had that spark that I learned to covet. These were people who did not feel the need to don cold steel armour around them every time they stepped out of their homes. These were people with warmth and caring, who exhibited a constant stream of the best of humanity's qualities, often at the expense of their own safety and protection. I had met one man of this ilk at Centre Point, during a very brief sojourn spent helping the young London wounded in my spare time. He was a guy who just kept getting blasted by the people he was helping and often by his co-helpers. He kept helping, rolling with each blow and giving of his best. He was a true humanitarian.

I'd met many such people, and I left London determined to remake myself in that mould.

I'd discovered what I wanted to be - a decent human being. I knew that it would be difficult to maintain this approach through the survival struggles ahead. I knew that I would backslide and often be the type of person, armoured and armed to the teeth, that I would want to avoid. I acknowledged all this - but I would try.

Things were going to be different now.

Perhaps I had buried some more demons in London?

SONG 14 - IT'S WICKED

You don't want to know - it's wicked
You don't want to know - nothing's what it seems
Please don't ask about my past - it's wicked

You've been everywhere, though you're still young
You've messed around you know - you've done wrong
You made your choices to escape the place you were
Kept bouncing back to you
You know what that does - it does you down
It does you down

You don't want to know - it's wicked
You don't want to know - nothing's what it seems
Please don't ask about my past - it's wicked

Leave stage left you've gone, you're heading back
You're taking everything you own in one small rucksack
You're running out, you're running down, you're running home
Exit stage left, the past has gone
The past has gone

You don't want to know - it's wicked
You don't want to know - nothing's what it seems
Please don't ask about my past - it's wicked

Please don't ask about my past - it's wicked

PART FOUR -
Everything that happens is packaged up inside me - Demons

CHAPTER LXIII

Where have you been, Les?

I was a minor celebrity for a while when I returned to Glasgow.

Most of my old cronies had not moved on. In fact, they were still mired in the same hippy scene that I had left behind me two and a half years before. It was sad to see that, far from moving on, the scene had degenerated even further and the biggest talking points among my friends were drug busts and drug deals, laced with violence and paranoia.

More than a few people from my past had gone completely crazy from overdoses of psychedelic substances, and far too many had fallen into the junk pit of heroin and morphine addiction. All of this served only to bolster my resolve that I was not back to stay, but was in transition till I could establish the beginnings of a path into the future that I wanted to embrace.

The guys from the old scene looked hungry when they asked about my recent past. I could see in their eyes that they saw me as someone who had escaped for a while. They would ask me questions about London and the scene down there, and it was obvious that they were trawling for a possible way out for themselves. I told some stories, minor incidents and brief descriptions of my time in the smoke, but I knew that, if I encouraged them to make the move themselves, I would be sending them to a place which could strip them of the very last strands of their ability to survive.

London was not for them. These were people who wouldn't try to find work, education or a group of new friends. These were not guys who were looking for the type of challenge that could change their lives; these were people who were looking for an easier environment in which to continue the kind of marginal survival pattern that they lived out in Glasgow.

London was anything but that! London was a fiercely competitive, money-orientated, aggressive and insular city - it would eventually destroy them. It was cool to be consulted as a man of the world. It was cool being a minor celebrity, even amongst the ruined and self-destructive guys from my past, so I tried to look cool, shrug my shoulders and say, 'Yeah, man; it was pretty cool down there, man.'

Meanwhile, I'd be thinking, 'You really don't want to know, mate - it's pretty wicked down there.'

A few pilgrims did follow my lead, however. I heard through the grapevine that Smiley and Walker had gone down to London to squat, deal some dope and make 'big amounts of bread'. Smiley was robbed and stabbed in the West End, trying to score some hash from a bunch of fake dealers, who were just junkies making a hit on a new kid from Scotland. Big deals, or - in fact - any deals, were not made in toilets in the West End, but Smiley had asked around and been given a tip by some other junkie, which he had stupidly followed up while holding a pocket full of cash. He lasted till he reached the hospital and then he died, drowning as surgeons tried to stop his lungs from flooding with his own blood.

Walker became a junkie himself, after meeting a heroin addict chick in a squat around Finsbury Park. What his fate was never made it back to Glasgow, but is very easy to predict. I doubt that Walker would have made it into his mid-twenties.

The old scene asked and I answered. They were looking for a way out of their sad existence in Glasgow. They were desperate for a chance to escape, but had not rationalized that it was their own weaknesses that they needed to escape from, their own daily choices that needed to be reviewed and changed. They were looking for a fantasy nirvana, and so they asked and I answered.

They didn't really hear me.

They didn't really want to know...

CHAPTER LXIV

Back in the Old Life

At first I stayed with a friend in Glasgow. I had a few friends who had not changed too much since my departure down south, but I also had a few who had grown up and were living a more mature existence. They were still a part of the drug culture and they were far from attaining any kind of real stability, but they had avoided the worst pitfalls and had stayed sane and addiction-free.

One of these was a friend called Linda. Linda was a girl two years older than me, who lived in the west end of Glasgow and was married to a guy called Jacob when I had left town. Jacob had always treated Linda like crap and had eventually left her to roam with some other chicks on the scene. Not that Linda was an angel. When I returned, she was having an on-off affair with a young guy on the scene, who was married and had two kids. She dismissed the slighted woman's plight by writing her off as a psycho - who was 'too uptight for her man to stay faithful'. The truth was - Linda just loved having sex with the guy and made any excuse to cover her behaviour.

Linda had a gay cousin called Peter, who also lived in the west end with his parents. He in turn had a close lady friend called Margaret, who idolized Peter and always held out some hope that he would, one day, stop being gay and would fall in love with her. Faint hope. Peter was a quiet gay only because of his circumstances in Glasgow. Glasgow was still very unliberated at this time, and, if it had been generally known that Peter was gay, or if he had been visibly camp, his life would have been even more miserable than it was with his sexuality hidden

315

from all but a few.

I lived with Linda for a couple of weeks until I got my own flat in the west end, and Linda, Peter, Margaret and I hung out together for a while.

I was still unemployed and so, for the first time in my life, I signed on at the employment exchange and collected the financial benefits package. I had accumulated enough points with my work in London to get full employment benefit; I had saved quite a bit of money and had that in the bank; and I received a very nice tax refund from the government - so I was financially sound. I thought I would take some time out before getting back into working to survive.

I had some fun in Glasgow. I became pretty close to the guys I was hanging out with, but their social problems were a real drag.

Linda kept drifting in and out of bad affairs with pretty dubious guys. When she wasn't doing that, she was in and out of relationships with her ex-husband and her married lover. She was never really happy and, although I had a massive crush on her myself, she always seemed too unstable or too immersed in some drama or other for me to pursue her. I tried to help her when I could, mainly by making threats to her ex-husband to try and stop him turning up and abusing her. Linda didn't help, though; she always saw a reason for giving the madman another chance. The result was always the same: a few days of them being together and he would abuse her, destroy her self-esteem and then take off again. She never seemed to learn, and our time as mates in Glasgow eventually stopped when she went off with him to live in the countryside farther north in Scotland.

Margaret and I had a very brief fling. I think that she was just trying to make Peter jealous. I think she succeeded, but the jealousy was not that I had Margaret; rather, it was that Margaret had me! It lasted only about a week and then I met a girl called Lucy, who moved into my flat, and Margaret went back to her fruitless pursuit of Peter. There were no hard feelings between us; we just continued to be good mates.

Peter was a highly intelligent, well-dressed and decently mannered lad of 19. He lived with an eccentric mother and a drunken, loud-mouthed and macho father, along with his little sister. Poor Peter had known that he was gay since he had been at school, but, like many others, he had kept it as his own dark secret through most of his youth. Even in the hippy scene there were very few people whom he trusted to tell, and not all of these reacted kindly to the news.

Some guys smiled to Peter's face and made the usual jokes and anti-gay statements behind his back. Some people just distanced themselves from him. The worst and most hurtful reactions were sometimes the well-meaning ones. Some friends, understanding nothing about his sexual proclivity, would ignore his identity and treat him like a camp freak. They would talk down to him, even though it was apparent that the disparity in intelligence between them was invariably in favour of Peter. They would ask him insulting questions about his sexuality and they would often treat him like a caricature of a woman. Peter tried to bury any adverse social reaction in his recreational pastimes of drink and dope.

The worst reaction Peter received was from the person who undoubtedly loved him most - his mother. Peter's mother was an eccentric. I think her eccentricity stemmed from being married to a lout who had ill-treated her and abused her for years. She had compensated by retreating into a semi-real world of being an elegant lady - well above her husband's rabble-like antics. She would dress in flowing cotton dresses and graceful shoes, with her long hair decoratively pinned in a sophisticated style. She could be seen floating down Byres Road in the west end, sporting a parasol and wearing white lace gloves. She was quite a character.

Her reaction to Peter's disclosure was one of misguided love. She knew nothing about the gay scene at all. She knew nothing about gay sexuality - so she reacted to Peter in the way that gossip and innuendo had prepared her.

'Never mind, Peter; you must just be whatever you want - mummy will still love you.'

'Thanks, mum.'

'Right. Come through here with me and you should just try on a few of my dresses.'

'But, mum - I don't think you understand.'

'No 'buts', Peter; you don't need to be embarrassed with me. You won't be able to wear them outside, of course, but you can always wear them in the house with me. Just don't let your father see you in them, dear - he might be a wee bit...'

Poor Peter. He couldn't make his mother understand that being gay did not mean wanting to be a woman. He knew that his mother loved him, but that she just couldn't comprehend him, so he went along with her dressing up that day and tried to avoid the subject thereafter. I think it was this incident that kept Peter in the closet for so long. He made up for it when he eventually came out - but that was much later.

In the interim, it fell to me to stop Peter from getting beaten up when drink loosened caution from his tongue or his attitude. I would never have wanted him to remain repressed, but he didn't seem to pick smart times to demonstrate his real sexuality. For example, I remember the night that Margaret, Peter and I were at a university dance in Glasgow.

The night had been a laugh. We had all sunk a few pints and I had danced with Margaret, Peter joining in occasionally and doing his wilting stagger around us. I knew that it was time to leave, though, when Peter started pinching guys' bottoms surreptitiously on the crowded dance floor, drawing strange looks and then smiles - at Margaret. I didn't want to get into any fights that night, so I started to usher Margaret and half push Peter out of the hall.

All went well until we approached the final flight of stairs leading to the exit. Peter was lagging behind Margaret and me, who were having a laugh at Peter's underhand antics. I looked over my shoulder and saw that Peter was talking to a chunky-looking drunk lad, who was weaving at his side and leaning an ear into his face to listen to what he was saying. Peter had a stupid drunken grin on his face and seemed to be enjoying having the thug's friendly arm across his shoulders.

Trouble!

I immediately dropped back, a worried-looking Margaret at my side. I stepped between Peter and his new friend, pushing my gay chum to one side.

'How are ye doin', mate?' I asked the stranger.

'Hey, pal, is that burd goin' tae gie me a blow job in the lavvy, then - like yer mate said?'

He thought that Margaret was giving him a blow job in the toilets? Then I quickly twigged.

'Are ye sure that's what he said, mate?'

'Aye; he said did ah want a blow job in the lavvy, pal - I said, 'aye'.'

Margaret was dragging a reluctant Peter through the outside door in front of us.

'Hey! Where's she goin' then, pal? Ah thought ah wis gettin' a blow job?'

With a smile I said, 'I think he meant that he would give you one, mate.' And, as a look of pure horror came over Mr Chunky's face, I made my own swift exit from the place.

I caught up with Peter and Margaret running down the street. They were both laughing their heads off at Peter's wee jest. I joined them in their laughter and described the look of angst on the victim's face, which kept us giggling all the way home.

What a laugh we had.

When we were sober the next day. Peter made a pact with us not to try anything that stupid again. It might have seemed funny in our drunken state the previous night, but it could all have turned pretty nasty. Poor Peter said that sometimes he just wanted to be able to be himself and pick up guys the way that I could meet and pick up girls. I pointed out to him that, if I tried to pick up a girl by just walking up to her and offering her oral sex, then my chances of success would be pretty well infinitesimal!

Peter was scratching at the doors of his closet. He needed to find somewhere where he could live as himself - without having to bury his sexuality. Glasgow discotheques were not the best choice of venue, however!

++++++++

Meanwhile, I had heard from an old friend who still lived in Cawder that my mother was pretty ill. I had exchanged a few letters with my mother since leaving Glasgow for London. My cupboard love had never been completely killed and, although these communications were few, they were still of importance to me. I had not bothered to communicate with my father, having no feelings at all towards him, but my mother still meant something to me. When I heard that she was ill, I decided that it was time to make a sojourn to Cawder.

Few things about Cawder had changed. A lot of the thugs from my time of living there had become hippy thugs. That is, they were still fighting, stealing and hanging around in gangs, but they said, 'man' a lot and they used any kind of drugs that they could get their hands on - especially amphetamines - to boost their fighting prowess. I was still known around the estate and my prior reputation seemed to have survived my absence, so I felt pretty secure returning to my parents' home.

It was a strange journey back. I had not been away for more than a couple of years, but everything looked different. Somehow it was a lot greyer than I had remembered. The streets and houses looked dingier, the graffiti looked more degenerate, and the people looked much more downtrodden than the image I had kept in my head. After living in so many different places and mixing with so many different types of people, all I could see around Cawder was hopelessness. My senses tasted depression as I walked up the street where I had once played 'tig', 'kick the can', or kerb football. As I walked into the close, which seemed to have shrunk in my absence, and climbed the two flights of stairs to my parents' door, everything seemed smaller, more shrunken and somehow much less than I had remembered.

My mother answered the doorbell and smiled when she saw me.

'Come on in, Les, and I'll make some tea. Your dad's in the living room.'

No more than that, but I was sure that she was pleased to see me again. She had alienated her adopted daughter, who had now returned from New Zealand and was living in the south side of Glasgow; and who was less like a sister to me than a distant acquaintance, as so much had changed since she left, and we were nothing like the people we had been as children. She had alienated a daughter, and I guess she saw that her only hope of having a family lay in retaining some ties with me.

Well, I'd see how she was and perhaps visit occasionally, but there was no possible return to a real mother/son relationship for us. That possibility had been buried under the comprehensive weight of a thoroughly miserable childhood, and I doubted that a few visits were going to make any difference to the depth of our relationship. I just couldn't see myself as a regular visitor to Cawder. Even as I waited for my tea, I couldn't remember ever feeling that this environment was actually my home.

But she was my mum and she was ill, so I hung around.

We had some tea and a few sandwiches, while we passed the time together. It was all very strange. Nothing was really asked about what I had been doing, or who I had become. It was as if my mother did not want to step over the mark, and my father was on 'good behaviour' and avoided anything that could spark contention between us. We just sat on the same old furniture, in the same old living room; with the smell of pipe tobacco smoke, compounded by my mother's cigarette smoke (she had recently started smoking); the gas fire's one jet heated the room and the sound from the constantly active television set filled the many gaps in our conversation.

I asked them about themselves. No change, except for a new second-hand car my father had purchased. They gave me local gossip and waxed lyrical about how well one of my cousins was doing as a laboratory technician and how successful another cousin was in some council office job. I answered in the right places, until the silences got long enough for me to feel that it was time to escape. I picked up my cup to return it to the kitchen and my mother came with me.

She talked quietly to me as I reached the sink.

'I've been pretty ill, Les.'

It was the first mention of illness from my mother. She had looked a little thinner and a little strained, while my father had looked as robust as usual. I had not really noticed much more damage than the normal ageing process and living on this estate in relative poverty could bring.

'What's up, mum?'

'They don't know, son. I've been having some tests, but it could be serious.'

My mother looked pretty worried, and for the first time in my life it actually looked like genuine worry, as opposed to the normal emotional manipulation I had been brought up with.

'Your dad doesn't really know how bad it is, son. He's no' very good with that stuff. I'm waiting to get my results before I tell him.'

Not much had changed in their open relationship, then. I put on my most sympathetic look and voice, as I tried to be a caring supporter. 'Well, let's not worry till we find out, mum - eh? I'll stay in touch and we can sort it out when we know. When do you get your results?'

'Ah'll get them in a few days, son. Do you want to stay back here for a while?'

That's when I really knew that it was serious. My mother's pride would never have allowed her to invite me back home after my ignominious departure years before, unless there was something really dark going on.

'I've got my flat, mum, and I'm living with my girlfriend, but I'll keep visiting. Are you OK for money..?'

'Just the usual, Les.'

'I'm going to get a job soon, mum, and I've got a bit put away. If you need anything just let me know - eh?'

After a brief and tentative hug, and without acknowledging my dad - I left.

I had mixed feelings about my visit. I was worried about my mother and her illness. I felt as remote from my father, and their environment, as I had ever felt in my life. It was all very strange and I wasn't too sure how I fitted into their lives at all. I hadn't really thought about getting a job, either, but - with my mother sick - I felt that I'd better get myself sorted out, just in case I had to hang around Glasgow for a while to support her.

I walked back to the west end, thinking deeply and pondering my next move.

CHAPTER LXV

From Hippy to Clippie

I was still a little confused about how I would offer support to my mother and I couldn't get my head around my long-term prospects; so, instead of working out what I should do next from a career point of view, I got myself a job on the buses. The Glasgow corporation was always a 'dead cert' for a job if you were unqualified or had my limited qualifications and experience. They would give almost anyone a chance of a job and there were generally vacancies for bus crews. The bus depots had a huge turnover of staff, mainly because their generosity was most often rewarded by the theft of a high percentage of their takings each day. It was a common 'perk' that was orchestrated between the bus conductors and drivers on their routes.

The corporation had a policy of firing thieves without prosecuting them. This was a humane policy that was well known on the streets and therefore well abused by their workers. As there was no real deterrent, many bus crews felt that they had been given a licence to steal, and would 'pockle' away until they eventually got caught and were sacked. Not many crews were looking to make a long-term future on the buses.

The common mode of theft was for the conductor to take a portion of the ticket price from a traveller without handing out a ticket. The conductor would pocket this cash without having to worry about his ticket issue matching his takings at the end of the day. This practice was taken as the norm by most of the Glasgow population, particularly within the city's vast housing estates. Nobody questioned this tradition, and the transaction was usually initiated by the travellers themselves with a, 'Here ye go, son - just keep the ticket.'

The punter got a cheap journey and the conductor had some more coins to add to his personal takings. Some of the greedier crews would work the, 'Sorry, mate, ma ticket machine's broken' trick, when they would take the full price of the journey from people and not even bother to try and hand out a ticket. There was also the used ticket scam, when the conductor would spend time at the bus terminus going round his bus and picking up discarded tickets, to be reissued on the return journey. The smartest lads would make sure that, when they issued these tickets in the first place, the ink cartridge that stamped the date and time on the tickets was blocked and would not print; then they could hand out the old tickets to punters, without worrying about an inspector coming onto their bus and catching them out.

There was no attempt at sleight of hand with any of these scams - the general public knew the score and very few complained. The few that did were issued with a 'pukka' ticket, a sneer of derision and more than one abusive comment from the conductor and some fellow-travellers. Like most petty crime, this trick succeeded because the general public either didn't care about the crime being committed or sympathized with the criminals. It was a socially acceptable 'pockle'. This was a working-class crime and the bus service catered mainly to the working classes. Who was going to grass up one of their own? The fact that the breadth of this crime undoubtedly affected both ticket prices and the rates that citizens paid to sponsor the service went right over the heads of the travelling population.

The biggest and most lucrative haul fell to conductors or drivers on their last day at the job. On this day the lads had a standard procedure for giving an employee a good send-off. Once away from the garage, the buses preceding the one that the leaver was working on would slow down, or even park up and wait. Ignoring any sort of capacity regulations, the leaver's bus would pick up as many people as they could cram into the confines of their double-decker metal carriage. The conductor would make no attempt at giving out tickets, using the broken machine routine as the excuse, and would simply collect an approximation of the journey's cost from as many punters as possible. All of the money collected went into his pocket as his 'farewell perk'.

One bus on the route would drive just ahead of the packed leaver's bus and, if an inspector was sighted, then the driver would pick him up to make sure that the leaver did not get caught out with a bus full of travellers who did not have a single ticket between them. The bus containing the guy who was leaving would then leapfrog the bus with the inspector in it and continue on its overloaded journey. The rest of the buses would violate timetable regulations and just amble behind the packed-out bus, picking up anyone who could not fit inside this overweight vehicle. The farewell convoy went on all day and the leaver could build up quite a small fortune - unfortunately, it would be mostly in change, but it was nonetheless a welcome nest egg.

A Glasgow traveller could always tell when someone was leaving the bus service. There would be no buses for an hour and then they would get a convoy of a half a dozen buses coming along; one bus would be full to bursting and trying to cram in more, with the rest of the buses sitting a bit behind with their doors firmly shut until the collecting bus had moved on. This situation brought a few half-hearted curses, but nobody really objected - 'After aw', it was the boy's farewell.'

'What were the inspectors doing?' you may well ask. These poor unfortunates, promoted usually because of time served and a perception that they were honest, walked a very thin line. Nobody liked the inspectors, or 'hats' as they were referred to by the bus crews. As far as the crews were concerned, they were there to spy on their daily activities and to get them into trouble if they saw an infringement of the rules. As far as the public were concerned, they were there to catch them out for not paying the correct fare for a journey and to throw them off the bus if necessary.

There was a pretty general hatred of ticket inspectors in Glasgow.

This may not have bothered a bus inspector in any other city. In Glasgow, it really wasn't healthy to be so widely hated. Glasgow was a city of spontaneous violence, especially within the housing estates. It was also a city of large alcohol consumption and, therefore, a large number of aggressively drunken passengers. An inspector who became too hated on any particular bus route needed to be transferred to another route quickly, before he was beaten to a pulp some night while trying to carry out his duty. He could expect no help from the bus crews - that was a certainty.

Inspectors were cautious. If they suspected anyone of cheating on fares, or if they had some beef about a crew's lack of adherence to the corporation rules, then they handed in their reports at the garage, without making the complaint known to the crew. If they got on a bus and found that it was full of thugs, or drunks, or just generally belligerent people, then they would have a cursory look around, talk to the driver for a few stops and then disembark quickly. Not many inspectors would risk their neck by trying to throw a thug or group of thugs off a bus for travelling without paying. That they could also expect no help from the general public was another certainty.

The other factor against a bus inspector being able to carry out his duty with any degree of success was the bus crew protection system. Bus crews were generally selected to work within their own housing estates or areas. As Glasgow housing estates were also ganglands, where you could really only survive if you were affiliated, crews were generally given their home turf to work in as a measure of protection. This also meant that the local gangsters could easily take exception to having any inspector on their mates' bus while they were travelling on it - especially if they were travelling together in numbers. Some crews took full advantage of this situation and had a permanent entourage of thugs travelling on their bus. The little 'hoods' would sit upstairs and smoke, drink and occasionally play cards. A smart conductor would hand out occasional cigarette money to them as payment for their protection services. This was the ultimate inspector deterrent, and gave the protected crew an undeterred licence to steal.

Shortly after my visit to Cawder and the realization that my mum was ill, I joined this happy bunch of working men as a Glasgow corporation bus conductor.

++++++++

I wasn't a good bus conductor. I don't think that I have ever taken a job less seriously than I took my employment with the corporation. This was just a very temporary stopgap for me. It was a way to earn some money while I waited to see how my mother's illness turned out and what my next decent move would be. I also gained a qualification! To be a bus conductor you needed to hold a licence, and so my initiation into the job involved some simple training on how to use a ticket

326

machine, how to count out change and on what bits of my uniform went on where! It was the simplest form of education, and I think that even an untrained monkey would have struggled to fail, but my mum was proud when I told her that I had a 'clippie' certificate.

'That's great, son - you're really gettin' on now - eh?'

It is the only time I can remember my mother ever being proud of me, and it was because I had passed an idiot test to become a conductor. Ah, well; I guess I should be grateful for small praises. I was never going to stay in this job, so she had disappointment to look forward to later, and plenty of time to come when she could slate me again for being a quitter.

I knew that my clippie job was not going to provide me with any kind of stimulation and, within the hierarchy of human needs, it was definitely level one and survival. I was right about the job, but it really was a great time in my life; I had totally underestimated the amount of fun that I would have as a clippie - especially at the weekends.

++++++++

Saturday night was chaos night on the buses. It seemed as if every drunk in Glasgow needed a bus home from the pub, and there were always a few who were either too drunk to pay, would pay with a couple of cans from their carry-out, or just didn't have any money left over from their alcohol binge for their bus fare. Most bus crews hated working the Saturday-night shift - but I loved it.

I had quickly learned to sling my ticket machine low across my body, with the bulky ticket dispenser hanging from loose straps at my right-hand side. This served as an able weapon of deterrence to any would-be thug who wanted to be belligerent or attack me for my takings. I also worked my own home estate route most of the time and so I felt pretty secure in my job from the potential for violence from travelling drunks. Security issues aside, I really loved these nights simply for the laughs they brought.

There were the singers. On a Saturday night you would always get the drunken crooners, happily smashed out of their heads, who would give full vent to their discordant voices and would serenade the other passengers with Sidney Devine renditions of old Scots favourites. Sing-songs were a big part of both Friday- and Saturday-night trips. I used to join in myself, strolling about my bus, paying lip-service to collecting money and enjoying more than a few beers with the customers. I never had a driver who enjoyed the sing-songs, though. I'd often get, 'Fur pity's sake, are you goin' tae shut them up, Les? That noise is drivin' me crazy, son.' To which I would simply smile and reply, 'You can shut them up if you want, mate - I don't mind it.' None of my drivers wanted the responsibility that shutting up a bus full of drunks entailed, and so my singalong bus just carried on into the night.

Weekends were fun - minus a few small drawbacks.

One downside was the pukers. There's nothing worse than having to ride back to the garage on a bus reeking with a drunk's watery vomit! Once this happened, it was a case of 'abandon both ship and passengers' and head back to base for either a new bus or the rest of the night off. It happened to everybody from time to time, but I witnessed my funniest occurrence of drunken stomach-shifting one Saturday night, on the last bus from the centre of Glasgow to Merryhill garage.

I'd collected my fares and was sitting upstairs chatting to some girls at the back of the bus - pulling being another nice wee perk of the Saturday-night shift. I was smoking and talking to these two wee honeys, trying to decide which one was likelier to fall for my charms, when one of them, looking over my shoulder, said, 'Les - ye'd better watch that guy doon there.' I swung around to see what the problem was and - sure enough - it was a bloody puker! He was sitting five rows down from me, head bent, swaying in an exaggerated manner to every movement of the bus, while holding on to the seat in front of him with one hand. He was making 'harrumph!'-type noises, as though he was clearing phlegm from his throat, and it was only too obvious from his completely ruined state that vomiting was about to follow.

The guy in front of my probable puker was also blind drunk. He was lying with his head back, snoring away the journey. He'd no doubt waken up at the terminus, miles from home, wondering why he had missed his stop. This was a common problem with drunks on buses. I'd often taken a drunk from terminus to terminus during the course of a night, wakening him up at the end of each leg, only to have him fall asleep again for the entire return journey. I'd usually give them a chance to sleep a bit of it off and then find out where they needed to be dropped off before I finished my shift. This particular journey was a one-way trip on the last bus, so my duffle-coated drunken sleeper would just have to take his chances at the terminus.

I had to deal with my potential puker.

I got off my seat casually with as much of an attitude as I could muster to try and impress the ladies. 'OK, girls, wait here; I'll be back in a minute,' I said, and I made to try and remove this drunk before he stank out my bus for the rest of the journey. I had just got to my feet when the bus lurched around a corner and my puker, unable to hold it in any longer, lifted his head slightly, grabbed his stomach with one hand and, with a cry for: 'Hughie!' puked his guts up - right into the hood of the poor duffle-coated sleeper in front of him!

The girls, all of the witnessing passengers and I fell about laughing. The puker, still completely out of his head, was awakened by the hilarity. He looked out of the window, burped and mumbled something incoherent, then lurched to his feet, weaving his way down the aisle to the stairs, with watery vomit splashed down the front of his shirt. I quickly pressed the bell above my head to get the bus to stop. If the puker was leaving, then I wanted him off right here; I wasn't waiting till the next bus stop.

Meanwhile the man in the duffle coat slept on - oblivious.

The rest of that journey was spent in laughter, while all of the punters upstairs swapped suggestions as to the likely reaction of Mr Duffle Coat when he awoke and found out that his hood was full of smelly vomit.

We neared the garage and still he slept.

Many of the punters left the bus disappointed not to see his reaction, but I wouldn't let anyone waken him up. I figured that, if he slept till the terminus, he could at least get cleaned up at the garage, and I didn't want him throwing a fit and spreading the mess around if I could help it. After a time with all of the windows opened up, we didn't really notice the smell too much.

I spent a pleasant time on the rest of the journey with the girls, managed a snog with one of them, and then bid them farewell just before the last stop, promising to get together sometime - which, as usual, turned out to be never.

I woke Mr Duffel Coat at the terminus. After a few dizzy seconds coming round, he became pretty animated when he saw what had happened in his hood. I told him that I hadn't seen who'd done it, but that I'd fix it up for him to get cleaned off in the garage. Without a proper target on which to vent his drunken anger, he had to be content with volleys of curses at the world in general, and in particular any dirty bastard who would do that to him.

Poor sod. I bet, if he has not learned to stay awake on a late-night bus, that he has at least learned either to sit in the back row or to wear a coat without a hood!

A lot of the punters were real characters, and I could probably write a book just dedicated to my short time in this job and the antics that I came across. I had flashers of both sexes to deal with, on each occasion catching an unwanted eyeful as I came up the stairs to the top deck of the bus and as my eyes reached crotch level. First I found a fat woman, who could have been a bag lady, sitting in the middle of the back seat, legs akimbo, with no underwear on - she almost put me off sex for life. Then, at another time, I caught a pervert who sat in the same back seat of the bus and opened his coat to flash his tackle at any young girl coming up the stairs. Each time I threw them off the bus with words of derision and a feeling of disgust.

The worst afternoons on the buses were summer afternoons on pension day. On these days my senses were assaulted by the overpowering, sickly sweet smell of old lavender. Even with all the windows and the doors opened, I could never quite rid the bus of this old people's smell.

The worst shifts of the day were on the school runs. At these times packs of maniacal kids would swarm onto the buses, making noise, fighting, arguing and bothering the other citizens. Vandalism from these little monsters was also rife, and on more than one occasion I had to throw the whole lot of them off and make them walk to school.

As well as the customers of character, there were also bus crews worthy of a book. The bus service seemed to trawl for every type of bizarre character that Glasgow had to offer. Although most of these demented souls never lasted very long in the job, there always seemed to be another mad bastard to replace any that we lost. I had my share of nutters as crew-mates.

There was the speed freak that I had the misfortune to be teamed up with for a while. He was constantly high on amphetamines - not a happy situation for a bus driver who was supposed to stop at every bus stop on the route and wait until people embarked and disembarked from the bus. This guy hated waiting. He used to berate me for helping people onto the bus - even old women, ladies with shopping plus children, and especially any disabled passengers. He would often just not stop at a bus stop if he saw that there was a huge queue waiting, much to the anger of any passengers who wanted to disembark! The funniest incident I experienced was the one when he got fed up with me helping people and just drove off as I was assisting a lady with her child and pram off the bus. I was just putting up the pram for my passenger when I heard the bus take off behind me. I could only stand and watch in disgust as the bus disappeared into the distance while my speed freak deliberately took off without me. I then had an embarrassing ten-minute wait for the next bus so that I could finally get back to the garage. The punters waiting at the bus stop and the crew who eventually picked me up all thought that this was hilarious. It was no real skin off of my nose, either, so I shared the laugh and just relaxed and had a cigarette on the way back.

Back at the garage, nobody seemed to have noticed what had happened, and, as it was my last run, I just cashed in and went home. Shortly afterwards I was given a new driver. The speed freak actually had a regular conductor, who had just been on holiday that week. I have always wondered if they eventually fired that crazy driver, but he was still there when I left the job.

There was also the conductor who had a heavy gambling addiction. He got his driver to stop outside a bookmaker's shop one day, went in to the shop, put all the money in his bag onto a 'hot tip', and then waited inside the bookie's for 15 minutes till the race was over. Meanwhile, the punters on the bus were getting pretty angry at being stranded, well away from the normal route, outside a betting shop. His horse lost and he came out of the shop, dropped his hat, jacket and ticket machine onto the back seat, then said goodbye to his driver. Amid condolences from his now sympathetic passengers - he went home. He was fired in his absence, but was never prosecuted for the theft of his ticket money.

I remember one crew who were much more sinister. In the garage they were renowned as 'the mugging crew'. They used to specialize in taking very drunk guys onto their bus, stealing their wallets and valuables when they were asleep, and then letting them off in a drunken stupor, far from where they needed to be. They were eventually caught and dismissed. This was the only time that I remember the police being involved, but even the union representative had no sympathy for their plight.

Characters working the buses and characters travelling on the buses - my time in this job may have been brief, but it certainly wasn't dull!

My mum was proud, too. She thought that I'd really begun to make something of my life now that I had a steady job - with a uniform. I remember how she used to say to me that I must have a big bank balance accumulating now that I had landed so well - 'And a job with plenty of overtime, son - ye're a lucky boy...'

Mums - what can you do..?!

CHAPTER LXVI

Dizzy Dora

My mother got the results of her tests; they were inconclusive. She started getting treatment for some stomach thing - some painkillers for her obvious distress - and she was put on a high-fibre diet to cure her chronic constipation. I felt sorry for her distress, but as there seemed to be nothing terminal going on I was starting to get itchy feet again.

I had been hanging around the old hippy scene and I had met a young girl, just out of school, called Dora. The wee girl was an aspiring hippy. She came from a good and prosperous family and had attended a very good girls' school. When her parents had decided to split up, however, she rebelled against her pampered upbringing and was determined to live the life of a hippy. She saw herself as a cool babe, taking drugs and partying with switched-on freaks, while sending a message of rebellion and independence to her parents.

She was very naive.

A 30-year-old guy called John, who hung around the fringes of the hippy scene, had seduced Dora while she was 16 and still at school. John was a lowlife who had a long criminal record and no respect at all for

Dora's innocence. He came on to her as the experienced hippy guy, feeding her with dope, stories and amateur guitar playing. Most of the hippy types whom Dora hung around were suspicious and disparaging of John - but Dora was in love and thought that the sun rose in his eyes every morning.

Dora's parents were mortified by her life choice. When they found out about her relationship with John, they did everything that they could to bring her back into the fold. Dora's father was an instrument-maker - fairly successful and reasonably well connected. Dora's mother was a very determined middle-aged lady - and also fairly well connected. They used these connections to bring police trouble into the scene around Dora and to try to wrench her away from her slimy boyfriend. They were well meaning, and only doing what any decent parent would do to protect their child from an obviously bad influence; but they made the same mistake of judgement that many concerned parents make - with the same results. The more they tugged and pulled and interfered, the more Dora pushed herself deeper into the hippy scene.

Dora's parents had, of course, involved the police in their struggle.

The police hated John. They saw him as an evil paedophile, seducing a young girl with drugs and defiling her with his lifestyle as well as his body. They really wanted to get their hooks into him and keep him away from this young girl. They watched him like a hawk for a long time, just waiting for him to put a foot wrong. They were hoping for something big such as a drugs bust, which they would have used as a powerful lever to make sure that he was incarcerated for a long time. They didn't get the drugs bust, but John was neither honest nor smart, and in the end they got the break that they wanted.

John loved cars. He was always boasting about the cars that he had driven. Not too difficult, if you have no qualms about ownership and the skills to enter and start a car without a set of keys. He owned a car - nothing special, just a second-hand Ford - but he was always 'Going to get something better.' John was a chancer of the highest order, but, when he decided to chance driving without road tax and insurance, this gave the police the opportunity that they had been waiting for. In the United Kingdom it is an imprisonable offence to drive without car insurance. For most people, the full weight of the law would hardly be applied. Most people would get a heavy fine, a warning and be told that the next time they were caught it could mean a jail term. The police badly wanted to jail John, though, so they made sure that, when they caught him, they were able to convince his judge that he should go to jail immediately.

John went to jail and Dora was devastated.

Dora's parents thought that the removal of John from her life would automatically bring their daughter back to them. How wrong they were. Dora always felt that her parents were to blame for John's incarceration, as they had involved the police for a long time. So, far from returning to the fold, Dora threw herself deeper into living the life of a hippy. She thumbed her nose at her parents, declaring undying love for John and a determination to wait for him to come back to her.

She took some stupid risks for this guy when she visited him in jail. On one occasion she smuggled in some hashish, which John told her never to do again - thankfully, she listened. Another time she caused a stir by arriving for a visit wearing a long coat, knee-length boots and nothing at all on underneath the coat. She said it was a birthday treat for John, but when she flashed at him, showing him her best features in the raw, she almost caused a riot among the other prisoners, who clamoured for a look! Apparently, her lover took serious stick from the other inmates for a long time after that incident - they actually had a big row over it during her subsequent weekly visit. Finally fed up, Dora stopped visiting him for a while.

That's when I met her.

Dora had been turned out of John's flat because of big rent arrears and the fact that the Drug Squad had busted her place, shortly after John was incarcerated. She needed somewhere to stay and I had a small but comfortable flat on the Great Western Road. I took her in, with a view to her taking the place over when I moved on. I knew that I had had enough of Glasgow by this time and I wanted to quit my boring conductor's job and go somewhere to start a new life - I just hadn't worked out where, as yet. I didn't think that I would be around long, and so I was happy to offer Dora my place in the long term, and provide somewhere for her to crash in the short term.

Dora's undying faithfulness to John was fading when she moved in. She started occasionally seeing another guy, who had sex not just with her but also with many other young ladies. He enjoyed having this young babe around, but had no interest whatsoever in forming a relationship. Dora was a romantic and had quite a wee crush on this guy. I think she must have thought that enough sex would turn him on to a bigger relationship. It never happened. In the end, all Dora was left with was guilt about betraying her jailed boyfriend and frustration from her inconclusive wee escapades with the 'other man'. She asked my advice on what she should do. Disliking John, I told her to find anyone else she could and dump her incarcerated loser of a boyfriend. She ignored my advice, though.

Romance wasn't Dora's only problem. When the police had busted her flat in Kelvinside, they had found some cannabis and had charged her with possession. The Drug Squad had been alerted to her indulgences by her well-meaning parents, who were still desperately trying to get some control of their wayward daughter's life. I didn't know anything about this parental link to the drug bust at the time and so, when her court case came up, I advised her that she should just plead guilty, take the fine and get on with her life. As it turned out, this wasn't the best advice from Dora's point of view. The judge had been well primed about her circumstances from reports that he had ordered from social services. As you can imagine, her parents painted a fairly damning picture of her lifestyle and had petitioned the court to help them get her back under control. Both her parents were in attendance at court, hoping that this would be the lever to get them their little girl back. The judge complied with their wishes. He ordered her, as a 16-year-old minor; to live under her parents' control for a probationary term. He also agreed to a court injunction by her parents that she was never to see John again.

It had all been a set-up, and Dora was trapped!

I think she was pretty cheesed off with me, blaming my bad advice for her predicament. I didn't feel any guilt at all. She had been caught not only in possession of drugs but also in a relationship with a dangerous slime-ball. I actually felt that it was probably all for the best, even as I doubted her soft-hearted parents' ability to ensure that the sentence was carried out. I moved out of my place to avoid her flak and left her to it. It was time for me to move on, anyway. This phase, the last of my life in Glasgow, was definitely due to end very soon.

I was right about Dora's parents' ability to carry out the wishes of the court. She hung around their home for a while, but she still stayed in close touch with the hippy scene and made her break a couple of months later.

For a while Dora took up begging for a living. She would dress up in tarty clothes and wait around at the Glasgow or Edinburgh train stations or close by, telling people that she had had her purse stolen and had no money for the train home. Given her very young age and her pretty and innocent face, she made a killing. Folk would invariably give her the money for her pretend ride home. She used to boast that Edinburgh's Princes Street was the best venue, but she had to quit there for a while after she almost got arrested for soliciting. She was still begging successfully when I lost touch with her and moved on in my own life.

I saw Dora very briefly some time later. She was back with John and she was eight months' pregnant. She came to visit me with the slime-ball and I let them spend a single night at my place. I was pleased to see Dora, but sad that she was back with John again.

I'm glad to report that she escaped that life eventually. I heard fairly recently that she was illustrating and writing children's books, with some success. I immediately went out and bought a copy of one of her books for my daughter, and got great enjoyment both from reading it and in thinking that Dora had really made something of her life.

Good on you, Dora!

CHAPTER LXVII

Heading out of Town

I moved in with Will, a hippy friend of mine, for a while.

It was somewhere to stay, but the hippy scene in Glasgow was getting just so old for me. I was not even comfortable around the guys I had known, who were all very much entrenched in the same pointless pattern of getting stoned every day and of doing anything they could to supplement their dole money - short of working - for a living.

My friend Peter had gone north to stay with his cousin Linda, who had once again dumped her ex-husband and was living in a cottage in the countryside. Margaret had decided that she was a lesbian, probably in a last-ditch attempt to get some parity with Peter; but, as a result, she spent a lot of time with her new bunch of girls and had practically no time for me. I had a few other decent friends, but this scene was not where I wanted to be any more.

One day, I got an opportunity to move on. Although I didn't know it when the journey began - it was to prove to be the start of the most fundamental change in my life to that date.

It all began as an ordinary morning in town.

Peter and Linda were home. Margaret called me and asked if I wanted to come down to Peter's mum's house and meet up with the guys for the afternoon. One of Peter's mum's eccentricities was that she enjoyed a joint with her son and his hippy friends, so I was more than happy to take them a smoke and hang out there for the afternoon. I missed these guys and was looking forward to catching up with their news.

It wasn't to be the happy day that I had envisaged, though.

Will and I stepped out of his place onto Byres Road, and started walking up this road to Peter's mum's house. We had only walked about 100 yards when two members of the Drug Squad cornered us to perform a random search. I was an unknown to these guys, having been out of the scene for a long time in London, but Will had always been around here since our schooldays and the police had pretty well sorted out the local names on the scene by now. Will was one that they knew only too well, having pegged him as a dealer and having failed to bust him for it so far.

They bundled us into the nearby entrance of a tenement building for a quick body search.

They were chiefly interested in Will, having had their eye on him and his dealing activities for some time. They searched him first, making me stand to one side, but warning me against any attempt at running away. We were both carrying. I had a quarter of an ounce of hash in my pocket, which I had intended sharing with Linda, Margaret, Peter and his mum. Will had some Ti-sticks in a tobacco tin, along with several tabs of acid, which he had intended selling that night at the pub.

While they were giving Will a pretty thorough going-over, I managed to surreptitiously remove the hash from my pocket, and I consumed it as quickly as I could chew. One of the DS guys asked me what I was doing. I tried to look as scared as I could and just nodded my head. He gave me a strange look for a moment, shook his head and then returned to his debasement of Will. I returned to my chewing, keeping my face turned as far away from the two police officers as I could. They found Will's stash and then they searched me, finding nothing as I had already eaten my bit of dope. They took us both down to the nearest police station.

By the time we got to the police station, I had no idea what was going on. I was getting higher and higher and could not have said anything coherent if I had wanted to. They processed Will, keeping me in another room. I remember some policeman asking me questions and I just kept my mouth shut and said nothing. They got my name from my driving licence, which had my parents' address on it, and then - satisfied with busting Will - they pretty much left me alone. After an indeterminate time, they released me. I can't even remember what they said - it was all a blur by this time.

On increasingly shaky legs, I made my way back to Will's place. I had it in my head that the police would pretty quickly turn over his flat for any more drugs, and I didn't want to get caught up in the middle if he had left anything there. I let myself in with the key he had given me, packed up my rucksack and exited - only minutes before the police raided the place and demolished his flat looking for more stuff!

I headed up to Peter's mum's house. I had no real idea where I was going to stay or what I was doing; I just wanted to get somewhere that I could lie down before I passed out completely.

By the time I arrived at their place it was getting pretty close to early evening. I was given a lot of quiet sympathy from the guys when I arrived, but Peter's dad was in residence and so the atmosphere was not very good. I vaguely remember Linda saying something about a big row with Peter's dad and that she and Peter were heading back up north that night. She asked me if I wanted to come with her. I must have said 'yes' - though, because of the state I was in, I am amazed that I could have communicated any wishes at all. I'm even more astounded that Linda wanted to travel with me in my semi-comatose condition.

Somehow or other I managed a few goodbyes, and then I set out with Linda. We were hitch-hiking back to her place, which was about a two-hour drive from Glasgow, and the guys had decided that Linda, who was most likely to get lifts, being a girl, would take me with her and that Peter would make his own way back.

To me the journey was just a blur. I remember being shaken awake a few times and hauled in and out of cars. Apparently Linda told drivers that I had food poisoning or something when they enquired about my condition. Why they even let us into their cars in the first place is a mystery to me. The only answer that I can think of is that my resourceful friend Linda was very pretty and had a warm and seductive smile; I have no doubt she was able to charm us through the journey and allay any fears that our benefactors might have felt.

I don't remember arriving at the cottage - the hash had all but put me into a coma by that time; I just remember waking up the next morning with a foggy head, wrapped up in blankets in Linda's bed, and thinking that I had had a dream about making love with her. Apparently I had made love with her, although I hear it was more a case of Linda making love to me and giving up when I eventually passed out completely!

I awoke into a new and unfamiliar environment. I remember looking around the sparsely furnished cottage, with its multi-purpose stove for cooking, heating and hot water, its two rooms, one of which was occupied by a sleeping Peter by this time, and its quaint galley kitchen and small bathroom. I remember looking out of a window across the summer gold of wheat in the fields, towards the deep blue of the sea - and thinking that I had never felt so much at peace. I put my sense of calm down to the fact that the dope was still very much alive within my system, but I was still completely enamoured with where I had ended up.

Linda made us some breakfast and offered to roll up a joint, but I wasn't interested; I wanted to explore my new surroundings. I took a cup of coffee and then went outside to drink in the fresh air, feeling somehow more complete than I had felt in a long, long time.

The cottage was situated in the countryside bordering the coast. It was about two miles from the nearest village, with nothing between the house and the coast but fields of hay or vegetables. I went for a long, lazy walk around the place in the warm summer sunshine, feeling as if I was on holiday and completely mellowed out.

This really was great. Although I had never been here before, I felt as if I had somehow come home. I was away from the noise, pollution and bustle of city life. I had left the games and the paranoia and the drugs behind me. I may only have been visiting Linda, but this really felt like a place where I could belong.

Peter finally arose, and we eventually all trooped off on the long walk down to the village for supplies. When we reached the small community, I lit up inside at the views of the sea. I strolled the little lanes and streets with a growing sense of well-being. Stone houses with red pan-tiled roofs; fishing boats on the water; gift shops on the prom; people going about their business with an air of familiarity; this environment sang out as a community!

This was something completely new to me. Of all the places I had been, and of all the scenes I had been a part of, I had never felt the over-riding sense of community that I was experiencing now. The more I saw, the more I came to love this place.

This was for me.

I was definitely going to stay.

SONG 15 - MY ROOTS

Home again, back to my country - Turn around, smells like
the sea
I sense it's just where I belong - Up here, can I be free.
Empty, like all the fields around me - I'm used up, dried
out, coming down
My short life, it is behind me - Can I start again?

Voice on my shoulder says - you belong,
Voice on my shoulder says - look around,
Voice on my shoulder says - close your eyes and feel the
place, feel your roots,
Voice on my shoulder says - stay awhile,
Voice on my shoulder says - make this your home,
Voice on my shoulder says - time to stop,
Voice on my shoulder says - you've travelled too far
already

Walking round, feeling deep inside - This place is just
where I belong.
The pace up here's started healing - The cracks of city life.

Made my bed, I'm here to stay now - Fresh air, my head is
getting clear.
Gently, I ease myself down - Back to my roots.

CHAPTER LXVIII

Back to my Roots

I lived with Linda for a few weeks. We shared a bed, but it was more as friends making love than as a relationship between lovers. Peter lodged in her spare room. Linda was still pretty messed up from her split with her ex-husband and I was bursting with the need for change. We were a strange group. All three of us were trying to escape from our recent pasts, and none of us had any real roots or a notion of how to build foundation for our futures. It was a hot summer, a great time to be in the countryside and by the seaside. We walked; Linda introduced me to the sprinkling of friends and acquaintances that she knew in this place; we hung out together; and we partied.

I paid only cursory attention to the people that I was introduced to. Most of them were hippy guys from various parts, who thought that it would be cool to live in the country. They had taken their city ways here with them, though. None had any work, living on the dole as they had in the city. I could not see any evidence of either the social skills that they would need to become a part of this community or the will in any of them to make that move anyway. They had made some local contacts, but they had done so through their drug habits. Their community contribution had been to introduce a ready supply of hash and acid into the local teenage community, and as such they had quite a few of the local lads and lassies hanging out at their village flats or country cottages.

They were not popular. There were many evenings when angry fathers would knock at their doors, looking for a young daughter who had got mixed up in their scene. They would steal from the local shops and I even heard that a recently departed cadre of junkies had been breaking into the local chemist shops. As in Glasgow, so too up here they were pretty bad news.

I was more interested in the local community.

The local people seemed great to me. It seemed that most of the young guys I met enjoyed easy camaraderie, born of living in a small community and growing up together. Fishing was the predominant source of employment at the time and these guys also worked and lived very closely together at sea. I thought that the timelessness and the lack of places to hide in a community where everyone knew everyone else's business created a much more balanced environment than I had been used to. The locals took living in this place for granted and were often disparaging about their own lifestyles - putting it down as too small, writing off their community as boring. Because of this, many of the young folk were drawn to the hippy incomers and hung around them looking for something different and the opportunity to be involved in a scene which, to them, was a bit more exciting. As a 19-year-old boy who had just been immersed in the background that attracted them, I could not see what could possibly be better in the hippy scene than the lifestyle they already had. It was just a case of opposites attracting, I guess.

Peter had made the decision not to go back to Glasgow, and instead to stay in the country. He had been looking around for a cottage to rent for some time before I arrived with Linda. He found a house, but it was pretty big, and he knew that he would need a couple of other people to share the rent. He asked me if I wanted to share with him, and I said 'yes'. He also brought in a young hippy guy whom we both knew as the third resident of our new home.

I don't really know why Peter chose this place to live, as it was certainly no more open to the gay community than the city had been. Perhaps it was the pace of life that attracted him. He definitely needed a change, though. He was so fed up and his identity was so stifled that he could no longer live a make-believe life. He probably felt that he had anonymity in this new place and that being so unknown would protect him. He, like the rest of us, knew nothing about small communities. Peter started telling the hippies about his sexuality, who in turn told the locals, who in turn passed it around generally - as is normal in village life. It didn't take long before he was defined by his sexuality and was well known around the area.

344

He hadn't really found the liberation he so desired.

At least it was a safe place for him to live. Although the community was small, it was still a community. There were many characters here and Peter was just another one amongst many. He was not hounded or persecuted. He was not shunned or singled out. He was simply left alone to be who he was. Peter could survive - but I'm sure it wasn't the kind of survival that he had hoped for, and he increased his alcohol consumption to compensate.

I had some funny initial reactions within this community too. At first the locals and the hippies assumed that, as I was living with Peter, I also had to be gay. It was a highly amusing time for me, to see the reactions of people and to read the judgement in their looks and stares. I have never been confused about my sexuality and so it didn't upset me to be so appraised. One very positive side effect of this belief was that the girls on the scene were very open and very approachable; by the end of the first month I had exploited this phenomenon to such an extent that nobody doubted my heterosexuality. Unfortunately, the ladies were also a lot more cautious in my company now.

It was the summer, I was in a new place, and I was in love with where I was. I settled into my new home and used the time to clean my head of the old and plan for the new. I had no idea as yet what the new might be, but I was sure of one thing - this picturesque place was where I was determined to live and start afresh.

I felt that here I was somehow back to my roots.

CHAPTER LXIX

Settling in

I started to adapt to my new environment. I was living a kind of dual life at the beginning, half in the local hippy scene and half outside it, looking for something different; but this was nothing new for me. I was getting to know the area and I was also trying to get to know the community itself. The hippy scene up here was not one that I planned to get involved too deeply in, but it had the advantage of being somewhat established, if on the fringes of the rest of the community. Through this group of people I met a new set of local folk about my own age. I dated local girls, especially after one disastrous and brief fling with a hippy lady, who had turned out to be completely crazy, but with whom I had returned to Glasgow for a month or so before I got wise and ended the whole thing. My relationship with Molly only reinforced my decision to keep well out of the hippy scene for good.

I started to get closer and closer to the local lads and work out just how I could fit in here. It was a great scene. The lads were like a mixture between my Glasgow friends and my London friends, with one basic difference - they were all a part of this place and, no matter what went down, they all stayed together. I became closest to two guys in particular - Tim and Chris.

Tim and Chris were both fishermen. I got to know them because they were both getting into smoking dope and were hanging around the incomer hippy scene. Between them they introduced me to the lads that they grew up with and, in return, I introduced them to the array of hippies who were constantly passing through at this time. I definitely got the better of the deal. The guys that I met were a laugh to hang out with and had much more about them than just lying around and getting stoned all day. They liked being on the fringe of the hippy scene, but it was for amusement rather than an immersion in this lifestyle. They, on the other hand, met a bunch of transient social outcasts, but - as I said - for them it was just a chance to play in a new scene; it affected their lives but they did not change radically from the experience. All Tim and Chris got was an introduction to deadbeats.

Tim was a really funny guy. He was up for anything, and I enjoyed many fun times with him and his pranks. He was a loyal friend to me and looked out for me during my assimilation into the local scene. He would take me to parties, introduce me to people, and would explain the different way of life up here, without judging me as an outsider.

Chris was also a good and loyal friend. He helped me to find work in his village and he was a friend whenever I most needed one. He taught me to mend nets when I decided to try my hand as a fisherman, and he taught me how to make fish pie and fish soup, and how to cook prawns so that they were edible. He was a great companion and made my integration into village life much easier than it could ever have been without his support.

Both of these guys, neither of whom were much older than I was, proved to be my best friends as I settled into this new rhythm of life.

I was changing.

After a few months of getting to know the place, I was ready to really settle down into my new environment. I had met and was dating off and on a local girl called Martha, who was 17 years old and was on the fringes of the incomer hippy scene. She had a best friend called Heather who was the same age as she was, and these two girls would often hang out and get stoned together. Both girls had already been out with a few of the hippies, and, whereas Heather's fraternization went unchallenged by her family, Martha's sojourn caused a lot of problems for the incomers.

Martha's father was appalled at her choice of friends. He would seek her out at night and cause her plenty of embarrassment - and her new friends some angst - by turning up at their flats while they were all getting stoned. Martha was undeterred by this; she kept hanging out with the smokers' scene, although she was certainly adding to hippy paranoia about being busted for possession of dope every time she turned up. I remember a hippy from Liverpool who'd just moved to the area saying once: 'All these schoolies are going to draw attention an' get us busted one of these days, man.'

He was right, but he was so interested in getting wee Martha into bed that he ignored his own warning. I guess his eventual drug bust was the fault of him putting his loins before his clandestine safety.

When I met Martha, Peter and I had moved to a new cottage, far away from the rest of the crew. Peter was just as fed up with the incursion of the hippy scene into his new surroundings as I was. He had got a new job and was trying to blend a little more into the local community. We got a new place out in the sticks and we both kept our distance from the scene. I dated Martha for a while and she would often spend time at our cottage. Her friend Heather would come around too. I liked Heather, but as I was enamoured with Martha I didn't really get to know her then. Heather was crazy about Peter. That social mix was to change radically over a short period of time.

Linda's ex-husband descended on the country scene again. By this time the man was completely off his head. Drugs and a natural tendency towards craziness had finally driven him over the edge. He was wandering about the country, stealing or begging his survival, and was staying with whoever would put him up. He arrived in our neck of the woods, decided to look up Peter, and ended up staying with us for an uncomfortable couple of weeks.

I hated this crazy man being around. He was nothing but trouble and I knew that he would be ripping off everything and everybody he could while he was here. I also knew that he would be poison to Linda and would inevitably cause her problems again. Peter seemed to like him around, though, so I just had to tolerate his presence. During his visit, he ended up taking Martha away from me.

I guess that I was more disgusted than angry. It didn't say much for me if a madman like that could so easily wrest my girlfriend away. Truth to tell, though, Martha wanted hippy excitement and I wanted local stability. This crazy guy must have seemed like a real adventure to the 17-year-old and so she jumped into his arms. The two of them took off back to Glasgow and Martha got the adventure she craved.

It didn't last, of course.

Mr Crazy ended up hitting her - a lot. Martha eventually wised up and left him to return back home, with a few more mental scars to add to her collection. When she returned she came out to see me. She seemed to want us to get back together, but it was too late. By the time she returned I had moved on and could never have trusted her in the kind of relationship that I now thirsted for.

I had begun dating different local girls when I split up with Martha. Heather was still on the scene too, and we had remained friends after Martha and I split up. She used to come around to our place because she fancied Peter. The strange phenomenon of gay guys being a major attraction to young heterosexual girls was in full evidence around Peter. Many of the young ladies in the area fancied him, but they would have been better off introducing him to their fathers and brothers, as Peter was never interested. I found his ability to charm members of the opposite sex very useful, as it kept a steady stream of dating possibilities around, and I was often able to take advantage of such a glorious opportunity. It was a pretty nice set-up for me - until Peter decided to up the gay stakes.

Peter had always been a bit camp, but not really effeminate. He didn't mince around or wear clothes that were too prissy; he just dressed smartly and affected a fairly suave air. Shortly after my break-up with Martha, however, Peter decided to get more and more outlandish and to experiment with his sexuality to a greater degree. I used to ignore it, figuring that it was still just Peter. The only thing that I was getting fed up with was his increasing drunkenness - for his sake more than anything. He seemed to be disintegrating before my eyes with his heavy drinking binges, and I could not see his liver lasting any length of time while he was consuming vast amounts of Carlsberg Special Brew. I was also alarmed about the amount of local men he seemed to be scoring with. These were often married men, whom Peter would take out of the pub in a drunken state and have sex with in the countryside. I could see him getting into serious trouble over that.

I think that Peter just needed to express himself somehow. He was completely stifled and just needed to be himself, regardless of the social attitudes around him. Knowing him for so long, and knowing the repression that he had lived with, I could never bring myself to comment on his behaviour. I tried to continue to accept Peter for who he was, but it was becoming so different from who I was that I was getting very uncomfortable with our home environment. I was getting fed up with the exhibition of him becoming increasingly camp and outlandish, so I guess it was just about time for us to go our separate ways and - hopefully - still stay friends.

It all came to a head one evening, and then the decision to strike out on my own was set in concrete. I had been in the pub and had met a new young lady. After a few drinks, a bit of banter with the lads in the pub and a bit of 'getting to know you' conversation, I took her back to the cottage to spend the night. I was merry and feeling very pleased with myself for pulling this good-looking chick. I had fancied this girl for some time and I was looking forward to the night to come with relish - until we entered the living room. We walked into a warm, log-fire-lit room, to behold a completely different Peter from the one I had left at home when I went down to the pub. He was sitting on the couch in a ladies' nightgown, lips adorned with bright red lipstick; he was wearing a face pack, his hair was tied back, and he was in the process of painting his bloody toenails with gold nail varnish! In all the time I had known Peter, I had never seen a sight like this. Perhaps he had indulged this transsexual fantasy in private, but in public - never!

I was shocked, but not half as shocked as the lady I was escorting. She took one look at Peter, threw me a look of complete disgust, and said, 'I'm off, you fucking perverts!'

'But, but...' but it was too late to change her mind. I resigned myself to a cold night alone.

That was that. This was a small community, word would spread, and I knew that, if I didn't get a new place for myself pretty quickly, I would be spending a whole lot of winter nights on my own. I stormed off to my room without a word to Peter, determined to find my own place to live as soon as possible.

Thanks to my local friend Chris, I soon found a place to live in a village on the coast.

Peter and I remained friends for a while, but we were never really close again. He was at the stage in his life when he needed to be outrageous, and I couldn't handle it. Our paths rarely crossed and, if they did, it was just for an occasional pint at the pub, or a brief visit from him to my home. I didn't go back to his place.

Peter eventually left the area and went to live in Amsterdam. He was a nice guy and I always hoped that he would find the confidence and freedom in the Netherlands that he could never find during his time in Britain. I would have liked to think that Peter met someone, formed a lasting partnership and lived happily ever after. Alas, it was not to be. I heard a couple of years ago from Linda, whom I have always kept an annual-type contact with, that Peter was dying of cancer. I flew over to Amsterdam to offer him my sympathies and to just chew the fat. I hadn't seen the guy for many, many years, but I still remembered that we had once been close friends. Peter was pleased to see me. We went to lunch and we talked about lots of things. During that visit he told me one of the saddest things that I have ever heard. He told me that he had two regrets. He regretted that the longest relationship that he had ever had in his life had only spanned two weeks. He also told me that he always wished that he could have had a child so that he could have left something behind; without this he felt that his life had been a total waste.

I don't think his life was wasted. Being a good guy counts for something, and I'm sure that there are many people out there who will remember Peter with fondness.

Peter died of lung cancer in 1999.

After leaving the cottage that I had shared with Peter, I settled into my new place and found myself spending more and more time with Heather. By this time, Heather had given up on Peter as anything more than a male girlfriend and so was open to other offers. She had had a brief fling with one of the hippy guys, who had really just used her and dumped her, so she was wary, but fairly interested. We hung around together for a while and then, eventually, Heather moved into my flat with me.

The reaction from Heather's family was mixed. Her father was depressed about it; her mother thought that it was, 'Better than doing it in the bushes;' while her brothers were happy to let her make her own choices. Martha was still Heather's best friend, but she ignored that inconvenient fact and was still proclaiming interest in us getting back together again. I honestly think I always liked Martha the better of the two, but, having been dumped once, I would never have gone back to her.

Instead, Heather and I fell into a fairly stable living pattern.

CHAPTER LXX

Crossing over

The relationship that I developed with Heather hastened my integration into the local scene. Although there were many local lads who didn't like the idea of one of their own taking up with an incomer, I also had strong allies in Tim and Chris, plus a number of other local friends and acquaintances to back me up - so I was accepted in the village. I loved being a part of this small community and was ready to sever my ties completely with the old hippy scene. As Heather had never been particularly enamoured of them anyway, she had no resistance to this change, and we gradually distanced ourselves from the whole drug-infested hippy culture.

I got a job in the village boatyard, and this also helped to bring me into the local community. This was Chris's village and he helped me to find both my rented house and the job. He had just started to settle down with a local girl himself, one whom Heather knew well from her schooldays, and so the four of us used to regularly hang out together.

I was enjoying my new lifestyle.

The boatyard was a laugh. I had told the foreman who employed me that I could paint and so he had taken me on as a labourer and a boat-painter. The truth was that, apart from the brief times when my father had put me to the task of scraping wallpaper or undercoating, I had never wielded a paintbrush and hadn't a clue about the trade! This fact became apparent when I was given the task of working on the first ever

352

boat to be painted on the new slipway that had been constructed by our company. The boatyard had not been faring well for orders, and this new slipway was a significant move by the owners to keep the business afloat. I felt really pleased to be given the first painting job.

The boat hull was to be painted blue, with a regulation red bottom and a white stripe separating the two colours at water level. Not knowing anything about the job, and having been handed the task without any real instructions, I set to in my own contrary style.

At first the job went well. I hosed off the barnacles, seaweed and other debris sticking to the hull. I let the woodwork start to dry while I prepared the metal and decking for its own overhaul. I then went to the paint store to get some boat paint. It never occurred to me that I should be using any kind of primer; I just picked up a few cans of white undercoat from the store and took them back to the slipway.

Amazingly, no one made any comment while I painted the boat white. I suppose the other guys either thought I knew what I was doing, or were looking forward to a laugh at the finished result. There were always pranks at the yard and I can imagine that the latter was the more likely of the two. Either way, my work went completely unchallenged. I went home that night feeling pretty satisfied with my day's work, and, unusually for me, I turned up early the next day to get started on putting on the final coat.

Working hard and working into some very welcome overtime, I managed to get the boat painted by the end of that night. As I surveyed my still-wet masterpiece, I felt pretty pleased with myself. For the slipway to be a success, we had to show the skippers that we could turn round the maintenance on their boats in quick order. Looking at the results of my labours, I felt that I had done my bit for the cause.

All was well until the launch the following day.

As the first boat to receive its maintenance on the new slipway, the company made quite a splash over its relaunch. Celebrations were always held when a new yacht was built, but this was going to be an especially big celebration. I waited at the pier with the rest of the team, enjoying a free beer and looking forward to seeing my handiwork afloat.

At high tide the framework holding the boat in place was gently lowered, with the boat, back into the water. Everyone was in a party mood at the success of this new venture. I watched the boat being lowered and felt a good deal of pride as its hull touched the water and it started to float out into the harbour.

At first there were cheers, and then the looks on the faces of the watching public and the boatyard workers changed to a mixture of amusement in some and eye-expanding horror in others. The boat was sitting in an inky pool of blue and red paint! I watched in horror as my handiwork melted off the hull and drifted, in an ever-widening pool of oily colour, across the harbour.

The skipper leaned over the side and cursed; he was furious - he was sailing an almost white boat! In this area, fishermen take a great deal of pride in their vessels. It was as common to refer to a skipper by the name of his boat as by his given name. Fishermen wanted their boats to look good and perform well. There was always competition amongst the crews and to be working on a good boat was a mark of high status. Because of my poor workmanship, openly displayed to the watching public, this skipper felt angry and humiliated.

In my ignorance, I had made a number of serious mistakes when painting this 45-foot fishing vessel. I had put on a normal undercoat instead of a boat primer; I had painted the undercoat onto the boat when it was still wet; and I had applied the topcoat when the undercoat had not yet hardened - and while it had been drizzling with rain. The end result was painfully obvious to all.

This was not the type of first-job-on-the-slip celebration that the company had intended.

Surprisingly, I was not fired for my gross incompetence. This was a small village and a small family firm. They were not a 'hire-and-fire' type of people. I was given a stern dressing down by the foreman and made to repaint the boat - under the supervision of a competent painter. We got it right the second time, but the subsequent launch was a bit of an anti-climax and there was no profit left in the job. I felt pretty bad about my mistake; although I made many more cock-ups during my time at the yard, at least I didn't make that one again.

I was never a good boatyard worker. My list of cock-ups was vast. I managed to crash a van while delivering rubbish to the dump. I almost caused a bunch of joiners to lose their fingers when I was given the task of filing the points off some aluminium struts and, in my boredom, only managed to file razor-sharp edges, which cut their hands to ribbons as they tried to fit them. The list could go on and on.

I managed to hang on, though, and I put this down to the kindness of the foreman, the owner of the company, and the attitude of the community in general. I was no good, but they gave me a chance and kept on giving me chances. This was my real break away from my past, living and working in a new community, and for that reason I will always be grateful to these people who tolerated my early incompetence.

I had many good times at the boatyard. It was a little sub-community of its own, with men who had been there since school and a host of traditions and established routines. It was not an action-packed environment - everyone had time to chat with each other and with any of the passing villagers. I fell right into this way of life and spent an equal amount of time sunbathing in front of the slip in the summer and warming my hands round the engineer's brazier in the winter, all the time chatting and getting to know the local community.

It's a pity that the boatyard eventually closed down. The yachts that were built there were of the highest workmanship and were highly sought-after pieces of boat craft. The problem was that they were expensive, and there were never enough orders to keep the place viable. I think that the pace of working life at the yard, in times that were getting ever more commercially manic, spelled the death knell of the company. It had become a ruthless world of tight deadlines and even tighter budgets that our wee boatyard could never adjust to. The business was eventually sold to a big consortium and, unfortunately, all the craftsmen employed there were turned into fitters on big steel boats.

It saddens me to say that, eventually, the boatyard was eventually closed completely, taking quite a bit of the heart of the village with it and ending a long-lived and proud family business.

For me, the job had marked a major transition in my life and the burial of another demon. I was finally a part of a community, and for the first time in my life I felt that I was somewhere where I belonged. I had abandoned hippy life and had crossed over.

I stayed on at the yard until the lure of bigger money from the sea drew me into trying my hand at being a fisherman. That was also to prove to be quite an adventure.

CHAPTER LXXI

Accepting Responsibility

During my time at the boatyard I had managed to make Heather pregnant.

I was overjoyed when I found out. I was only 20 years old, but I sometimes felt as if I had lived for 50 years. I was tired of running around and I welcomed the chance to start a family and really put down some solid roots.

Heather was not so sure.

She was only 17. I suppose she felt as if she still had a lot of living to do before she settled down. At the time I was not smart enough to really understand her misgivings. I put her reluctance down to just being a bit afraid of actually giving birth to a baby. Heather made no moves to force me into a permanent relationship, but I wanted to get married. I was high with the idea of having a family of my own, and I was so immersed in making something of my new life that I failed to see any possible negatives. I was too young and too selfish to consider what it really meant for Heather, or what our life together would really be like. I didn't even stop to consider if I actually loved this girl and genuinely wanted to spend the rest of my life with her. I was having a family, and I just wanted to make it happen quickly and start to build the life I craved.

If only things were that easy.

Heather agreed to marry me. That's all she did, though. There was never any joy-filled warmth or hopeful expectation in her compliance. She was pregnant and she agreed to marry me.

At least her parents seemed pleased with the announcement.

I, on the other hand, was high. I was full of optimism and hope for our future. I really wanted this: I was settled, I was going to have a baby, and this was going to be my home. This was a responsibility that I was more than happy to accept.

Bad news took me briefly back to Glasgow, though, even before the wedding banns were read.

CHAPTER LXXII

The Death of a Family

My final visit to Glasgow was when my mum died.

I had never given my parents or any of my relatives contact details in case they wanted to get in touch with me. I had kept minimal contact since I moved to the countryside, and in fact my parents had only met Heather once, when I returned to Glasgow to pick up the things that I had stored for a while with friends. When the news is bad enough, though, I guess someone always finds some way to make sure that it catches up with you. In this case I was glad that they did, even though it was not the kind of news that anyone really wants to hear.

A knock on our door heralded a policeman. By this time I was drug-free and did not have any of the paranoia associated with users and visits from the police. I was surprised to see the two policemen there, but ushered them inside without a qualm when they politely asked leave to enter.

'I'm sorry to say that we have to give you some bad news, Mr Smith. I'm afraid that it's your mother. She was taken into hospital a couple of days ago with cancer, and your family asked us to get in touch with you, as they don't think that she will last much longer.'

I was stunned.

I had known that mum was still ill, but there had never been any mention of cancer. Apparently the doctors had discovered it very late on and her bowel cancer had mutated with alarming speed, wasting her away almost overnight.

Somehow, regardless of what ever goes on between you, a mother always is and will always be a special person in your life. Although I had never held any outward affection for my parents since I was very small, that cupboard love still existed somewhere inside me and I was stricken to hear that she was about to die. I had known of and been around many deaths in my short life. My grandparents had not lasted into my teens. I had friends and acquaintances who were no longer alive. Death was not exactly a stranger, but the imminent death of my mother still felt overwhelming.

I thanked the policemen, let them out and immediately started to pack for the quickest trip I could make to Glasgow. Heather decided that she would come with me.

We arrived at the hospital on the night that my mother died. By the time I reached her side she could not even recognize me, and her body was so wasted that I found it almost impossible to recognize her. Heather and I kept a long vigil and then left in the evening to stay at my parents' house and return again next morning.

During that night she died.

When I heard the news I cried. It was a brief show of tears, as my relatives and their neighbours were quick to remind me that I should be strong for my father and my sister. I was full of unexpressed grief and confused emotions. I didn't know what to think or how I should act. In the end I fell back on my armour of anger and stayed stern throughout the next few days, until my mother was laid to rest in the cemetery bordering the street where I once lived as her son.

With the death of my mother I put that family firmly behind me. I had neither love nor sympathy for my father. He had always been an arrogant and aggressive man - selfish, insincere and unloving. I would not spend any more of my life with him. Although I loved my sister for the times we had shared until I was 13, she was now a stranger to me. She had her own family life and had grown into an adult that I never really got to know. We promised each other that we would keep in touch, but it never happened.

As for the rest of my relatives, I had one aunt who I remembered for her kindness. Apart from that - nobody.

For a while the experience that Heather shared with me over my mother's death brought us fairly close together. We returned to our home, left my old ghosts behind and prepared ourselves for a new life with our baby.

My old family had gone, but now I had a brand new family to look forward to. Perhaps, at last, I would have one filled with love instead of confusion and anger.

CHAPTER LXXIII

A Life on the Ocean Wave

Shortly after the death of my mother, Heather and I were married in the local registry office. It was a very low-key affair. We didn't have much money, so the only wedding ring handed over was Heather's, which she purchased out of her own savings. We had no fancy clothes and the only guests that we invited were our immediate families, who also acted as witnesses. We had a small get-together at Heather's parents' house and then went off home, Heather pleading sickness through her now noticeable pregnancy.

I was happy to be married, but the signs even then were not good. On our wedding night, instead of celebrating and lovemaking, we had an argument about something trivial and Heather went to bed early with a headache.

Unfortunately, this was to be the norm throughout our blighted relationship.

Meanwhile, I had a child coming and was feeling the need to earn more money to support us than I was earning at the boatyard. My new responsibilities had thrown my mind into long-term planning mode and I had formulated a path that would improve our lot and give our child the best possible lifestyle. My plan was to save up enough so that I could return to full-time education and then get myself into a decent career. I figured that, with hard work, I could rise up the ranks and give my clan the stability and opportunities that would flow into our lives as a reward for my diligence. As always, I was full of optimism. The difficulty lay in trying to find some well-paid work in the area to kick me off, without having any relevant qualifications. This was an area of fishermen, farmers and tradesmen; I had none of these skills.

My mate Tim came to my rescue.

'You should try the fishing, Les. You can make a good bit if you get on the right boat. I'll help you get started.'

True to his word, Tim helped me out, and I became a temporary fisherman.

Tim and Chris taught me the basics and then Tim got me a berth on a boat with him. I had a new adventure in front of me and - I hoped - a great start towards my longer-term goals. The sea was a completely new experience. I'd loved to watch the boats sail in and out of the harbour and I had been on a few trawling trips with both Chris and Tim. The sea drew me, as it draws many, and I always wondered what the life of a fisherman would be like. Most of my friends and acquaintances were either fishermen or had been at sea at some point. I couldn't wait to start.

I was worse at being a fisherman than I was at working in a boatyard!

Although I was extremely enthusiastic to begin with and I tried my best to learn the skills required of the job - I was hopeless. My poor skipper had a Frank Spencer for a crewman. Apart from cooking and sorting prawns, I was practically no help at all throughout my time at sea. Even my cooking made him angry at first, as I was used to a greater degree of hygiene than he was prepared to accept. I remember how much I pissed the skipper off when I cleaned out his prized multi-layered fat from the frying pan to cook him up some prawns that we had caught for his supper.

'What the fuck dae ye think ye're doin', Les? It takes ages to build up a flavour in the pan like that. And what are ye daein' cooking up the prawns! For fuck's sake - that's our livin', ya daft bastard!'

Tim laughed his head off at that one.

I was always tired when I worked at sea. I remember sleeping in often and missing both the tide and the boat. On one occasion I got a lift from another boat and jumped across into mine. I remember singing, 'A life on the ocean wave,' as the boat rocked and Tim and I gutted fish and picked prawns, while ingesting an unhealthy mixture of exhaust fumes from the engine and cold salty air. I loved the feel of the sea, but unfortunately this meant that, if I went down to the cabin for 40 winks, it was almost impossible to wake me up again, having been rocked into a deep slumber by the motion of the waves.

I had so many mishaps that it is surprising I didn't sink the boat and cause the death of all of us. I had a great time through it all, though, and Tim was the best possible and most tolerant crew-mate I could ever have been with.

I remember: dropping stuff over the side of the boat at sea; sleeping so deeply on the boat that they could hardly wake me up to work; getting stoned a couple of times with Tim and then the two of us driving the skipper crazy with our giggling; getting blind drunk after work on a Friday in the local bar and having a great laugh with the lads; throwing up with seasickness and then throwing up with land-sickness when we docked; being cold to a level where I couldn't feel my numb fingers and was in danger of slicing them off with my gutting knife; washing prawns; feeling tired; and loving the sea at night, as the small armada set out for their evening's work in the dark, and then watching the boats separate till there were only the tiny pinpoints of the ships' lights for my eyes to see.

They are still great memories.

I remember when the exasperated skipper said, 'At least we'll get our boat painted well this year, wi' you havin' worked at the yard, Les.' The poor guy was wrong again - he really did pick a lemon to crew his boat.

I wouldn't have lasted as long as I did without Tim. Tim sheltered me from my gross incompetence and, through his good graces and his pull with the skipper, I managed to last till I had saved up quite a bit of money. I knew that I could never have made a career as a fisherman, though, and so I was not too annoyed when my long-suffering skipper had finally had enough and fired me. If I had been him I might not have been so patient for so long.

Being fired seemed to carry no stigma in the fishing community. I remember one fisherman who said, 'It's a good guy that gets fired, Les; it's a poor guy who has tae gie up!' I still loved sailing, and I might even have spent some more time working at sea, but that year, on a cruel gale-swept night, the sea took my two best friends into its bosom.

The boat they sailed on had a new skipper and a new but experienced crew. Chris and Tim had jumped at the chance to get onto this trawler. The fishing was going well and boats were making good money. Both of the guys hoped that this berth would be a lucrative one. They both had young families, as had many of the crew. When the boat disappeared that night and the message got back we were all stunned. It was a tragedy deeply felt within the community when the guys were lost at sea on that stormy night, and neither the remains of their boat or their bodies were ever found. I remember crying myself when I found out. It seemed so wrong that the sea could claim such young lives and could tarnish the future of so many young families. It was the always-dreaded tragedy that this community perpetually lived in fear of - I didn't envy the fishermen and the families of these fishermen who continued to work at the sea.

I missed Chris and Tim; they had been good friends and had made a huge difference to my ability to settle in the area. I owed them a lot. It was the end of a short era for me, though; from that point onwards I had no more yearning to go to sea.

SONG 16 - IT'S COLOURED BLUE

It's dark outside now, I don't have to hide now, look at black -
it's coloured blue
All around me, there's not a single sound it seems, but listen
carefully, you'll hear blue

It's a void outside the sun, can't feel anything at all - everything
is old
All my senses gone to hell, colour senses blue as well - I feel cold

I'm drawing back now, I won't risk my neck now, heart's been
beaten black and blue

Behind my armour I'm a man, playing to the audience - take a
bow
But behind my doors again, I relax, disintegrate - just like now

It's dark outside now, I don't have to hide now, solitude - relief
from pain
It's dark inside too, you'll know if is this happening to you, look
at black - it's coloured blue

Look at black
Look at black
Look at black - it's coloured blue

CHAPTER LXXIV

Married Life

My marriage to Heather proved an unmitigated disaster. We were both very young people, just kids really, and neither of us had ever been shown any marital role model to build upon. That aside, we were also very different people with extremely different hopes and dreams.

It could never have worked out between us. Heather wanted freedom and adventure, where I only wanted the closeness and warmth of a loving family. Heather developed a slight detachment from me at the beginning of our married life, unhappy with the circumstances that had taken her to this point, which only grew colder and more distant as time went on. I started our marriage full of an optimism that dwindled each day, as I became less and less able to ignore the growing rift between us. There was little emotion shared between us and we generated even less physical warmth or passion.

The only saving grace was our child.

Heather gave birth to a beautiful little baby girl. We adored her.

From the first moment I saw this beautiful little person and was able to hold her in my arms - I knew that I had gained something very special in my life. She was golden to me. She encapsulated all the love and goodness that had been lacking in my life. At last, I had someone to love unconditionally.

Heather loved her, too. It was a trial for her at first - she suffered from post-natal depression for a long time. She struggled with being responsible for a baby at the age of 18, when she was still just a child herself, and she mourned the loss of her freedom. She was hurting, but I have no doubt she loved our daughter as much as I did. We went through the daily routines of a married relationship, but each day it became more and more apparent that this precious gift of life was the only real bond between us. Although we were doomed to fail, we tried to make our marriage work - each of us in our own way.

Heather had come from a broken family, and so she clung onto our marriage to avert the same marital split for our daughter that she had grown up with. She went about the routines of motherhood and of keeping house while I worked, but there was no joy in the process and she never had any love to spare for me. She made friends with other mums and built a sort of social life within the village. I tried to share this with her, and as a result we had two faces to our relationship - one for our friends and the general public, and a very different one when we were alone.

I lavished all my affection on my beautiful little daughter. She was the spur that drove me to improve our circumstances and to deliver the plan for our future that I had formulated. Whenever I could I took her wherever I went. I enjoyed every special moment that we spent together. My daughter became my family, but, with Heather, even the potential for falling in love just kept on fading.

I, too, went through the routine of being a good husband and always did my best to provide both Heather and my daughter with the best material life that I could forge. Although I never really bonded with her family, we always shared the important events with her relations; having them for Christmas or going to their houses for visits, and combining birthday parties and other celebrations. We were dutiful, but we were also very far from having a genuine partnership.

Although we were unhappy together, neither of us would contemplate a marital split that would take us away from daily contact with our child. We loved her and we knew that we would always make sure that we could share her time.

With a beautiful child to love but a nightmare relationship to live, it was a time of mixed blessings.

CHAPTER LXXV

Implementing the Plan

After my experience in the fishing industry had come to an end, I plunged into my master plan for developing a career. I enrolled at college to finish off the business studies qualifications I had started to build up during my sojourn in London. After that my plan was to do a computer science degree and then go on to do a computer science postgraduate qualification. I was pretty sure by now that technology was the career path for me. I had tasted this type of work in London and I had loved it. I was sure not only that I would enjoy this career, but that it would bring the material rewards that I ached for and could use to give my family a very comfortable quality of life.

Completing my programme of education wasn't easy. I had very little money at the time and the education authorities had told me that, although I would receive a government grant for the first year of my studies, I would not receive any further grants for subsequent years. In terms of my master plan, this meant that I would get support to finish my business qualification studies - but nothing else.

I was determined to succeed regardless of the obstacles, so I got part-time jobs and worked while I completed my studies.

My routine for four years became one of: attending classes when I was scheduled to; working on any days off that I had, and working most evenings; studying after I had finished work in the evenings; working the occasional weekend when I could; and spending any of my remaining time with my daughter. I suppose, even if I had had a good relationship with Heather, it would have become pretty tattered through the implementation of this intense routine. But I didn't love her; she seemed not to care, and that simply enabled me to attack my plan more aggressively.

It turned out that I had a strong aptitude for both the subjects that I studied, and for study itself. After the first month of my four years, I found that I could understand more than 100% of what was being taught by attending 20% of the lectures and classes, then reading in my own time. The business studies were a breeze and the computer science was a joy - without the pain of any struggle. I had chosen well, it seemed, and at least this part of my journey proved to be very easy indeed.

I discovered that a perk of my studies being relatively effortless was that I had more of my time left over for work and for giving even more attention to my lovely little girl. The time I spent with her was always special; her little smiles and hugs made everything I was working towards worthwhile and kept me focused on making a success of my life.

I also enjoyed my little academic and career victories during this time, which compensated me for my complete failure at making a go of my marriage. I was so proud of myself when I managed to set up my own small PC software maintenance and development company during the first year of my computer science degree. Programming came naturally to me and I found that I had a flair for design. I combined these talents and managed to find work setting up small company microcomputers and programming business solutions for them. This was in the very first days of personal computers, and the market was wide open to me. Small and medium-sized businesses were just branching into high-technology solutions and work was not hard to find. I had a lot of fun, I grew quickly in skill and confidence, and I made enough money for my family to survive.

Because of the pattern of my life, I was genuinely my own man and could schedule work and study to suit myself. I had many days when I could take our baby for long walks, and had plenty of time for playing games and generally adoring her. This lifestyle I was living also brought me long student breaks for family fun. The more time I spent with my child, the more that I loved her. These were special days indeed.

I also had a college social life of sorts, to supplement the tedium of my sad marital life. Although I could not immerse myself in the antics of my fellow students, I was on the periphery and had parties and sessions enough to fill my social, if not spiritual, vacuum.

There were some hard times, too. Money was often scarce, despite the work that I did. We had enough to survive and had enough for a few extras, but we had no large disposable income. When it came to transportation to college, I had no car, and the bus journey could take an hour and a half - so I hitch-hiked. I used this mode of transport through all the seasons, and I can remember many miserable days, standing by the side of the road in snow, rain, or gale, hoping to get a lift before my fingers froze off altogether!

I eventually managed to scrape enough money together for a small motorbike. This was a huge improvement in the summertime, but on the bleak days of winter it was a nightmare of discomfort. This mode of transport lasted until I skidded off the road on a patch of black ice and wrecked my bike against a wall. I was lucky to be able to walk away that day. My helmet actually split down the middle because of the impact, as I flew through the air at high speed and smashed head first into a stone marker on the verge. The accident also left my leathers worn through to the skin - quite a bit of which I left glued to the tarmac. I didn't get another bike after this one, and so I continued to hitch-hike for the rest of my time as a student.

However hard anything else in my life was, though, the darkest times were always at home.

An unbridgeable chasm had developed between Heather and me, but our problems were never discussed in any depth, nor given any sort of a chance for reconciliation. Heather was not mentally equipped for self-analysis, and, whenever I tried to get an in-depth discussion going about our marital problems, she would shy away. She was always too tired, or too depressed. There was never a right time for such discussions. As I said before, we were both very young.

Our problems went untended and our relationship continued to deteriorate.

I believe that it was as early as the first year of our marriage, which spanned 20 years altogether, that Heather and I evolved our unspoken agreement that we would stay together for our family, but would live our own separate lives. It didn't happen overnight, but gradually Heather developed her favoured friends and I nurtured mine. Heather concentrated on her interests and I concentrated on mine. We came together for 'family' events and we acted out the married-couple role with the few mutual friends that we cultivated, but that was all. I was

370

not really interested in how Heather spent her private time and she had no real interest in how I spent mine.

We were both growing up and changing, but at the same time we were becoming enemies rather than friends. We would snipe at each other in private and put each other down. We showed no respect for the hopes and dreams of one another, other than for our children to have as good a quality of life as possible. I lost sight of who Heather was and never even noticed who she was becoming. Our marriage was over before it ever really began.

But, even though the demons of my marriage to Heather were just being born, it was still a time for celebration. I still had a family in the form of my daughter and - at last - my oldest demon could be defeated.

END OF BOOK 1

Stepping out and hanging up my clothes
Feels so light now as all the armour goes
Not a stranger, there's someone else who knows
THERE'S NO DEMONS

SONG 17 - FULL CIRCLE

My child you are beautiful, so beautiful to me
Holding you, hugging you, you smell so sweet

Child I can understand, what life is all about
Child you have brought me - full circle

Five little children, five times discovery - of how it should
be

I'm grateful to share the time, of five very special lives
Children you've brought me round - full circle

Full circle

EPILOGUE

I completed my education, and I came out of it with top marks and as the top student in my year. It was the springboard I needed to launch my plan, and I used it well. Through time I would manage to reach the pinnacle of my chosen career in business and technology. That's a story for the second of these books, however (The Death Of Demons, book II - The Biggest Journey).

My marriage was not looking as though it was going to be a success, but I had a career to look forward to and a family to support and spur me on. I cannot speak for Heather, as I'm sure that, if she was to write about our relationship, she would see things quite differently from me, but I know that her pain mirrored mine.

My past was gone and, although I was to gather more demons in my life, many of my demons from my youth had been buried. The lessons remained, however. These were lessons about sharing, loving and being able to give unselfishly and unconditionally. They were lessons about how important it was to choose friends carefully and how to make sure that I retained my identity and never let it become submerged in someone else's value system.

I learned lessons about failure and wasting one's life from the time I had spent within the drug culture. I learned about how not to be a parent from my own bitter experiences. For example, I would never hit my child. Physical abuse towards little ones is something that I could never tolerate. I've never found that there is even any need to consider it. A stern word when necessary, coupled with an assurance that they are loved, cared for and have parents who are genuinely interested in them, always suffices. Kids who are loved want to please their parents. In treating them this way, you receive back far more love than you could ever have hoped for.

With the birth of my first daughter, I was able to have a share in childhood that I had earlier been denied. I was able to share the magic and the joys I had missed. My daughter was my greatest prize, one that brought me 'Full Circle' and provided me with the catalyst to become a winner. Her birth was in fact the gift of life for both of us and the death of my first ever demon - that of family rejection. That demon was gone forever; I had my own family now.

++++++++

Now

I think that's probably enough for now. The rest of the story is best kept for The Death Of Demons, book II.

I look out of the small window beside me and I can see Valerie playing with our baby in the garden. The sun is shining and they are smelling flowers and laughing together.

Whatever it took to get here, however convoluted the journey, I know I am in a very special place and I'm enjoying a very special time.

Life is good.

Val, you are

Death of my Demons

Thank you for loving me - even knowing who I have been

ALBUM ACKNOWLEDGEMENTS

This album is dedicated to Valerie Murray - the Death of all my Demons - and to the five beautiful children who brought me 'Full Circle'.

All songs were written and arranged by Eric Moran, except for 'Looking Inside The Fast Lane', which was written by Eric & Rachael Moran.

All performances on vocals and instrumentation are by Eric Moran, with the exceptions of:

Jonathan Miller on bass in 'The Death of Demons' and 'Full Circle';

Rachael Moran on vocals in 'Schoolboy Blues', 'Looking Inside The Fast Lane' and 'It's Wicked';

Julia Rogers on Organ Blues Beats in 'Schoolboy Blues'.

My heartfelt thanks for your excellent contributions.

Special thanks go to Rachael - you were with me throughout this journey and were my creative counterpoint on many of these pieces.

Special thanks are also due to Valerie - you were and still are the source of my confidence, my biggest supporter and the reason that it's always worthwhile fighting through the pain barrier to realize my dreams.

Very special thanks go to Jonathan Miller. Without his musical genius, his post-production support, his classy bass licks, his patience while we battled to finalize this work, and the strength of his technical skill I would not have been able to finish this project. I owe you big time, Jonathan.

Finally - thanks in advance to all of you for buying this book and album; I hope you enjoy them.

OTHER ALBUM INNERS

(page numbers refer to the page of the book where the lyrics to each song are included)

1 - The Death of Demons 12
2 - Born Into Blues (1) 14
3 - What'll Happen Now? 18
4 - Born Into Blues (2) 27
5 - Hard To Care 32
6 - Born Into Blues (3) 62
7 - On The Streets 65
8 - Schoolboy Blues 89
9 - Catching Fish With My Mind 175
10 - Makes Me Strange 185
11 - Brain Pudding 209
12 - Time To Change 212
13 - Looking Inside The Fast Lane 308
14 - It's Wicked 312
15 - Back To My Roots 342
16 - It's Coloured Blue 365
17 - Full Circle 372
Album Cover Design by Eric Moran